VOLUME TWO

PLANNING THE MODERN CITY

PLANNING THE MODERN CITY

VOLUME TWO

Harold MacLean Lewis

CONSULTING ENGINEER AND CITY PLANNER

JOHN WILEY & SONS, Inc., New York
CHAPMAN & HALL, Ltd., London

PREFACE

Tremendous strides have been made in city planning throughout the world since the publication of *The Planning of the Modern City*, by the late Nelson P. Lewis, issued in 1916, with a second revised edition in 1922. Much of the progress lies in the wider acceptance of planning as a prerequisite to the orderly and efficient development of both urban and rural areas. Many communities, nevertheless, are still without plans, and much remains to be done in this field.

There has, however, been little change in the general principles governing the theory or the practice of city planning, so that this new book, based on the old one and prepared by the son of the original author, has required little change in the statements regarding these principles. Many references have been replaced with later examples, and statistics have been brought up to date. Chapters have been added dealing with basic information needed, the control of subdivisions, and the problems of parking motor vehicles, the relation of the airport to the city plan, public responsibility for housing, and the redevelopment of blighted areas. New developments and trends in zoning, express highways, and urban transportation have been described.

The present work is presented in two volumes. The first contains a general introduction to city planning, an analysis of its objectives, and a discussion of all the main elements which establish the framework of a master plan for an urban community. The second volume deals with the special physical, social, legal, economic, and administrative problems which should be considered by a city planner and a planning commission.

Nelson P. Lewis wrote with the background of many years spent in municipal work, and his book drew fully on his rich experience as a civil engineer and municipal official. It was recognized as an outstanding engineering contribution to city planning literature. As the first Chief Engineer of the Board of Estimate and Apportionment of the City of New York, a post created in 1902 after the creation of the present city by the consolidation in 1898 of the former city, then comprising only Manhattan Island and The Bronx, with the counties of Kings (including the city of Brooklyn), Queens, and Richmond, Mr. Lewis became one of the outstanding municipal engineers in the United States. He promptly assumed leadership in the city planning field. With his wide knowledge and study of the plans of many other cities, both in this country and abroad, he knew urban problems thoroughly and was active in their solution. His book was frankly written with the idea that the fundamental problems of city planning are, and from their very nature must be, engineering problems. At the same time he fully appreciated that planning is a co-operative process involving the active aid of members of all related professions dealing with design as well as of specialists in economics and sociology.

Cities, large and small, present many urgent planning problems. At the same time, because of the magnitude of their public works programs and their ability to draw on the best technical advisers, they possess great opportunities for benefiting from sound planning. This new book, like the former one, is limited to a discussion of urban planning. Many of the illustrations in the earlier publication were selected to illustrate principles and are retained in the present volumes. Many others were intended as a record of planning accomplishment and have been replaced with later and more timely selections.

I was privileged to have a small part in assisting the original author in the preparation of the second edition of his book. As a son who was fortunate to be associated with his father in some of his later work for the Regional Plan of New York and Its Environs, and as one who has specialized in city planning, I have found the preparation of this new book to be a labor of love. The opinions of the original author have been retained, and nothing has been added which would conflict with these.

HAROLD MacLEAN LEWIS

New York, New York
October 7, 1948

ACKNOWLEDGMENTS

Acknowledgment is made of the assistance received from the published works of others as referred to throughout these volumes. Special acknowledgment is also due to the following: Lloyd F. Rader, Professor of Civil Engineering, University of Wisconsin, and Elisabeth M. Herlihy, Chairman, Massachusetts State Planning Board, for their helpful suggestions and the loan of illustrative material; my office staff members, Charles M. Herrick and Charles L. Austin, who did much of the research work involved in the preparation of new material, Alfred Czanczik, who prepared many of the maps and diagrams, and Grace E. Hutchinson, who, as my secretary, has handled all the secretarial and stenographic work involved; Russell Sage Foundation for permission to use material in the volumes of the Regional Plan of New York and Its Environs; and the many others who have made available photographs and maps used as illustrations.

CONTENTS

Part Six—Legal, Economic, and Administrative Problems

Part Four

Community Planning and Replanning

13

NEIGHBORHOOD AND COMMUNITY PLANNING

WITH THE DEVELOPMENT OF THE LARGE CITY certain important qualities of village life have been lost, and the advantages of city life have been offset, to a greater or lesser extent, by attendant disadvantages. One of the characteristics which distinguishes mankind from the rest of the animal world is his social quality—the need and ability to live with other people. The primary expression of this need throughout known history has been the family; in primitive society the secondary organism was the tribe, which became the community or village as civilization developed.

In a village everyone is more or less intimately acquainted; the abilities and failings, the surpluses and lacks, the interests and doings of each individual are common knowledge. Each village develops distinctive characteristics and an awareness of its standards, opinions, and attitudes which comes from living "face to face" with all its residents. In the large city much of this knowledge is lost, and with it some of the individual and collective capacity for happiness, group action, and self-regulation which is so vital to a healthy society. It is in the urban areas, which lack this quality of neighborliness, that the indices of social breakdown—juvenile delinquency, boys' gangs, crime, poverty, wife desertion, divorce, abandonment of infants, vice, etc.—are found to be highest.

In addition to such serious social consequences, resulting, at least in part, from the lack of neighborhood living, cities suffer physical disadvantages from excessive centralization. The one to three hours a day which are spent in traveling to and from work in some of the larger urban areas of this country represent a disproportionate amount of the workers' leisure time. Equally disproportionate is the investment in transit facilities which is required when most of the productive activities are concentrated at one point. Suitable recreational facilities for both children and adults often are not to be found convenient to their homes, and the route which must be followed by many children on their way to school involves dangerous street crossings.

The alleviation of the lacks and dangers of overcentralized urban areas is a complex problem which must be approached from many angles. The various phases of this problem, which is one of the major sociological considerations of modern city planning, are discussed in this and subsequent chapters. This chapter deals with the physical organization of urban residential areas for social purposes. The following chapter considers the more detailed question of housing. Chapter 15 relates housing and neighborhood planning to blighted areas, which are one of the unfortunate results of overcentralization and lack of planning. Chapter 18 discusses, as one of the special problems involved in urban planning, the more radical cure of decentralization. The subjects covered in these four chapters are interrelated and together comprise an aspect of city planning the importance of which has been recognized only recently.

Importance of the Neighborhood in the City Plan

As the larger urban areas have grown in population, individual villages have met each

Eliel Saarinen has compared the plan of a healthy city to the pattern of a cross-section of living tissue. Each is a series of cells, the city cell being the neighborhood unit. The cells are surrounded by the lymphatic system, the major street system of the city, through which they have their necessities provided and their products distributed. But each cell is a somewhat complete entity in itself, with its own interior circulation and parts.[1] The advantages of such a cellular organization for the city are convenience, safety, stabilization of values, and preservation of amenities.

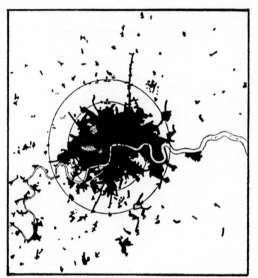 

From "The City—Its Growth, Its Decay, Its Future," by Eliel Saarinen,
published by the Reinhold Publishing Corporation, New York.

FIGURE 13·1. EXPANSION OF THE BUILT-UP AREA OF LONDON

Separate centers in existence in 1880 (*left*) had become connected and submerged by 1929 (*right*).

other at their outskirts. Whereas formerly a trip outward from the downtown area of the central city would have taken one through successive thickly settled areas, separated by relatively open areas of parks or farms, one now passes almost imperceptibly from one center to another. Not only has the sense of neighborhood and community character been lost by this process, but in addition the trip has become a monotonous one of continuous passage through built-up areas. Where this merging has not progressed too far, it should be stopped. Where it is already an accomplished fact, the neighborhood quality must be re-created.

Where such a structure is lacking in the city pattern, almost all the evils of lack of planning will occur more readily, and spreading areas of blight are almost inevitable. As the city starts to grow outward, pressure of the central commercial and industrial area causes speculative rises in land values in the residential areas on its fringe. With the anticipated transition in use these areas are no longer in demand for residence, and evidences of blight appear. Even though horizontal expansion of commerce and industry fails to materialize to the extent an-

[1] *The City—Its Growth, Its Decay, Its Future,* by Eliel Saarinen, Reinhold Publishing Corporation, New York, 1943, pages 8–19.

ticipated, speculative values and blight continue to spread into the residential area, driving residential uses still further out from the center. If vertical growth of the central area causes horizontal shrinkage, additional blighted areas will appear at its outer edge.

Such experiences can be largely avoided in the future if the city plan designates the neigh-

In 1935, the City Plan Commission of St. Louis divided that city into residential neighborhoods and industrial districts. Figure 13·2 shows the boundaries of the 82 residential neighborhoods and 17 industrial districts of St. Louis as of 1940. The Mayor's Committee on City Planning laid out 725 neighborhoods in the city of New York in 1936, and 514 neigh-

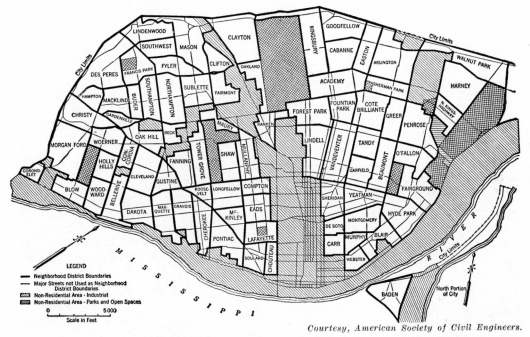

Courtesy, American Society of Civil Engineers.

FIGURE 13·2. BOUNDARIES OF NEIGHBORHOOD DISTRICTS IN ST. LOUIS

As laid out by its City Planning Commission.

borhood pattern for the entire city, to include both developed and undeveloped areas. Such a plan encourages orderly cellular growth and renewal of older or blighted areas according to a reasonable pattern. Changes in requirements as the city grows or contracts can thereby be met in an orderly manner, and stability encouraged over a maximum area. No matter how good the individual house or block, rentals will fall if the surrounding houses or blocks deteriorate. This infection has a tendency to spread and to "snowball." The establishment of definite neighborhood boundaries and characteristics acts as a barrier to such infection and may confine it to one neighborhood, rather than permit it to spread throughout a larger area.

borhoods were delineated for Chicago by its Plan Commission in 1946. Other planning commissions are making studies for neighborhood delimitation of their cities as this book is written.

Principles of Neighborhood Unit Planning

The neighborhood unit principle was developed originally by Clarence Arthur Perry for the Regional Plan of New York and Its Environs. It was described in detail in one of the Regional Survey reports[2] and discussed further in Perry's book, published 10 years

[2] *The Neighborhood Unit*, Monograph One in Vol. VII, Regional Survey of New York and Its Environs, 1929, pages 21–140.

later.[3] In working out his formula, Perry strove to describe the requirements of a residential area which would contain: [4]

> . . . all the public facilities and conditions required by the average family for its comfort and proper development within the vicinity of its dwelling. . . . The formula for a city neighborhood, then, must be such that when embodied in an actual development all its residents will be taken care of as respects the following points: They will all be within convenient access to an elementary school, adequate common play spaces, and retail shopping districts. Furthermore, their district will enjoy a distinctive character, because of qualities pertaining visibly to its terrain and structure, not the least of which will be a reduced risk from vehicular accidents.

The essentials of the neighborhood unit formula were outlined by Perry as follows: [5]

> 1. *Size.* A residential unit development should provide housing for that population for which one elementary school is ordinarily required, its actual area depending upon its population density.
> 2. *Boundaries.* The unit should be bounded on all sides by arterial streets, sufficiently wide to facilitate its by-passing, instead of penetration, by through traffic.
> 3. *Open Spaces.* A system of small parks and recreation spaces, planned to meet the needs of the particular neighborhood, should be provided.
> 4. *Institution Sites.* Sites for the school and other institutions having service spheres coinciding with the limits of the unit should be suitably grouped about a central point, or common.
> 5. *Local Shops.* One or more shopping districts, adequate for the population to be served, should be laid out in the circumference of the unit, preferably at traffic junctions and adjacent to similar districts of adjoining neighborhoods.
> 6. *Internal Street System.* The unit should be provided with a special street system, each highway being proportioned to its probable traffic load, and the street net as a whole being designed to facilitate circulation within the unit and to discourage its use by through traffic.

The size of a neighborhood unit may vary considerably, depending on the size of the school, the ratio of school population to total population, family size, population density, and other factors. Each of these should be scrutinized for the particular community involved when considering neighborhood planning. The school problems have been discussed in Chapter 11, "The Location of Public and Semi-public Buildings."

Other factors controlling the size of a neighborhood are the desirable walking distances to various neighborhood facilities. The maximum distance which a child should be expected to walk to school generally is taken as $\frac{1}{2}$ to $\frac{3}{4}$ of a mile. Playgrounds for children five to 15 years of age will serve a $\frac{1}{4}$- to $\frac{1}{2}$-mile radius. The maximum distance to a shopping center should be $\frac{1}{2}$ mile. From the foregoing standards it readily can be seen that the ideal size for a neighborhood is something under $\frac{1}{2}$ mile square, since that will permit combination of the playground with the school at the center of the unit. However, should circumstances require it, a neighborhood unit as large as one mile square can be designed to meet these requirements. Such a size will be found necessary only in areas of very low density.

Table 20 shows the total population and school population which may be expected in a residential neighborhood $\frac{1}{4}$ square mile in area ($\frac{1}{2}$ mile square), if developed at different densities. In sections where the average net site area per dwelling unit is much over 2,500 square feet, a neighborhood unit of more than $\frac{1}{4}$ square mile in area probably will be required. On the other hand, while the school population to be anticipated may not be excessive in a section where the average net site area per dwelling unit is less than 1,300 square feet, it is desirable to keep the neighborhood unit as small as possible in order to derive the maximum convenience and social benefit. Thus it probably will be best to plan a neighborhood unit of less than $\frac{1}{4}$ square mile in area when higher densities are contemplated.

An adequate system of open spaces for the active play of children and for passive recreation and amenity should be provided within the neighborhood unit. In the neighborhood park system there should be at least 50 square feet of playground for every child in the five- to 15-year age group. Such playgrounds should have an absolute minimum area of three acres, with five to seven acres a desirable minimum, and will be most useful and most easily supervised if they can be located in connection with

---

[3] *Housing for the Machine Age,* by Clarence Arthur Perry, Russell Sage Foundation, New York, 1939.

[4] *Ibid,* page 50.

[5] *The Neighborhood Unit,* Monograph One in Vol. VII, Regional Survey of New York and Its Environs, 1929, pages 34–35.

TABLE 20

QUANTITATIVE ESTIMATES OF USE AREAS AND POPULATION FOR A RESIDENTIAL AREA ½ MILE SQUARE AT VARIOUS POPULATION DENSITIES

	Net Site Area per Dwelling Unit in Square Feet				
	5,000	2,500	1,300	1,000	600
Area in acres of					
Streets	40–48	40–48	36–48	32–48	32–48
Parks, playgrounds, schools, and shops	18	18–20	18–22	20–24	20–26
Residential use	94–102	92–102	90–106	88–108	86–103
Number of dwelling units	820–890	1,600–1,780	3,020–3,550	3,840–4,710	6,250–7,850
Estimated number of persons per dwelling unit	3.5–4.0	3.4–3.9	3.3–3.8	3.2–3.7	3.0–3.5
Probable total population	2,860–3,560	5,450–6,950	9,960–13,500	12,300–17,400	18,750–27,400
Probable school population [a]	260–360	490–695	900–1,350	1,100–1,740	1,700–2,740

[a] At nine to 10 per cent of total population.

the elementary school. It may be expected that children of this age will walk from ¼ to ½ mile to use such a playground. In addition, there should be a neighborhood park, with a minimum area of five acres. In high-density neighborhoods, where individual yards of sufficient size are not provided, there should be, in addition, playlots to the extent of at least 25 square feet per child of five years and younger. Each of these lots should have an area of 5,000 to 10,000 square feet, although 2,500 square feet can be useful in special cases, and will serve an area of ⅛ to ¼ mile in radius. Perry estimated that about 10 per cent of the gross area of a single-family neighborhood should be in recreation space.[6] From the theoretical standpoint, the provision of park and play areas should be more generous in high-density than in low-density areas. However, site costs frequently may force a compromise.

The school should be located as centrally as possible. If the neighborhood is able to support a separate community-center building and a church or churches, these should be grouped with the school so as to afford maximum convenience to all parts of the neighborhood and give architectural character to the neighborhood civic center. In the event that a separate

[6] *Housing for the Machine Age,* by Clarence Arthur Perry, Russell Sage Foundation, New York, 1939, page 59.

building for community purposes cannot be supported, the school should be so designed as

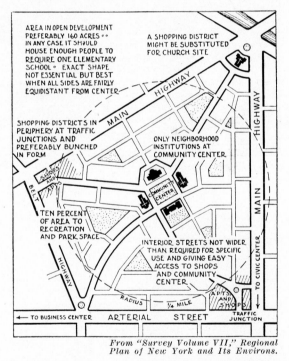

From *"Survey Volume VII," Regional Plan of New York and Its Environs.*

FIGURE 13·3. A DIAGRAMMATIC PRESENTATION OF NEIGHBORHOOD UNIT PRINCIPLES

to be adaptable for club meetings, civic gatherings, and other neighborhood social functions. A common is desirable at the civic center for outdoor social functions in good weather.

The shopping district or districts should be studied with considerable care. Their location adjacent to similar districts in bordering neighborhoods is advantageous to the consumer and preferred by most merchants as well. For convenience, it is desirable for them to be at or near any principal railroad or transit stops, and sufficient parking space for automobiles ger of through traffic. The interior street pattern should be so designed as to allow the most direct possible communication between homes and areas of common use, but should discourage through traffic. Street capacities should not be excessive, lest they encourage through traffic. Within the neighborhood, the primary consideration in street design should be safety

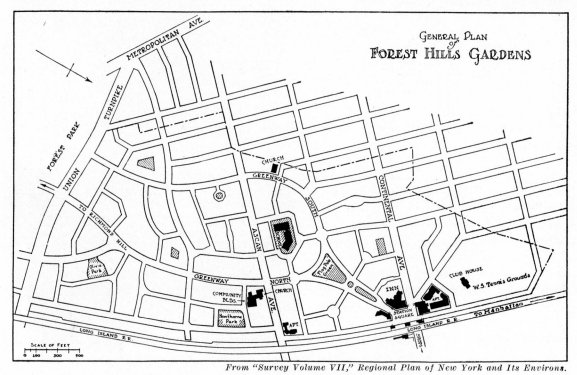

From "Survey Volume VII," Regional Plan of New York and Its Environs.

FIGURE 13·4. AN EARLY EXAMPLE OF A DEVELOPMENT EMBODYING NEIGHBORHOOD UNIT PRINCIPLES

Forest Hills Gardens, in the borough of Queens, New York City, as laid out in 1911.

should be furnished, with access so designed as to minimize congestion and conflict between pedestrian and vehicular traffic. Service streets should be provided in the rear of the stores. Space requirements should be worked out carefully so as to include all facilities required without allotting excessive space to business use.

Main traffic arteries form good boundaries for a neighborhood unit, but should never go through one. Ideally, a thoroughfare of the parkway type is the most desirable boundary street because it insulates the neighborhood most thoroughly from the adjoining one, as well as from the relative unpleasantness and dan

and convenience for pedestrians, rather than speed and directness for vehicles.

The standards which have been outlined in this section are ideals which will not often be found in existing cities, nor will they always be possible of achievement in a new development. Figure 13·3 shows diagrammatically a theoretical neighborhood embodying the principles and standards which have been discussed. Although a complete neighborhood will seldom be developed in one operation, it is possible to accomplish the end over a period of time, provided a plan exists. With such a plan, piecemeal development is possible which eventually will result in the whole. This is as true for redevelopment of blighted areas as for new developments, with the existence of a plan particularly important for blighted areas, so that repetition of past mistakes can be avoided and real and permanent improvement made. (See Chapter 15, page 40.)

Examples of Existing Developments

One of the oldest examples of neighborhood unit development in this country is Forest Hills Gardens, located in the borough of Queens in New York City about 15 minutes' ride on the railroad from Pennsylvania Station in the heart of Manhattan. This development was started in 1911 by a subsidiary corporation of Russell Sage Foundation, and was regarded by the Foundation as a business venture with an educational purpose.

Figures 13·4 and 13·5 show the plan of Forest Hills Gardens and a view of its shopping center. Figure 13·6 indicates the character and variety of its development. The tract has an area of 164 acres and a population of about 5,000 persons. It is well bounded on the south and west by a main thoroughfare and a railroad, but its eastern boundary is not clearly defined. The total park area is about five acres, inadequate by modern standards, but all the facilities for neighborhood life are present and well organized. At the time it was built, Forest Hills Gardens actually was more of a suburb than a part of the urban area, but since that time the city has engulfed it. In writing about the general street plan adopted, Frederick Law Olmsted said, "Probably one of the most notable characteristics of Forest Hills Gardens will be the cozy, domestic character of these local streets, where the monotony of endless straight, wind-swept thoroughfares which represent the New York conception of streets will give place to short, quiet, self-contained and garden-like neighborhoods, each having its own distinctive character."

In spite of being cut by four main traffic streets, the area has retained its neighborhood character and borne out Olmsted's prediction. The management of the community property and the enforcement of rights and deed restrictions, by which the character of the development has been preserved, were turned over in 1923 to a corporation whose membership consists solely of property owners in Forest Hills Gardens. That corporation has been highly successful in its purpose, and forms an excellent civic nucleus for the neighborhood. The residents of Forest Hills Gardens show a high

Courtesy, Sage Foundation Homes Company.

FIGURE 13·5. THE SHOPPING CENTER OF FOREST HILLS GARDENS IN NEW YORK CITY

degree of the social attitudes which the neighborhood unit formula aims to foster.

Another example of neighborhood unit development is the Fairview section of Camden, New Jersey, sometimes referred to as Yorkship Village. This area was developed in 1918 by a subsidiary of the New York Shipbuilding Company, with financial assistance from the United States government, as a housing area for employees of various shipyards in Camden. Figure 13·7 shows the plan of the area as developed in 1922, and Figure 13·8 an air view of the central section.

The site consists of about 225 acres of land with an elevation of 10 to 20 feet above high tide. It is bounded on the north, south, and west by salt marshes and streams and on the

east by Mount Ephraim Pike, a main thoroughfare from downtown Camden and Philadelphia.
The highly formalized and symmetrical plan
is suitable to the relatively level topography
and the colonial style of architecture of the
initial development. All the required neigh-

The proportion of the total area in streets—
34 per cent—is high, owing to the generous
use of wide streets and alleys. Public areas,
including the school site, amount to almost 20
per cent. The 36 acres of public open space
comprise about 48 separate parcels, ranging in

Courtesy, Russell Sage Foundation.

FIGURE 13·6. AIR VIEW OF FOREST HILLS GARDENS, NEW YORK CITY

Showing the curved streets and variety of residential development.

borhood facilities were provided in the original
plan, including sites for a school, church, community building, and stores. In 1922 there
was a total of 1,438 residential units, of which
1,021 were in row housing, 300 were in semi-
detached units, 61 were detached, and 56 were
in apartments. The population of Fairview in
1936 was about 6,500 persons.[7]

[7] *Urban Planning and Land Policies,* National Resources Committee, United States Government Printing Office, Washington, D. C., 1939, page 64.

size from a front yard to the school grounds,
an arrangement which makes for excessive
maintenance costs and which may also be criti-
cized for not being of maximum utility. In
December, 1922, the various properties were
sold at public auction with deed restrictions
controlling the uses. The school had been
taken over by the city, and the church by its
congregation. About 1936, home values ranged
from $1,800 to $3,750, and monthly rentals
averaged $28 for units owned by several realty

companies, and $24 for those privately owned.[8]

There have been two principal failures in Fairview. As a result of lack of provisions in the deed restrictions to regulate the character of building, subsequent construction frequently has been architecturally inharmonious with the rest of the development. If this new building had been confined to one section, the results would not have been so unfortunate. The other

personal interference or attempts at social co-operation by others, and are not sufficiently capable of organizing themselves." [9]

Planned Communities and Subdivisions with Neighborhood Characteristics

The development of communities embodying neighborhood characteristics in their design

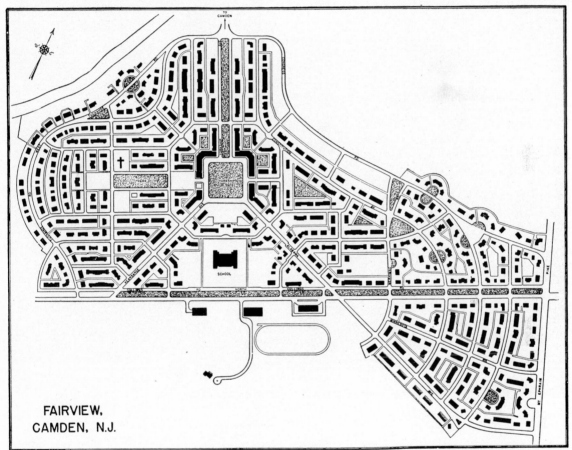

FAIRVIEW, CAMDEN, N.J.

From "Urban Planning and Land Policies," National Resources Committee, 1939.

FIGURE 13·7. PLAN OF YORKSHIP VILLAGE IN FAIRVIEW SECTION OF CAMDEN, NEW JERSEY

Showing conditions existing in 1922.

failure of Fairview has been its lack of neighborhood organization, which has resulted in the failure of the community facilities in their purpose. It was the opinion of a person who had "been on the ground at Yorkship since its inception and knew of the hopes and desires of its designers that . . . the people resent any

has by no means been confined to the United States. In Germany the various colonies established by the Krupp Company are admirable examples of such developments. (See Figures 13·9, 13·10, 13·11, and 13·12.) Workingmen's colonies, which may, perhaps, be considered the real parents of garden cities, were es-

[8] *Ibid,* page 66.

[9] *Ibid.,* page 67.

tablished by the Krupps at Essen as early as 1856. However, they bear little or no resemblance to the colonies later built by this company which, while located, many of them, in the heart of busy industrial cities, are admirable examples of community planning. The streets generally are laid out with the studied

to 107), also are examples of neighborhood and community planning.

A recent example of community planning features in housing in the United States is Parkchester, completed in 1940 by the Metropolitan Life Insurance Company in the borough of The Bronx of the city of New York. (See

Photo by J. Victor Dallin, Landsdowne, Pennsylvania.

FIGURE 13·8. AIR VIEW OF THE CENTRAL SECTION OF YORKSHIP VILLAGE IN CAMDEN, NEW JERSEY

irregularity so distinctive of German city planning, and trees, shrubbery, and open spaces and occasional statues and fountains make some charming street pictures. The individual homes are exceptionally attractive, notably at Margarethenhof, which is a residential colony for the officers and the principal employees of the company, and at Altenhof, which is exclusively devoted to houses for superannuated employees, a cozy home being provided rent free for each aged couple.

The garden cities developed in England, which are discussed in Chapter 18 (pages 103

Figures 13·13 and 13·14.) Parkchester's 12,-269 residential units are entirely in seven- to 15-story apartment buildings and house some 42,000 persons at a gross density of 310 persons per acre, with buildings covering 27.4 per cent of the area. The project includes stores, a movie theatre, a powerhouse, and five garages with a capacity of over 2,500 cars, but there is no provision for schools, churches, athletic field, or auditorium.[10] Parkchester has been sub-

[10] *Housing and Citizenship,* by George Herbert Gray, Reinhold Publishing Corporation, New York, 1946, pages 18 and 170.

ject to severe criticism by various city planners for these lacks, and on other grounds. Its density is considered excessive for its location, and the addition of this large population in an

oped housing community of the multi-family type in the city of New York.

One outstanding example of subdivision guided by planning principles is the Country

FIGURE 13·9. PLAN OF COLONY GEWERKSCHAFT, EMSCHER-LIPPE, GERMANY

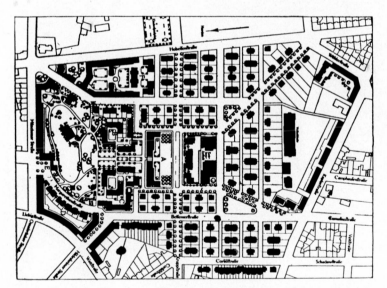

FIGURE 13·10. PLAN OF COLONY ALFREDSHOF, ESSEN, GERMANY

area served by only one rapid-transit line has severely taxed that facility. However, it has fairly low coverage for an apartment development, and its street system is such as to give no encouragement to through traffic. As of 1947 it was probably the best privately devel-

Club District, located in an area extending from three to five miles south and west of the downtown area of Kansas City. (See Figure 13·15.) This development has been the work of the J. C. Nichols Investment Company, starting in 1906 with a 10-acre tract and expanding to

FIGURE 13·11. COTTAGES IN ALTENHOF, ESSEN,
GERMANY

Retired employees of the Krupp Company were provided with houses free of rent in this development.

about 4,000 acres in 1936, of which 2,500 acres had been developed. A report of the National Resources Committee described it as follows: [11]

The district comprises an integrated development of some 16 subdivisions which have been devel-

[11] *Urban Planning and Land Policies*, National Resources Committee, United States Government Printing Office, Washington, D. C., 1939, page 84.

oped over a period of 30 years. The principal structure of the plan is formed by the main arteries of Ward Parkway and Brookside Boulevard, which converge at what is known as the Country Club Plaza or central business district and connect with Mill Creek Parkway and Broadway, which lead to the heart of Kansas City. Secondary cross thoroughfares outline residential areas of from about 200 to 400 acres. Business development has been limited to the plaza at the northern boundary of the district and to small local shops located at the intersections of the major and secondary streets.

FIGURE 13·12. TYPICAL HOUSES FOR WORKMEN
IN COLONY ALFREDSHOF, ESSEN, GERMANY

The upper view shows a dwelling to accommodate five families.

In 1936 the Country Club District had a population of approximately 25,000 persons, housed principally in some 6,000 to 6,500 single-family dwellings, although there were about 100 apartment units at the entrance to the

Courtesy, Metropolitan Life Insurance Company.

FIGURE 13·13. GENERAL PLAN OF PARKCHESTER, NEW YORK CITY

Courtesy, Metropolitan Life Insurance Company.

FIGURE 13·14. INTERIOR VIEW OF PARKCHESTER, NEW YORK CITY

Showing apartments grouped around a central court.

district, and a small section was set aside for duplex housing. Deed restrictions include control of land use, minimum cost of dwellings, setback lines, building projections, free space, outbuildings, billboards, and racial restrictions.

The district houses a decidedly high-income group. Just before 1936, housing built there was entirely single-family dwellings selling for $7,500 to $47,500. In 1936 there were 11 schools, 11 churches, eight shopping centers, 200 small parks, and four 18-hole golf courses included in the district, which is organized as a series of modified neighborhood units. The operation and maintenance of the district are

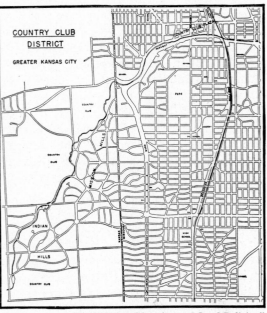

From "Urban Planning and Land Policies," National Resources Committee, 1939.

FIGURE 13·15. GENERAL STREET PLAN OF THE COUNTRY CLUB DISTRICT, KANSAS CITY, MISSOURI

supervised by associations of home owners, the duties of which organizations include the enforcement of restrictions, rubbish and snow removal, care of public plantings, maintenance of recreational areas, and upkeep of vacant property. The associations have the right to collect assessments and enforce payment.

Two other outstanding subdivision developments which have followed planning principles are Roland Park in Baltimore, and Palos Verdes Estates, near Los Angeles. The first unit of Roland Park was established in 1891, another in 1914, and a third in 1924. Successive developments were modified by the lessons of earlier experience. Palos Verdes Estates, which was established in 1923, is particularly interesting because of the great thoroughness with which the planning was done and the care with which the details of control were worked out. The interested reader will find a rather complete summary description of both projects published in 1939 by the National Resources Committee.[12]

The examples of community planning described in this section have been confined to those which were not attempted as self-sufficient communities, but which were, rather, residential areas within or near existing urban centers. Examples of self-sufficient, or satellite, planned communities are discussed in Chapter 18 (see pages 97 to 102). The student of neighborhood planning will find the plans of the United States Housing Corporation of particular interest. The projects of this organization were designed during World War I, and although all of them were not completed, plans were made in great detail in anticipation of actual construction.[13]

Community Co-operation in Local Planning

The importance of the neighborhood in developing civic responsibility and effective action of the citizenry has been emphasized at the beginning of this chapter. Citizen interest and participation are equally important to successful planning for the community. It has been demonstrated repeatedly in the United States that the effectiveness of planning is directly proportional to the support it receives from the people, and, conversely, that the best plans never will be followed if they lack public support.

The neighborhood is the logical level for citizen participation to start. Everyone believes himself to be an expert on his own neighborhood, and in a sense he is. He is interested in it, and the collective factual knowledge of the neighborhood by its residents cannot be duplicated in any number of surveys. The planner who fails to avail himself of this knowledge by working with the residents in formulating the neighborhood plan is committing a sin of

omission which will hinder the effectiveness of his work in three ways: (1) by not getting the information which the residents can supply, he omits some of the factual base on which the plan should be built; (2) by not allowing the residents to participate in the formulation of the plan, he jeopardizes its chances of support and execution by them; and (3) by not thus showing the people that planning is a democratic process through which they serve their own collective interests, he fosters the misconception that planning means autocratic regimentation.

The most effective means of securing the co-operation of the community is through existing organizations: church, fraternal, business, real estate, and labor groups, the parent-teacher associations, women's clubs—all may be used as the means through which planning is introduced to the community and through which the community takes part in planning. The wider the range of interests represented by these organizations, the better it is for both plan and community. The meetings will need forethought and management to keep them balanced and constructive. The whole process should be clearly and simply presented. The presentation of tentative plans should be made as interesting and kept as short as possible. Discussion should be invited, but should be directed so as to avoid interminable and nonconstructive argument on some minor detail. The planner must show his attitude to be that of the professional adviser without bias. As the plan develops, the groups should be progressively informed and given opportunities to discuss it. If such a program of co-operation with the public is carried out successfully, the plan will be sound, and the probability of its execution enhanced.

The maintenance of the physical characteristics of a neighborhood unit depends very largely on the participation of the residents and property owners of that neighborhood. The most successful neighborhood and community developments have had active organizations for the purpose of fostering the care of physical equipment and the interest and constructive action of the individual in the social unit. The lack of such organization in the Fairview sec-

[12] *Ibid.*, pages 85-92.
[13] Complete presentation of these projects will be found in *Report of the United States Housing Corporation,* Vol. II, Government Printing Office, Washington, D. C., 1919.

tion of Camden, discussed earlier in this chapter, has resulted in some failure to realize the potentialities of a well-planned neighborhood, whereas the strength of the organization of the Forest Hills Gardens property owners continues to promote the desirable neighborhood qualities of an area which has no better physical plan. The newly developed neighborhood or community which forms such an organization will benefit from the pride and interest which it fosters in all the new residents. These same feelings can be sustained by the effective operation of the neighborhood-improvement association through the years.

Selected References

Building New Neighborhoods—Subdivision Design and Standards, the Chicago Plan Commission, Chicago, June, 1943.

"Community and Neighborhood Planning—the Key to Progress in Urban Residential Areas," *Information Bulletin* 47, Regional Plan Association, Inc., New York, November 6, 1939.

DAHIR, JAMES: *The Neighborhood Unit Plan: Its Spread and Acceptance,* Russell Sage Foundation, New York, 1947.

Houses, Site-Planning, Utilities, Vol. II, Report of the United States Housing Corporation, United States Department of Labor, Government Printing Office, Washington, D. C., 1919. (Describes war-emergency housing projects of World War I.)

PERRY, CLARENCE ARTHUR: *Housing for the Machine Age,* Russell Sage Foundation, New York, 1939; *The Neighborhood Unit,* Monograph One in Vol. VII, Regional Survey of New York and Its Environs, 1929, distributed by Regional Plan Association, Inc., New York; *The Rebuilding of Blighted Areas—A Study of the Neighborhood Unit in Replanning and Plot Assemblage* (Architectural and Planning Studies under direction of C. EARL MORROW), Regional Plan Association, Inc., New York, 1933.

"Planning Profitable Neighborhoods," *Technical Bulletin* 7, Federal Housing Administration, Washington, D. C., 1938.

Urban Planning and Land Policies, National Resources Committee, 1939. (Includes descriptions of principal existing planned neighborhoods.)

Questions

1. What are some of the social and physical ills which have resulted from the growing together of communities into unbroken urban areas?
2. Describe a cellular organization of a city into a series of separate neighborhoods.
3. List the essential features of a neighborhood unit under modern planning standards.
4. What is the controlling feature in the size of a neighborhood unit? In the number of such units which may form a logical planning district?
5. What principles should govern the street plan of a neighborhood unit?
6. How will good neighborhood and community planning prevent blight?
7. Give examples of some of the good features and some of the faults of planned communities as developed in the United States and abroad.
8. Describe the importance of citizen participation in community planning and some of the most effective ways of obtaining it.

14

HOUSING AND THE CITY PLAN

SINCE A NEIGHBORHOOD, AS DISCUSSED IN THE preceding chapter, is primarily an area of homes, the subject of housing is closely related to neighborhood planning; and as by far the largest single use of a developed urban area is residential, housing is also a major part of urban redevelopment, discussed in the following chapter. Thus these three chapters are closely interrelated. Many volumes have been written on housing, and the subject cannot be covered thoroughly in a book on the general subject of city planning. However, this chapter aims to discuss those portions of the field of housing which are of importance to the city planner.

The improvement of social and living conditions has long been a recognized objective of urban planning, and planning commissions have been giving more and more attention to this phase of the subject, particularly as it affects the well-being and healthy growth of the urban organism. Since the well-to-do still are, as they always have been, able to afford housing of a high standard, the principal emphasis will be on low-rental housing. The provision of such housing in urban areas is being increasingly recognized as a field for public action. It has long been so recognized abroad. In England, for example, public housing authorities built three houses for every one built by private industry in the period between World War I and World War II.

The importance of proper housing to a city can hardly be overemphasized. Its distribution, character, and density are important factors in the preparation of the city plan. Other major factors which must be correlated with the pattern of housing include transit lines, the street system, parks and playgrounds, and zoning. The study of population distribution, population characteristics, family incomes, and other vital statistics is necessary in preparing a housing plan for any community. In planning a new city it would be desirable to establish first the areas of use and then to connect these with a suitable system of street and transit facilities. But in practice the planner is usually faced with established communication systems which can be modified only slightly because of the great investment they represent. As a result, the location, size, and character of proposed housing are generally determined largely by existing service facilities.

Sites for low-rental housing must meet certain specifications. They should be either within walking distance of a major center of employment or convenient to mass-transportation facilities capable of carrying the required volume of passengers to and from work. They should also, in common with higher-cost housing, have easy access to major highways but be isolated from them for the safety of those living in the area, and should be provided with the recreation, educational, and social facilities belonging in a planned neighborhood, as described in detail in Chapter 13 (pages 3 to 6).

Sound city planning is one of the means which must be used if the deterioration of housing into slums is to be prevented. James Ford has said: [1] "The customary approach to the problem by city planners is, naturally enough,

[1] Reprinted by permission of the publishers from *Slums and Housing*, by James Ford, Harvard University Press, Cambridge, Mass., 1936, page 495.

the city or region considered as a unit. There may be merit in approaching the problem from its opposite angle, the individual and the family." What size of family, what income groups, and what occupation groups want to live where? How much can, or will, they pay for shelter and other facilities? There is need for a thorough knowledge of the answers to these important questions in planning for the modern city, and for vision in interpreting such information if there is to be progress in the standards of urban living. The architect, the contractor, labor, and mortgage capital have all been accused of uninspired following of past standards and practices in housing. The city planner should make sure that he does not accept what has been done as the best that can be done.

Slums—Cause and Effect

The slum has probably been with civilization as long as the city. Certainly we know of it as far back as we have written history. Among relatively recent testimony are reports of slum conditions in New York at the end of the eighteenth century [2] and the classically descriptive works of Charles Dickens and Victor Hugo. Not only has the slum been with us for a long time, but in some instances the same area has remained a slum for over a century. The infamous Five Points, located at the present intersection of Worth and Baxter streets in Manhattan, was the center of the worst slum area of New York in 1827. Today a park and courthouse occupy the spot, but much of the area just east thereof is still a part of New York's outstanding slum areas.

The causes of slums are complex and interacting. Man's unwise use of physical features may be a causative factor. Polluted streams or harbors or excavations which scar the landscape may be surrounded by the dwellings of those "who, because of their poverty, can make no choice, or who, because of their ignorance, do not deplore the injury done to their site." [3] The same is true of the areas which are made undesirable by various noxious activities, such

as heavy traffic, elevated railroads, or factories which are noisy or noisome. Rapid growth of population, particularly by immigration, has caused slums by making the demand for housing too great for the supply, and encouraging speculative, low-standard building for quick profit. Also the growth of cities has pushed business and industrial uses too close to the homes of the well-to-do, causing these buildings, which were designed for spacious living, to be abandoned to those who could not afford and did not know those standards. This same growth has increased land values in these transitional areas, requiring overcrowding in order to collect sufficient total rent. Poor architectural planning, resulting in inadequate light and air, even for dwellings which were not overcrowded, made these buildings intolerable when large numbers of people were crowded into areas meant to house only a few. Most of the factors which cause blight are contributors in making slums. (See Chapter 15, page 33.)

The following statements by James Ford summarize the underlying reason for the development of slums: [4]

Survivals of old principles of land ownership and control are at the bottom of our difficulties. Land owned in fee simple is exploited for the owner's, rather than the public's, benefit. . . . Vested interests, even in slum housing, are at many points inviolable. . . . There can be no solution of the slum problem until the primacy of public interests over private interests in property is recognized and incorporated in the thought-habits of our people and in fundamental law.

One of the principal reasons for an increased awareness of the slum problem has been the growing disparity between the best and the worst in housing as civilization advanced. The concept of democracy, as developed in the last two centuries, has also been a contributing factor. But when the home environment of the well-to-do child is compared with that of the child of the slums, equality of opportunity is still somewhat of a mockery. The myth that slum dwellers "live that way because they want to" dies hard, but it is dying. The economic drain of the slum on the city has been shown by figures. The social cost is less easily proven,

[2] *Ibid.,* pages 40–71.
[3] *Ibid.,* page 444.

[4] *Ibid.,* pages 452 and 506.

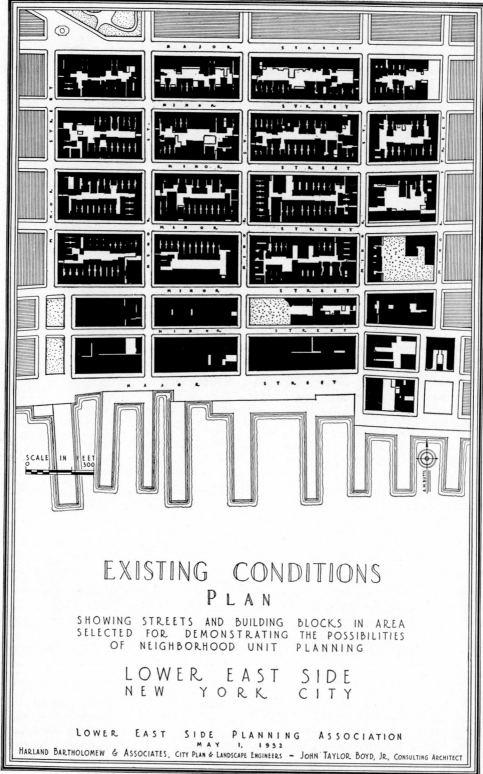

FIGURE 14·1. INSUFFICIENT PROVISION FOR LIGHT AND AIR IN A TYPICAL SLUM AREA

but far more important. The democratic form of government puts the well-being of the nation in the hands of the electorate. To the extent that this electorate is well informed, intelligent, and healthy mentally as well as physically—social in the broadest sense of the word—and only to this extent, can this well-being be furthered.

A graphic description of a slum and its deleterious effect on a city's welfare is given in the following description by Howard Whipple Green of a section of Cleveland: [5]

One small section of slum area in Cleveland in which the community invested over $5,000,000 in public and semi-public buildings produces a tax-rate income of $225,000. It costs the city, county, and Board of Education $1,357,000 to render such direct services as good municipal housekeeping and education require. Thus, this area shows a net cost to the taxpayer of $1,132,000 annually—a loss of well over a million dollars a year. Private funds increase this cost to $1,747,000 a year—a total approaching two million dollars a year.

When fire protection in a residential suburb costs $0.63 per 1,000 dollars of appraised value of land and buildings, $50 seems too large for a section of slum area. When police protection costs $4 per family in a suburban city, $58 seems high.

Since only 5,244 families live in the area, each family is being subsidized to the extent of over $333 per year by tax funds and private funds. And yet these families have no right to be content. They should demand more—a decent environment in which to live. They live in "cast-me-down" dwellings which in the heyday of high rents cost them over $25 per family per month.

They suffer from crime—over 21 per cent of Greater Cleveland's murders during the past 12 years were committed in this tiny section with an area of only 0.55 per cent of the area of Greater Cleveland and a population of but 2.1 per cent of the population of Cleveland, Lakewood, Cleveland Heights, East Cleveland, and Shaker Heights. Among them were not necessarily the murderers. The murderers may have lived in the fine residential suburbs, but the murders were committed in the section. It provided an ideal place to commit a murder, with its dark alleys, tumbled-down buildings, junk yards, and other obstacles to peace and order.

They suffer from vice—over 26 per cent of the houses of prostitution located in eight under-cover surveys made in this community during the past few years flourished in this area. Doubtless, the residents do not patronize the prostitutes—they lack the funds. . . .

They suffer from delinquency—more than six per cent of the boys brought into Juvenile Court lived

[5] *A Sheet-a-Week*, prepared by Howard Whipple Green, Vol. I, No. 52, September 22, 1934.

in this area, a rate three times the average for the entire community. Only 89 boys appear in Juvenile Court per 1,000 boys 10–17 years of age in the community, 307 in this area.

They have illegitimate births—10 per cent of the mothers giving birth to an illegitimate child lived in the area.

They have large numbers of deaths from tuberculosis—nearly 12 per cent of all during a four-year period.

They suffer most from unemployment—5.5 per cent of the jobless lived in the area in April, 1930, as compared with 2.2 per cent of the gainful workers. They had many jobless in January, 1931, 120 per 100 families.

These people need relief—food, clothing, and shelter. As many as 8.0 per cent of all relief families in 1932 were in this section where 1.9 per cent of all families live. Over half of the 5,244 families were on relief in 1932.

They need help—a decent place to live, in a decent environment, with decent opportunities for all.

What kind of citizens are those described above, and how do they contribute to our society? Even if the adults are assumed to be incorrigibles (by no means a justifiable assumption [6]), what chance have their children to avoid the warped minds and characters engendered by such an environment? How far may this infection of sickness, delinquency, vice, and misery spread as the members of this community come in contact with those outside and more fortunate? That the slum attracts certain incompetents, criminals, and degenerates cannot be denied. However, it seems reasonably certain that these types are more the result of slum environments than the cause of slums. The United States Housing Authority reported in 1940 that among 40,000 children in 25,000 families moved from substandard housing to 61 local Housing Authority projects, the number of juvenile delinquents was virtually zero. Although these tenants were a

[6] In *Housing and Citizenship*, Reinhold Publishing Corporation, New York, 1946, George Herbert Gray reports on the experience of the Dutch with public housing. There they found about nine persons in 10,000 had mental or physical deficiencies which made them undesirable tenants in new standard housing. This group was placed in special housing and given special supervision, "graduating" when they were sufficiently improved. Eighty-five per cent of these "undesirables" "graduated" within a few years, leaving only about 1⅓ families in 10,000 who required a longer period, or were incurable.

FIGURE 14·2.   CONDITIONS IN URBAN SLUMS

Upper view shows alley dwellings in Washington, D. C., in March, 1942, near Delaware Avenue.   Lower view shows a tenement on South Elmwood Avenue, Buffalo, eliminated by one of the city's public housing projects.

picked group, certainly this extremely low incidence of delinquency cannot be attributed to
that fact alone. A decent environment gave
them back their self-respect, and they grasped

in the slums as to offer no hope of their elimination. In New York City in 1909 there were
641,344 family units in tenements built before
1901 and considered substandard in their de-

FIGURE 14·3. DISORDERLY REAR YARDS TYPICAL OF URBAN SLUMS

A portion of the site of one of Buffalo's public housing projects.

the opportunity to become constructive members of society. To the extent that equal opportunity is not given to all members of society,
a country suffers.

FIGURE 14·4. SPECULATIVE "LOW-COST" HOUS-
ING, PRODUCING FUTURE SLUMS

Illustrated by a development in Miami, Florida;
view taken in April, 1939.

The slum is not disappearing automatically
in our cities today. Although in the better
sections obsolescent buildings are replaced with
new ones, this process is proceeding so slowly

sign from the standpoint of admission of light
and air. In 1932 there were still 524,894 family
units in these "old-law" tenements.[7] At this
rate it would take over 100 years to replace all
these unhealthy warrens. In some cases, the
slum actually has been profitable to the landlord by returning high rents for uses which
would not be tolerated in more reputable sections of the city.

Good housing, then, is a matter of public
concern. If private initiative cannot furnish
adequate housing for all (and the existence of
slums is proof that it cannot), then the government must take a hand. George Herbert
Gray has said, "When the policy of adjusted
rents is carried out to the point of making public housing development available to families
with incomes from the lowest up to those able
to pay the *economic rent*, . . . then our public
housing policy becomes comparable in principle to that of our public schools, which are
available to all, though all could not enjoy

[7] *Urban Blight and Slums,* by Mabel L. Walker,
Harvard University Press, Cambridge, Mass., 1938,
page 75.

their benefits if required to pay their per capita share of the cost." [8]

Low-cost Housing and the Building Industry

Low-rental housing supplied directly by a public agency has been provided with some form of public subsidy to take care of the differential between an economic rent for *low-cost* housing and a rent that is within the means of the *low-income* group to be served. The problem of providing low-cost housing that will not have to be subsidized is tied up with the economics of the building industry. It is impossible, under existing practices, to produce new housing of a satisfactory standard which can be sold or rented at a price within reach of roughly the lower fourth of our family-income groups.

In 1941 the lowest-priced new houses being built by private developers cost between $3,000 and $4,000. Using the accepted ratio of two years' income as the maximum amount a family should spend for a house means that the lowest-income family which could afford a new

TABLE 21

DISTRIBUTION OF AMERICAN FAMILIES IN TOTAL UNITED STATES AND IN URBAN AREAS, BY INCOME GROUPS, 1941 [a]

Incomes in Dollars	Percentage Distribution	
	All Families and Single Consumers	Urban Families of Two or More Persons
Negative income	0.3 ⎱	
0– 500	15.4 ⎰	3.7
500–1,000	18.2	10.9
1,000–1,500	15.8	13.2
1,500–2,000	14.7	18.3
2,000–2,500 ⎱		17.0 ⎱
2,500–3,000 ⎰	21.1	13.8 ⎰
3,000–5,000	10.5	16.6
5,000 and over	4.0	6.5
Total	100.0	100.0

[a] From Table 443 in *Statistical Abstract of the United States, 1944–1945*, United States Department of Commerce, Bureau of the Census.

[8] *Housing and Citizenship*, by George Herbert Gray, Reinhold Publishing Corporation, New York, 1946, page 140.

house then was in the $1,500- to $2,000-per-year group. Table 21 shows that in 1941 about 28 per cent of the urban families of two or more persons had lower incomes than this and therefore could not afford to buy even the cheapest new house. Nor could they afford new privately developed rental housing at the minimum rents then available. On the basis of 1947 construction prices, it has been estimated that only families in the top 12 per cent income group can afford to purchase or rent new housing. [9]

Let us examine the factors which make up the cost of a house as built by private initiative today. They are as follows:

1. Site.
     Land.
     Existing improvements.
2. Materials.
3. Labor.
     Non-creative.
        Legal service.
        Promotion.
     Creative.
        Directive.
           Engineering.
           Architectural.
           Administrative.
           Governmental.
        Executive.
           Skilled labor.
           Unskilled labor.
4. Capital.
5. Maintenance.
6. Taxes.

In almost every item of the above list there are factors which add to the final cost. Land often is held speculatively for a price higher than is merited. Existing buildings on the site must be razed and may cost something to buy although useless to the purchaser; street improvements as installed may be more elaborate than warranted. The materials which go into a house are of almost incredible variety, and efforts at standardization are only beginning. Furthermore, they pass through many hands from producer to ultimate consumer, and at each exchange some profit is taken. Before money is loaned, titles must be searched—a troublesome and sometimes expensive procedure. And of course the promoter must make his profit.

[9] "Where's the Housing?" by Eugene Raskin, *Progressive Architecture*, February, 1947, page 41.

Under the subheading of creative directive labor, the engineer and the architect cannot afford to spend much time on the individual house, and so it is seldom that sufficient creative thought is given to possible new ways of saving in design and equipment. Administration, such as it is, is split between the owner or promoter, the architect, and the general contractor, and with the building process carried on in the small tailor-made manner which is the mortgagee. These guaranteed loans in 1946 bore interest rates of at least $4\frac{1}{2}$ per cent, whereas Charles Abrams, former Counsel, New York City Housing Authority, is of the opinion that the rate should be not over $3\frac{1}{4}$ per cent.[10] Maintenance adds a substantial figure to the effective rent of housing, whether it be owned or rented by the user, and the close profit margin of low-cost housing encourages construction "economies" which may, in the

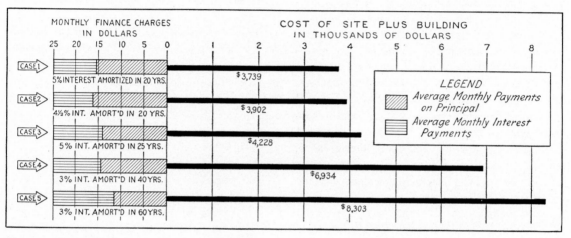

FIGURE 14·5. EFFECT OF VARIOUS INTEREST AND AMORTIZATION RATES ON HOME COST WHICH CAN BE FINANCED FOR $25 PER MONTH

Case 1—regular mortgage; case 2—FHA insured mortgage; case 3—possible alternative FHA insured rate; case 4—possible rate on project financed by an insurance company; case 5—typical USHA rate.

customary today, organization which might affect real economies is very unlikely. Building codes generally are out of date and too rigid, specifying materials and sizes when standards based on performance would give flexibility and permit economies. The various wasteful practices of construction labor are so well publicized as hardly to need mention. Labor's fear of technological unemployment has prevented many possible money-saving factory assemblies, and labor's reluctance to accept lower hourly wages in favor of more regular employment on an annual basis adds to the housing bill.

The cost of capital is a very large item in the total cost of housing. Mortgage money only recently has become available at less than six per cent, and then only when the government, through the Federal Housing Administration, has undertaken to guarantee the principal to

long run, result in an added expense because of excessive maintenance requirements. The accepted United States system of providing the bulk of municipal revenues by taxation of real estate places a heavy burden on housing. Tax rates vary from 2.5 to 4.5 per cent on assessed value, a perpetual fixed charge on housing, which is diminished only in part as the building depreciates in value. This means that taxes on a $3,500 dwelling unit amount to $7 to $13 per month. Some five per cent of our urban families of two or more persons could not afford to pay rent sufficient to cover taxes alone on such a dwelling in 1941. (See Table 21.)

There are many items that go to make up the rental charge for a dwelling. Assume that a tenant can afford $25 a month for the carrying charges of interest and amortization, alone.

[10] *The Future of Housing*, by Charles Abrams, Harper Bros., New York, 1946, page 43.

The total cost of home (site plus building) which this sum would finance under different combinations of interest rates and periods of amortization is shown in Figure 14·5.

If one includes all the elements involved in the creation of housing in the term "construction industry," it becomes quite apparent why that industry has failed to keep pace with others in producing a better product for a lower price. The answer is that there is no such thing as an integrated construction industry in this country. The factors contributing most effectively to the conspicuous success of the automobile industry—vertical organization of the entire process, from raw material to consumer, and mass production through standardization—are not present in the building industry. In all fairness, it must be admitted that certain complications are present in housing which do not exist in the automobile industry; for instance, housing requires land, the housing unit is usually too large for factory completion, and the cost per unit is very much higher for housing than for automobiles. Nevertheless, much could be done in the way of organization and mass production which is not done today. Abrams has stated that the land owner, organizer, contractor, architect, and consumer of housing are unorganized and highly competitive, whereas the materials manufacturers, financiers, and labor are highly organized, with competition limited or non-existent. He also has stated that the consumer has no effective voice in the housing field, since the real estate boards which claim to speak for the land owners and tenants are dominated by brokers and lenders.[11] While these conditions continue to prevail, we can expect little progress in low-rental housing from private enterprise.

Other Approaches to Low-rental Housing

Taking 1941 conditions as a basis, a considerable proportion of the 28 per cent of urban families who, as pointed out on page 22, do not have enough income to afford to buy or rent new privately built housing also cannot afford to rent second-hand housing meeting

[11] *Ibid.*, page 122.

modern standards. This proportion may amount to 10 to 15 per cent of the total number of urban families with two or more persons. This group will always contain some unemployables who will remain public dependents. Others must be housed either in new subsidized public housing or through subsidizing their rents in private second-hand housing until they can advance sufficiently in income level so that they can pay economic rents. The relation between family income and rent (expressed as monthly rental, whether it be rented housing or owner-occupied housing) paid by United States non-farm families in 1940 is shown in Figure 14·6. About 30 per cent of the total had incomes of less than $1,000 a year, and over a third of this group paid less than $10 a month in rent or its equivalent.

As new housing is provided for medium rentals, there will be vacancies in older dwellings as families move from them into the new dwellings. This will permit a "filtering down" process by which members of the group between the 10 and 15 per cent and the 28 per cent, referred to above, may find dwellings within their means. Further than that, "filtering down" cannot be effective. On the other hand, there is no justification for attempting to provide all the lowest-income group with subsidized new housing having conveniences and gadgets better than can be afforded by the next higher income group, who must pay their own way.

The fact that housing is a long-lived product also works against the "filtering down" process. A structure which could be built for $5,000 in 1932 might cost $10,000 in 1947. This $10,000 building, in some future period of deflation, will have to pay finance charges on its original cost, regardless of the fact that the same structure then can be built for perhaps half the price. This encourages speculatively sharp changes in the volume of building. Building booms dry up as soon as any surplus housing appears in the new-unit price group. As Abrams says, "The building industry is geared to an economy of continuous shortage."

It is obvious that unless and until radical improvement is made in all factors involved in the cost of housing, there will have to be some kind of subsidy of low-rental housing. Today most persons are agreed on this principle, but few groups can even begin to agree on how this subsidy should be paid, to what extent, and by whom. Abrams has listed the following five criteria for subsidies: [12]

1. The subsidy should serve a public purpose.
2. The subsidized operation should be administered or controlled by the public.

for building, and managed the projects after they were built.

Between the extremes of profit enterprise and government housing are two other methods of attaining low rentals: philanthropy and co-operative enterprise. Although the philanthropic approach has been useful in leading the way toward better standards and methods by

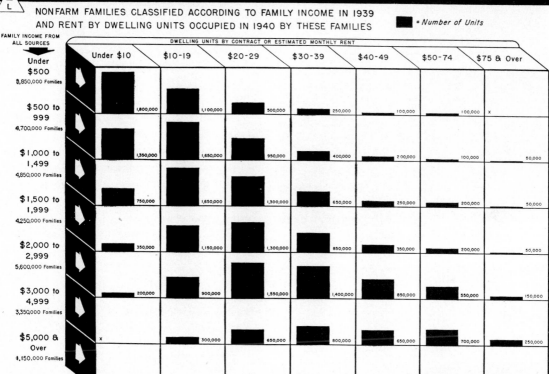

Family Income and Rent of Existing Housing

NONFARM FAMILIES CLASSIFIED ACCORDING TO FAMILY INCOME IN 1939 AND RENT BY DWELLING UNITS OCCUPIED IN 1940 BY THESE FAMILIES   ▮ = Number of Units

FAMILY INCOME FROM ALL SOURCES	DWELLING UNITS BY CONTRACT OR ESTIMATED MONTHLY RENT						
	Under $10	$10-19	$20-29	$30-39	$40-49	$50-74	$75 & Over
Under $500 3,850,000 Families							
$500 to 999 4,700,000 Families	1,800,000	1,100,000	500,000	250,000	100,000	100,000	x
$1,000 to 1,499 4,850,000 Families	1,350,000	1,650,000	950,000	400,000	200,000	100,000	50,000
$1,500 to 1,999 4,250,000 Families	750,000	1,650,000	1,300,000	650,000	250,000	200,000	50,000
$2,000 to 2,999 5,600,000 Families	350,000	1,150,000	1,300,000	850,000	350,000	200,000	50,000
$3,000 to 4,999 3,350,000 Families	200,000	900,000	1,550,000	1,400,000	850,000	550,000	150,000
$5,000 & Over 4,150,000 Families	x	300,000	650,000	800,000	650,000	700,000	250,000
TOTAL FAMILIES 27,750,000	x	x	100,000	150,000	150,000	350,000	400,000

X = Less than 25,000

SOURCE: Estimates of National Housing Agency

From "Hearings before the Subcommittee on Housing and Urban Redevelopment," United States Senate, 79th Congress.

FIGURE 14·6

3. The subsidy should be defined and certain (not hidden).
4. The subsidy should burden the taxpayer as little as possible.
5. The subsidized operation should be capable of being administered practically.

On the basis of these criteria, probably the form of low-rental housing that comes closest to satisfying all requirements is directly subsidized housing done by municipal housing authorities which have acquired the land, let the contracts

[12] *Ibid.*, pages 326–329.

example, it never has satisfied more than the smallest fraction of the need, nor can it do so. For the co-operative method there is more hope. Among the outstanding examples of successful co-operative housing in this country are two projects by the Amalgamated Clothing Workers Union, the first built in 1926 in The Bronx and the second in 1930 on the Lower East Side of Manhattan. But with maximum allowable rentals per room of $11 in the Bronx project and $12.50 in the Manhattan project, even these apartments are not used by really low-income families. However, the purchase price per room of $500, a decidedly low figure for the standard of housing offered, demonstrates the economies possible by co-operative methods. (See Figure 14·7.)

The co-operative approach to the housing problem, when pursued intelligently and vigorously, has demonstrated an ability to furnish

Courtesy, Amalgamated Housing Corporation.

FIGURE 14·7. AMALGAMATED CO-OPERATIVE APARTMENTS, BOROUGH OF THE BRONX, NEW YORK CITY

View in interior court, taken in 1927.

better results at lower costs than private housing. In the period 1926–1935, co-operative societies produced 10 per cent of all new housing in Sweden and 75 per cent of all new housing in Holland.[13] It has been found that the social development of the tenants is an important factor in the success of housing. In the rehabilitation of former slum dwellers, supervision of trained social workers who take care of the details of management and rent collection and engage in friendly co-operation with tenants in the solution of their many personal problems has been shown not only to be of social benefit but also to have economic advantages in preventing the destruction of property and in improving living conditions.[14] The co-operative housing project starts with the advantage of its essentially social approach and conveys an awareness of civic responsibility to its members which carries over to the benefit of the city and the country in general. Abrams has favored as the ultimate aim of all public housing its eventual conversion to co-operative ownership.

It should be emphasized here that the so-called "co-operative apartment" built by a developer and then sold to various tenants, which has flourished in times of inflation in this country, is not a true co-operative and has almost none of the advantages which are described above. It is primarily a device to enable the builder to unload his building at a profit while prices are high. The weakness of the true co-operative movement in this country has been in part a result of the success of the private enterprise system in furnishing goods and services at low prices, and in part due to the traditional individualistic character of the American citizens. In the field of housing, private enterprise has failed to live up to the general standard. As this realization spreads throughout the public, we may see more co-operative housing.

Legislative Regulation of Privately Built Housing

While several European countries have been far ahead of the United States in public housing, this country has led in setting housing standards by law. This is particularly true in the city of New York, where the slum problem has been especially large and acute as a result of the city's age and the fact that it has been the principal immigration center of the country. Discussion of this phase of public activity in housing therefore will deal principally with developments in New York, where the laws have, in general, been the first and the models upon

[13] *Housing and Citizenship,* by George Herbert Gray, Reinhold Publishing Corporation, New York, 1946, page 73.

[14] This approach was originated by Miss Octavia Hill in London in 1864. For a thorough discussion of her work, see *Slums and Housing,* by James Ford, Harvard University Press, Cambridge, Mass., 1936, pages 573–580.

which those for other municipalities have been patterned.[15]

Realization that housing affects the welfare of the public as well as the individual came early in New York. In 1647 the Director General and the Council of New Amsterdam (New York was then under Dutch rule) appointed surveyors to superintend the location of houses and fences in order to correct the "disorderly manner . . . practised in building and erecting houses, . . . in placing pig pens and privies on the public roads, . . . [and] in neglecting the cultivation of granted lots. . . ."[16] Lots remaining unimproved nine months after the original grant were ordered to revert to the original grantor. Thus, three centuries ago, the problem of idle urban land was recognized and dealt with more effectively than can be done today. Another order required the removal of wooden and plaster chimneys, which had been found to be a public fire hazard. Building regulations from the standpoint of fire protection developed early, through necessity to protect the public from the sins of omission or commission of the individual.

An early government slum-clearance project was authorized in New York in 1800 by the state legislature in an effort to prevent disease-breeding conditions in areas where buildings were erected "upon lots of ground so short, as to deprive such buildings of the free circulation of the air, and to compel the occupants of them to make the cellar or other parts thereof receptacles of filth and dirt."[17] The city was authorized to purchase, freely or by eminent domain, all properties in certain areas so afflicted, to raze the buildings, and to dispose of the properties in any way which would benefit the health and welfare of the city. In 1804 the

city enacted regulations requiring the licensing of taverns and boarding houses. These licenses were to show, among other things, "the number of lodgers authorized in each house" as fixed by certain municipal authorities.[18]

The latter half of the nineteenth century brought about great concern over the slum problem in New York, and with this increased awareness of the evils of the tenements came a great deal of regulatory legislation aimed at improving the standards of light, air, sanitation, and, indirectly, population densities in these dwellings. These five decades of investigation and regulation culminated in the Tenement House Act of 1901. Among other features, this law required that tenements constructed thereafter:

1. Be of fireproof construction if over 60 feet high, or fire-safe at specified strategic points if less than 60 feet high.
2. Cover not more than 70 per cent of the area of interior lots or 90 per cent of corner lots.
3. Have specified rear yard sizes and court sizes.
4. Have at least one window of specified size in each room, to open on street, yard, or court.
5. Have specified minimum room sizes.
6. Provide running water and a water closet in each apartment.

In addition, the Tenement House Act of 1901 required the following improvements in existing buildings:

1. Windows to be cut between windowless rooms and those having outside light, or directly to outside light.
2. Radical improvement of sanitary facilities to specific standards.
3. Specific minimum standards of cubage of air per person occupying.

This law was very carefully drawn, provided for building permits to be issued by the city before any construction could be started, and prohibited occupancy of the building until a certificate of compliance had been granted by the city. It also provided in detail for administration, enforcement, and penalties, both civil and criminal. The Tenement House Law of 1901 represented the high point of comprehensive housing legislation of restrictive nature up

[15] A detailed description of New York City housing legislation will be found in *Slums and Housing,* Vol. I, by James Ford, Harvard University Press, Cambridge, Mass., 1936. The following four paragraphs have drawn on this material.

[16] *Ibid.,* page 28. (Statement quoted from *Records of New Amsterdam from 1653 to 1674,* edited by Berthold Fernow, New York, 1897, Vol. 1, page 4.)

[17] *Ibid.,* page 80. (Statement quoted from *Laws of the State of New York Passed at the Sessions of the Legislature Held in the Years 1797, 1798, 1799, and 1800, Inclusive,* pages 541–543.)

[18] *Ibid.,* page 81. (Statement quoted from *Minutes of the Common Council of the City of New York, 1784–1831,* III, 350–352.)

to the time of the writing of this book, since the Multiple Dwelling Law of 1929 replaced many provisions of the 1901 law with less strict ones.

Legislative Promotion of Housing

The first legislative effort at promoting low-rental housing in the United States was the establishment of the New York State Board of Housing in 1926. Under this law, housing corporations whose dividends were limited to six per cent, by complying with certain standards and other requirements, could enjoy partial tax exemptions for as long as 20 years at the option of the municipality. Rents per room per month were limited to $12.50 in Manhattan, $11 in the remainder of New York City, and $9 in smaller communities. Although several of the projects built under this law without governmental subsidy made contributions to the housing field by their examples in planning, financing, or management, few were built to rent for less than the maxima set.

President Hoover's Conference on Home Building and Home Ownership in 1931 led to an active federal interest in low-rental housing. In 1932, as part of the government's relief program, the Reconstruction Finance Corporation was authorized to make 10-year loans to corporations formed to provide housing for low-income families, and Knickerbocker Village in New York City, involving the clearance of two congested blocks in the Lower East Side of Manhattan, was built under this procedure. In the following year there was established the Housing Division of the Public Works Administration to advance funds to local limited-dividend housing corporations under state control. The state legislatures hurriedly acted to legalize acceptance of such federal moneys, but only seven projects received final approval under this program.

When this program was discontinued in 1934, a United States Emergency Housing Corporation was created, with power to acquire sites and to develop federal low-rent housing projects, using PWA funds. Projects under this public corporation were undertaken only after local sponsorship, but they were federally

planned, built, and owned until taken over by local sponsors. Initially there was an outright 30 per cent capital grant, which was later increased to 45 per cent, and a 45-year amortization period for the cost of materials and labor; a three per cent ground rent was charged in lieu of amortization of the land. Later amendments to the powers of the USEHC stipulated a charge based on the ability of the tenants to pay in lieu of municipal taxes, and allowed greater flexibility in the period of amortization and interest rate. The centralized administration of this corporation, labor troubles caused in part by the use of PWA labor, and charges of politics in the choice of tenants were among the factors which made it necessary to change this system.

Gradually the idea evolved that the proper agency to plan, build, and operate public housing, however it might be financed, was a municipal public housing authority. Recognizing this principle, the United States Housing Authority was established in 1937, and intended as a permanent agency. It was authorized to loan and grant funds to local public housing authorities for slum clearance and rehousing, with the objective of providing new rental housing at rates which former slum dwellers could afford. Cost per family unit was limited, and housing so furnished could be rented only to those occupying substandard housing and having incomes not over five or six times the scheduled rent. Slum clearance was assured by requiring, with certain exceptions, that one existing substandard family unit be eliminated for each one constructed. The USHA advanced a loan running for not over 60 years and amounting to not more than 90 per cent of the cost, the remainder to be supplied by the local community. To reduce rents to the required point, annual subsidies were to be split 20 per cent by the local government and 80 per cent by the USHA. The local portion of the subsidy usually took the form of remission of taxes and charges for public service, while the USHA generally furnished sufficient subsidy to assure payment of interest on the loan.

Under the USHA, projects had to be initiated, completed, and maintained by local authorities, which required passage by states of enabling acts for local authorities, granting them the necessary powers, including land acquisition by use of eminent domain and the right to issue bonds. As of January, 1942, there were 622 local housing authorities co-operating with USHA, and 491 projects completed or

for public service as the local subsidy does there seem to be a question, in that this is to some extent a hidden subsidy.

The efforts described above were aimed to promote low-rental housing. The federal government also has aided housing for moderate-

Courtesy, New York City Housing Authority.

FIGURE 14·8.　FOUR STAGES IN HOUSING DEVELOPMENT AS SHOWN IN A FEW NEIGHBORING BLOCKS IN NEW YORK CITY

1—Old-law tenements banned in 1901; 2—New-law tenements with larger courts and improved ventilation; 3—Dunbar Apartments, a privately sponsored development with community features; 4—Harlem River Houses, a public housing project of the New York City Housing Authority.

under contract.[19]　In 1942 the Federal Public Housing Authority was created as part of the National Housing Agency and took over the functions of USHA. Measurement of USHA projects by Abrams' criteria for subsidies (see page 25) shows that the requirements have been quite well satisfied on the whole. Only in the practice of remitting taxes and charges

to high-income groups through various agencies. The Federal Housing Administration was created in 1934 to mitigate some of the evil effects of what was then standard mortgage practice on homes. It was designed to help only those owners or renters who had sufficient income to pay their own way. The FHA merely insures mortgages of certain types and on certain kinds of residential construction. The lower interest rates of FHA-insured mortgages have made them very popular, and its program may be

[19] *Housing and Citizenship,* by George Herbert Gray, Reinhold Publishing Corporation, New York, 1946, page 235.

considered a decided success. It has aided permanently in putting the mortgage business on a sounder basis, both by reducing the risk and by requiring regular amortization payments, and it has raised the structural, architectural, and planning standards in housing. Furthermore, it has done this without expense to the taxpayer. As of January, 1944, the excess of income over operating expenses of the FHA was $13,753,310.[20]

The Home Owners' Loan Corporation was established in 1933 to forestall foreclosure of mortgages on small homes, such foreclosures being at a peak because of the severe economic depression. Its chief positive contribution to housing has come as a result of its policy of renovation and resale of homes on which it has foreclosed. The Federal Home Loan Bank System has functioned as a credit reserve system. It has reduced interest rates and raised construction and design standards. Both the HOLC and the FHLB are self-supporting, but neither has made any direct contribution to housing for the lowest-quarter income group.

A Perspective of the Housing Problem

The city planner has small hope of seeing his dream city realized until the problem of low-rental housing is solved. In the land use pattern, residential uses take up about 60 per cent of all developed areas in our cities, and a substantially greater proportion when suburban areas are included. As long as one-fourth of a city's population is compelled to live in housing which does not meet adequate standards, some 15 per cent of the developed areas in such a city will therefore tend to remain blighted, no matter how successfully the rest of the city plan may be carried out. Some form of subsidy, direct or indirect, seems essential to eliminate these blighted areas. This is a matter of real concern to the city planner.

What basic competitive difficulties does shelter face in our national economy when compared with the two other common necessities—food and clothing? First, shelter is not readily

[20] *National Association of Housing Officials Year Book,* 1944, page 49.

movable, so that it cannot be manufactured complete in an economically advantageous location and shipped as a unit to the consumer, nor can an excess of shelter in one location readily be moved to another. Second, shelter requires land in a particular location. The amount of available shelter-land in a desirable location is limited, this limitation being modified by the density of use and the transportation facilities of the area. Third, shelter is long-lived; physically it may last at least as long as the full lifespan of a person, but it is subject to severe obsolescence, and therefore may become undesirable long before it is actually "worn out" or "consumed." Fourth, shelter, as such, is subject to a direct tax, to which the other two basic necessities are not, in the real property tax, from which about one-fourth of all tax revenues in the United States was raised in 1941.

What can be done to reduce these unique difficulties which impede the production and distribution of shelter in the United States? To reduce the difficulty of the relative immobility of shelter, it is at least possible to manufacture partial housing assemblies at one location and ship them to the final location. As has been noted in an earlier section of this chapter, this procedure has been impeded considerably by the objections of the building trade unions and by lack of standardization. A notable start in this direction has been made, however, by one manufacturer who assembles a plumbing "core," in which are the heating facilities and all necessary plumbing connections for the bathroom on one side and the kitchen on the other. Wide use of such standardized assemblies could mean an appreciable saving in initial cost and in maintenance.

The question of the limited quantity of desirable land for purposes of shelter is quite complex. It is the responsibility of the planner to see that this quantity is kept as large as possible by proper design for transit and highways, which will provide maximum accessibility to areas of intensive use, and to keep these areas of intensive use from becoming needlessly concentrated, overconcentration having the effect of decreasing the available supply of desirable shelter-land.

The problem can also be attacked by changes in the tax system, a method which will be discussed in more detail in Chapter 24, "Municipal Land Policies" (see page 192).

To minimize the obsolescence to which shelter is so subject because of its long life requires that the planner, the architect, the engineer, and the builder use all their intelligence and skill to assure that new housing embodies the best known techniques and the most enduring standards in its design and construction. (See Chapter 15, page 37.) They must discard the husk of fashion and seek the grain of usefulness for living. This will require that the public be aware of the importance of this work, and that more of the time and energy of the technicians involved be spent on housing.

In addition to reducing these four competitive inequalities of housing, the building industry must be integrated and revitalized, ways must be found to accomplish slum clearance and urban reconstruction, the real estate pattern must be stabilized, and a better mortgage system must be evolved. Unless and until these goals are substantially accomplished, we will have to subsidize housing for a considerable proportion of our population. We cannot afford to do otherwise. Gray has written, "From our point of view, any public policy which puts financial investment ahead of social investment in citizenship misses the point and dodges the issue." [21]

Our current public housing program has but scratched the surface. It has been estimated that in about 1940 some 45 per cent of the total substandard housing in this country was occupied by those ineligible for USHA (now FPHA) housing and unable to afford commercial rents.[22] These persons will have to be adequately housed before our "investment in citizenship" through housing can be considered sufficient.

[21] *Housing and Citizenship,* by George Herbert Gray, Reinhold Publishing Corporation, New York, 1946, page 164.

[22] *Ibid.,* page 143.

Selected References

ABRAMS, CHARLES: *The Future of Housing,* Harper Bros., New York, 1946.

"A Housing Program for the United States" (a report prepared for the National Association of Housing Officials), *Publication* 48, Public Administration Service, Chicago, 1935.

BAUER, CATHERINE: *Modern Housing,* Houghton Mifflin Company, Boston and New York, 1934.

FORD, JAMES: *Slums and Housing* (two vols.), Harvard University Press, Cambridge, Mass., 1936.

GRAY, GEORGE HERBERT: *Housing and Citizenship, A Study of Low-cost Housing,* Reinhold Publishing Corporation, New York, 1946.

"Neighborhoods Built for Rental Housing," *Land Planning Bulletin* 4, Federal Housing Administration, Washington, D. C., August, 1947. (Gives plans, photos, and statistics for nine modern garden-apartment projects.)

Slums, Large-scale Housing, and Decentralization (reports of committees on blighted areas and slums), President's Conference on Home Building and Home Ownership, Washington, D. C., 1932.

WOOD, EDITH ELMER: "Slums and Blighted Areas in the United States," *Housing Division Bulletin* 1, Federal Emergency Administration of Public Works, Washington, D. C., 1935.

Questions

1. What other features of the city plan are closely related to housing?
2. What are the principal specifications which sites for low-rental housing must meet?
3. What is a slum? What are the principal causes of slum areas?
4. About what proportion of families in the United States could afford to purchase or rent new housing under 1941 conditions? Under present-day conditions?
5. Describe some of the reasons why the building industry has failed to keep pace with other industries in producing a better product for a lower price.
6. What criteria should govern the granting of subsidies for low-rental housing?
7. How has co-operative enterprise met the problem of lowering housing costs?
8. Describe some of the legislative requirements for standards of housing construction.
9. What efforts has the United States government made to promote low-rental housing? How successful have these been?
10. What are some of the planner's approaches to a solution of the housing problem?

15

REDEVELOPMENT OF BLIGHTED AREAS

THE STUDY OF THE PROBLEM OF REDEVELOPMENT of blighted areas in cities to some extent is an outgrowth of earlier studies of slum clearance and housing. The first idea was to get rid of slums. This objective led to consideration of the principles of adequate housing, which in turn led to realization of the importance of planning for neighborhoods and communities of neighborhoods within the urban area as one of the important phases of the housing problem. Both slum clearance and urban redevelopment too often are thought of as housing projects.

Photo by John B. Sanromd.   Courtesy, Trustees George Robert White Fund.

FIGURE 15·1. THE PRADO IN BOSTON, MASSACHUSETTS, CONNECTING HISTORICAL CHRIST CHURCH (OLD NORTH CHURCH) WITH ST. STEPHENS CHURCH, AN EARLY TYPE OF BULFINCH ARCHITECTURE

Constructed by the Trustees of the George Robert White Fund and turned over to the City of Boston in 1934, this involved the demolition of 17 buildings, including tenements, and the elimination of an old public street 10 to 12 feet in width at a total cost of $265,000. Christ Church is in background, and a statue of Paul Revere in foreground.

Although it is true that residential uses absorb the largest part of the developed urban area, it is not necessarily true that a slum or a blighted area therefore should be rebuilt with dwellings. It may be that major portions of the area in question should be developed for business or industry or as parks.

Proper redevelopment depends on proper planning, which will show to what uses the area in question is best suited. The city plan shows generally how the area should function in the city pattern, and the community and neighborhood plans will show the details of land use and development within the area. Only in this way can the chaos which contributed to the blight be avoided in the new development. The problem of urban redevelopment therefore involves neighborhood and community replanning.

Nature of Urban Blight

A blighted area may be defined as a section of a community where, "as a result of social, economic, or other conditions, there is a marked discrepancy between the value placed upon the property by its owner and its value for any uses to which it can be put, appropriate to the public welfare, under existing circumstances." [1] Major-general U. S. Grant, 3rd, has listed the following four major symptoms of blight:

1. Areas of decreasing taxable and use values, without corresponding decrease in municipal operating and maintenance costs.
2. Areas gradually being abandoned or relegated to uses incongruous with the character of surrounding neighborhoods.
3. Areas incapable of adequate development in the normal way because of initial faulty subdivision, topographic obstructions, or the thoughtless intrusion in the past of artificial obstacles to normal development.
4. Slums, with their squalid and overcrowded conditions, breeding crime, disease, and only too often bad instead of good citizens.

It should be emphasized that all four symptoms need not be present in any one area to make it a blighted area; any one of them is sufficient. However, the first or second symptom listed

above almost always will be found. The fourth symptom is an extreme condition found in residential areas.

In her book *Urban Blight and Slums*, Mabel L. Walker lists these four criteria for blighted areas:

1. Falling land values over a long period.
2. Detrimental shifts of business or population.
3. Failure to make or maintain improvements over an extended period.
4. Substandard housing.

Again, the last item may not be present in some blighted areas which are not primarily residential in character.

Blighted districts are a severe problem in our urban areas today. A study of a group of large cities showed that slum districts contained about one-third of the city's population, absorbed about 45 per cent of its resources in the cost of such services as fire and police protection, poor relief, and sanitation, yet paid in real estate taxes only six per cent of total city revenues. [2] Table 22 compares 1942 figures for

TABLE 22

COMPARATIVE STATISTICS FOR A BLIGHTED AREA AND AN UNBLIGHTED AREA IN LOS ANGELES IN 1942

Characteristics of Area	Blighted Area	Unblighted Area	City Average
Area in square miles	3.0	2.2	Not reported
Population	48,900	33,000	" "
Median age in years	30	38	" "
Percentage white	92	100	" "
Percentage native	69	84	" "
School years completed	7.6	11.7	" "
Persons per gross acre	26.8	20.6	" "
Average rental per dwelling unit in dollars	23.60	37.50	" "
Income per capita to city for current expenditures through			
Revenue from taxes in dollars	4.25	11.30	13.00
Other revenues	3.63	3.63	3.63
Percentage of city average	47	90	100
Expenditure per capita in dollars by city for			
Direct services [a]	9.87	6.28	9.13
Indirect services [b]	7.35	7.35	7.35
Percentage of city average	104	83	100

[a] Includes police, fire, health, library, parks, and playgrounds.
[b] Includes executive and administrative departments, public works, tax collections, etc.

[1] Reprinted by permission of the publishers from *Urban Blight and Slums*, by Mabel L. Walker, Harvard University Press, Cambridge, Mass., 1938, page 6.

[2] Testimony of Major-general Philip B. Fleming, Federal Works Agency Administrator, before the Senate Subcommittee on Housing and Urban Redevelopment, January 11, 1945, page 1525.

a blighted area and an unblighted area in Los Angeles. The two areas were carefully selected to obtain, in so far as possible, comparable conditions from the standpoint of income and living habits of the inhabitants.[3] The figures show some of the financial effects of blight on the municipality. In the blighted area income represented only 46 per cent of expenditures on a per capita basis, whereas in the unblighted area the ratio was 109 per cent.

In the blighted area police arrests were 3½ times as frequent and juvenile delinquency almost seven times as frequent as in the unblighted area, and health costs were found to be 2½ times as great, although the blighted area had less than 1½ times the population. Since the budgets of city departments, especially health and police, are limited and do not begin to satisfy the need, the above comparisons still do not give the entire picture.

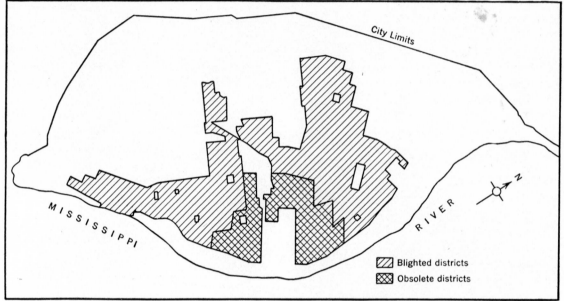

From "St. Louis After World War II," 1942. Courtesy, St. Louis City Plan Commission.

FIGURE 15·2. MAP SHOWING EXTENT OF OBSOLETE AND BLIGHTED DISTRICTS IN ST. LOUIS

The social effects of blight are less amenable to cost analysis, but are even more important. The same study reported incidence per 10,000 persons of the following fire, police, and health services in the two areas of Los Angeles:

	BLIGHTED AREA	UNBLIGHTED AREA
Fire alarms	256	142
Police arrests	350	100
Juvenile delinquency	67	10
Visits of home nurse for		
Communicable diseases	69	14
Tuberculosis	705	91
Visits of doctor for		
Communicable diseases	66	28
Indigent cases	59	0

[3] *Urban Land,* Vol. 5, No. 5, Urban Land Institute, May, 1946.

Blight is a festering sore on our urban civilization which is infecting our citizens, both present and potential, and which is draining a disproportionate share of our economic strength. And it is spreading. While population and property values decrease in centrally located blighted districts, new development takes place on the fringes of the city. Existing utilities are not fully used in the blighted center, while additional facilities are required for the newly developed areas. Transit lines and highways also are extended, while tax returns decrease and tax delinquency mounts in the blighted district. The incidence of urban blight is not a new phenomenon, but as long as our cities grew rapidly in total population, it was not widely recognized as a serious problem. With the stabilized urban populations which are expected within the next few decades the proportional magnitude of this problem will increase.

Causes of Blight

Urban blight may be caused by physical influences, lack of planning in the original development, intrusion of deleterious uses, city growth and change in area use and value, social deterioration, normal obsolescence, land speculation, or a combination of these factors.

Examples of physical influences which may cause blight are found in areas subject to flood or areas of excessive slope. An inadequate street system or awkward block or lot shapes are results of lack of planning or poor planning which may inhibit good development and encourage blight. The construction of an elevated railroad through an area or an industrial use having objectionable features is a deleterious influence on the immediately surrounding areas and may result in blight. With heavy

population growth in one direction the central business district may shift its position considerably, as in New York City, where the main shopping center has moved from 14th Street to about 50th Street in the half-century since 1900. When such a shift occurs, the old district tends to become a blighted area. The relationship between "social deterioration" and blight

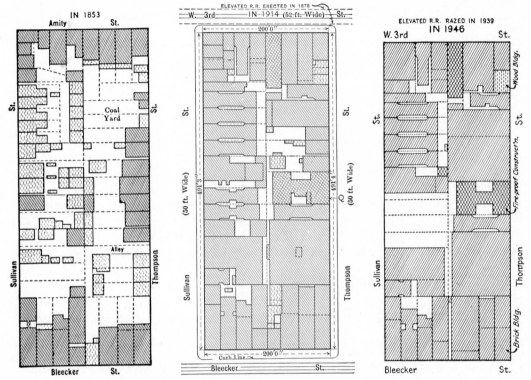

FIGURE 15·3. CHANGES IN SUBDIVISION AND IN AREA BUILT UPON IN A TYPICAL BLOCK IN NEW YORK CITY, 1853, 1914, AND 1946

can be seen in almost any city in areas originally consisting of large single-family residences built by the wealthy and abandoned by them to become rooming houses, or in areas adjacent to "ghettos" of any nationality or race.

The physical changes which have taken place in a typical block in a blighted area of New York City are shown in Figure 15·3, where the coverage and nature of occupancy in 1853, 1914, and 1946 are shown in three separate diagrams.[4]

[4] The 1853 and 1914 plans are from a committee report, "Best Methods of Land Subdivision," presented by E. P. Goodrich, *Proceedings of the Seventh National Conference on City Planning,* Detroit, 1915, facing page 48.

In this case a residential district of the better class was converted into one of cheap tenements or combined shops and flats; some of these were later displaced by warehouses and factories, and eventually demolition of abandoned buildings was started.

An area may become blighted merely through normal obsolescence; to quote Alfred Bettman, "obsolescence is not merely a structural obsolescence, but an obsolescence of the design of the areas themselves as well as of the whole urban territory." [5] Not only do structures and improvements in an area grow old, but with advancing design and technologies the facilities themselves may become out of date. An example of such obsolescence is the "parlor" of the nineteenth-century house, which today has become for most people a relatively useless room. Similarly, the separate dining room is no longer always wanted, and the individual back yard of the row house is giving way to the common landscaped area and playground, as its individual furnace is being replaced in group housing today with central heating. With the increasing use of the automobile, the business building on a narrow street has found itself at a disadvantage compared to one on a wide street.

Finally the important factor of land speculation is a cause of blight, in that properties are held for prices at which there is no possibility of appropriate and economic development in the location. The speculator anticipates sale for a higher-value use than exists, and so reduces his expenditures for maintenance to a minimum. He is uninterested in the property as presently used in the existing community, hoping only to make a profit on his invested capital by sale. The tragedy of this practice is that there is little or no possibility of any such sales except in isolated and fortuitous cases, yet each such high-priced sale is used by scores of owners in the neighborhood as an indication that they also may expect a windfall. Raymond Unwin has shown that, at the rate of growth of commercial uses in metropolitan Chicago between 1923 and 1936, if all future commercial growth could be concentrated in the central areas of that city which were blighted in 1936, it would take until at least the year 2080 to redeem the full extent of these blighted areas exclusively with commercial uses.[6] Yet property owners in blighted areas continue to hold out for prices based on an anticipated commercial use and therefore higher than can be paid for economically feasible residential redevelopment. Such speculative holding is encouraged in cities which are overzoned for business and other intensive uses, or which are not zoned at all.

Certain financial practices also have encouraged and aggravated this hopeless tendency to hold property for an uneconomic price. Until recently it was usual to continue mortgages without amortization, counting on the land value to rise at least as much as the improvement depreciated. That such a rise in land values would continue indefinitely seems often to have been assumed by mortgagor and mortgagee alike, but in areas where this has not happened, there frequently is no equity left because there has been no reserve for depreciation. The rental value of the structure may reveal this, but there is general failure to base capital value on rental value. There has been too much of this "capitalization of expectations" in our mortgage and real estate bond structure.

James Ford said, "The ignorance of [designer,] landlord, tenant, or public official; the lack of perspective in each; speculation, greed, corruption, apathy, fashion, and imitation; the rise of standards which create obsolescence—all originate in our social system." [7] His statement sums up the causes of urban blight, but it cannot be emphasized too strongly or too often that the crux of the problem is the discrepancy between the value which the owner places on the land and the uses to which the property can appropriately and economically be put. This discrepancy always is present in blighted areas. Realization of the fact that the asking price for property in a blighted area

[5] Statement before the Senate Subcommittee on Housing and Urban Redevelopment pursuant to Senate Resolution 102, Part 9, January 12, 1945, page 1605.

[6] Housing and Citizenship, by George Herbert Gray, Reinhold Publishing Corporation, New York, 1946.

[7] Reprinted by permission of the publishers from Slums and Housing, by James Ford, Harvard University Press, Cambridge, Mass., 1936, page 454.

is vastly above its true value is painfully slow in the land owner. The East Side of Manhattan between 3rd and 14th streets had been a blighted area for over 25 years in 1947, yet in that year land prices still were too high to permit redevelopment as even moderate-rental residence, the only reasonable use to which most of this area can be expected to be put.

Problems of Prevention

Since successful redevelopment of any blighted area depends on the ability of the new development itself to resist blight, it is worth while to examine carefully the problems of prevention. Consider a neighborhood newly developed in the usual manner with single-family houses, each lot separately owned. Such a neighborhood is developed principally by families with young children, who need room, both in the house and outside, for their offspring. Twenty or thirty years pass. The children have grown up and gone away, and the parents are reaching the age where a house is too much trouble for them to care for and is bigger than they need. It is at this time that the critical point is reached. In a space of five to 10 years the character of the neighborhood may change completely. New owners may open some of the houses to roomers, a few may be remodeled as two-family houses, or apartments may be built on one or two sites. Any of these changes will tend to depress the value of the remaining single-family residences for single-family use, but the location may not be such as to warrant any generally more intensive use. This is the beginning of blight.

It will be argued that a proper zoning ordinance will prevent intrusion of more intensive uses, and this is true, but a proper zoning ordinance requires planning and determined administration if it is to remain fully effective. If we assume such control to be effective, then the question becomes, Who will use these existing single-family houses, which now are about 25 years old? Certainly their value for either sale or rent has decreased considerably, since an economic group equivalent to the original owners will not live there because they can

afford something more modern. If the original cost has not been amortized sufficiently by this time to permit sale or rental at a figure which will permit the same degree of services and maintenance for a much lower income group, then blight will follow.[8]

The factor of obsolescence as a cause of blight cannot be eliminated completely, but it can and should be minimized. While physical aging of a structure is unavoidable, the other aspect of obsolescence may be avoided to a large extent, but only by very competent design and adherence to the most advanced principles and standards of the day. However, since there has been reasonable reluctance on the part of investors to finance unproved designs, it seldom has been possible to build for the future to the extent which would fully minimize obsolescence.

Land speculation being a basic cause of blight, considerable thought has been given to its prevention. One of the more radically direct solutions proposed for this problem is the increment tax. Under this proposal the owner of a property could receive for its sale only the amount he had paid for the land, plus the present value of the improvements. Any amount over this would go directly to the municipality. In favor of this proposal are the arguments that it would assess the cost of local public improvements and values created by the city equitably, in addition to maintaining land costs at true market value. In parts of New Zealand and Australia, taxes are levied ad valorem on land, but no tax is levied on improvements on the land. This penalizes unimproved or poorly improved land, encourages a higher degree of improvement than our own system of equal rates on land and improvements, and discourages speculative holding of land for a higher price than is economically justified.[9] "Time zoning" may offer some relief from blight caused by speculative holding by preventing use of a building after a certain period of time. Regulations permitting such limitation by certain municipal authorities were enacted in Denmark

[8] This problem is fully discussed in Chapter 14, "Housing and the City Plan."

[9] In the city of Pittsburgh land is taxed for city purposes at a rate twice as high as improvements, a step toward the land tax system.

in 1939, and in Australia legislation was adopted in 1940 authorizing a limitation of rentals for substandard structures. In both cases the powers applied to dwellings only.

Problems of Redevelopment

Urban redevelopment must be approached from the broadest planning viewpoint. Since the area to be redeveloped is a part of the city, its present and future conditions depend on the degree to which it performs as a healthily functioning part of the city, and its problems must be studied in terms of the economy of the whole area of which it is a part. It must be so designed that it will fit into a pattern of neighborhoods for the entire city, if a haphazard development such as failed before is to be avoided. Figure 15·4 shows a general redevelopment plan for blighted residential areas in downtown Chicago, in which the degree of blight has been related to anticipated rental ranges and neighborhoods, and the area as a whole has been considered. This type of study illustrates the comprehensive approach which is required in planning for the rehabilitation of blighted areas.

Successful redevelopment of a blighted area involves all the problems of prevention of blight which have been discussed in this chapter, in addition to others. Some of the more important of these additional problems are site costs, construction costs, financing, taxation, and resettlement of existing users.

The question of site costs already has been mentioned to some extent. The fact that in all blighted areas the owner's price for a site is in excess of its value for any appropriate use is a stumbling block of major proportions. It might seem that acquisition for redevelopment by exercise of eminent domain would result in somewhat of a reduction of this cost, but this is not the case generally. The court must award the owner a fair price for land so taken. The owners, the mortgagees, the real estate dealers— all the people who are supposedly competent witnesses in such matters—for years have had their ideas of value geared to the potential use under favorable circumstances, rather than to

what the use probably will be. Hardly a witness can be called disinterested among those who may be called "expert" in the matter of real estate prices and values—not even the tax assessor, and his evidence is not always admissible. In a given area, what owner will depreciate the value of his neighbor's property in an eminent domain proceeding? His own may be next. What mortgagee dares admit that the whole neighborhood is overvalued when he may not recover the amount of his mortgage in a sale at a true value? And for the real estate dealer to make such an admission merely cuts his commission at the next sale, unless his view is far-sighted enough to see that there are no sales whatever at the inflated values. All this is not to say that everything is willful misrepresentation. Most of it is rather a blind optimism, but its result is the same. The court gets an inflated idea of the value of the property in question, and then, to be very just, it adds a little more.

It would seem, then, that for purposes of urban redevelopment at least, some method should be worked out whereby the true, fair value of a property could be determined, and the owner forced to sell for this price. However, every legislative effort to set any maximum price for a property to be taken by eminent domain has been held unconstitutional by the courts. In the opinion of Ira S. Robbins, former counsel for the New York State Board of Housing, this situation could be changed only by amendments to the federal and state constitutions.[10]

The land tax and the increment tax might relieve the problem of high site costs to some extent, if they were to be adopted. In the meanwhile, there is strong pressure from real estate and public housing interests for governmental subsidy, either in the form of tax exemption or cash grants, in order to make possible redevelopment of blighted areas. Yet, "on what grounds . . . can it plausibly be argued that the government should tax its citizens to

[10] For a thorough discussion of this difficulty, see *Urban Blight and Slums,* Mabel L. Walker, Harvard University Press, Cambridge, Mass, 1938, pages 184–190.

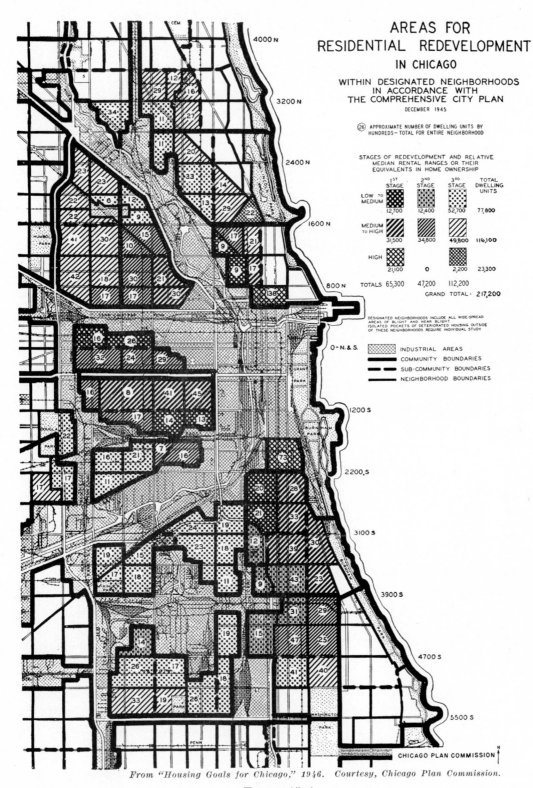

AREAS FOR
RESIDENTIAL REDEVELOPMENT
IN CHICAGO

WITHIN DESIGNATED NEIGHBORHOODS
IN ACCORDANCE WITH
THE COMPREHENSIVE CITY PLAN
DECEMBER 1945

From "Housing Goals for Chicago," 1946.   Courtesy, Chicago Plan Commission.

FIGURE 15·4

bail out the land owners, many of whom have suffered no actual loss, but have merely failed to realize the extravagant gains which they had anticipated?" [11]

In so far as an area properly can be redeveloped for industrial, business, or relatively high-cost residential purposes, the element of building cost will not be an obstacle. However, the greatest part of the blighted areas which exist today will have to be redeveloped as medium- and low-cost housing, since this use takes by far the largest proportion of non-public urban areas. This fact makes the housing problem almost inseparable from the problem of redevelopment of blighted areas. Until the cost of constructing housing is reduced, urban redevelopment is going to be considerably retarded. At present the higher rental uses must help substantially to carry the low-cost housing if most redevelopment projects are to be self-supporting.

To apply the best planning-design principles in redevelopment, the area dealt with must be large, and this requires an unusually large amount of capital. Private sources of such amounts are not plentiful. To date, the principal private investors in large housing projects which may be considered a sort of urban redevelopment have been insurance companies. Unless organizations can be found with large amounts of credit or cash available with which they are willing to back such schemes, most redevelopment will have to be done by public agencies. The government has two advantages over private capital in this field: it can obtain money at considerably lower rates of interest, and properties owned by the government are not subject to tax, nor are incomes from such properties. However, it is obviously impossible for the city to allow extensive areas to be redeveloped and removed from the tax rolls.

Finally, there is the problem of resettlement of existing users in areas to be redeveloped, which is principally a problem of housing. In the years immediately after World War II this problem became a major one, and very difficult to solve.

[11] *Ibid.,* page 130.

Efforts to Accomplish Redevelopment

Considerable study has been given to the processes by which urban redevelopment may be achieved. Some of the earlier suggestions for facilitating the unified redevelopment of areas advocated various co-operative schemes. Essentially most of these methods involve the formation of corporations or trusts in which all properties in a given area are turned over to the company, the various owners receiving stock or certificates proportional to the value of their properties. The three principal difficulties with such devices are: (1) the establishment of valuations on the individual properties; (2) the securing of development capital; and (3) the compulsion of "hold-out" owners in a given area.

Two means of minimizing the amount of development capital required have been proposed, both being devices by which the cost of development can be spread over a period of years. One scheme provides for progressive sectional redevelopment of the area as shown in Figure 15·5. The other provides for initially using the best structures, after their rehabilitation, and a progressive reconstruction of the rest, starting with the worst. Conditions before redevelopment and at an intermediate stage of redevelopment are shown for a study area in the southwest section of Washington, D. C., in Figure 15·6.

Recognition of the necessity for the use of eminent domain in order to acquire all the property necessary for proper redevelopment of blighted areas has resulted in enabling legislation for this purpose.[12] There are two general types of enabling acts of this kind. The first gives the local governments the power to assemble land, issue bonds, and sell or lease land to private enterprise for redevelopment according to a comprehensive plan. The Urban Land Institute reported that, as of August, 1946, this type of legislation had been enacted in eleven states and the District of Columbia. The other type of enabling act is designed to encourage large financial institutions to participate in urban redevelopment by giving cor-

[12] Types of such legislation are discussed further in Chapter 20, "City Planning Legislation," page 147.

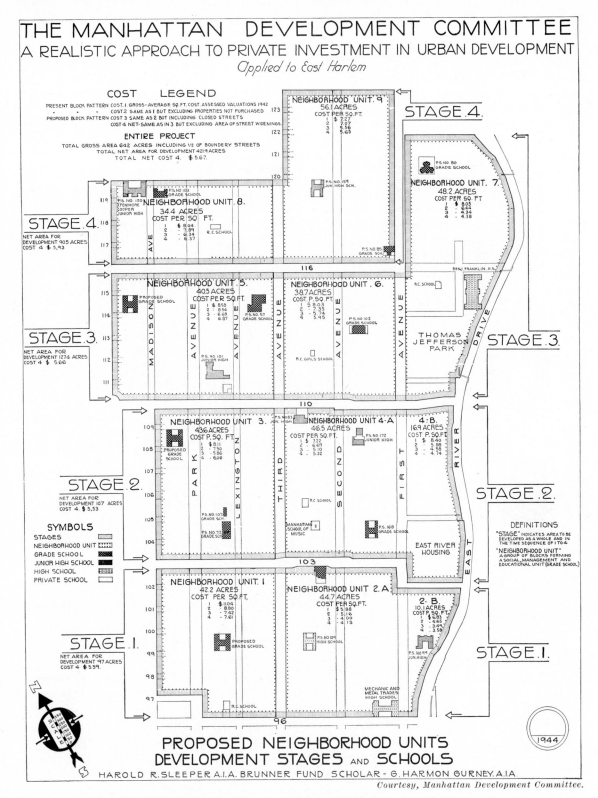

FIGURE 15·5. PROPOSED SECTIONAL REDEVELOPMENT OF A BLIGHTED AREA

Illustrated by a study of the Manhattan Development Committee for the East Harlem area, New York City.

41

porations organized for this purpose access to the power of eminent domain in certain cases, as well as other benefits. Twelve states had passed such legislation by August, 1946, according to the Urban Land Institute. Both types of legislation provide for detailed supervision by

would act on a regional basis. The latter would make a master plan and could order non-conforming uses terminated within 10 years; it could buy, lease, rent, condemn, and sell land in blighted areas, hold land in reserve, zone regardless of existing ordinances, replan and re-

Project Area as Redeveloped

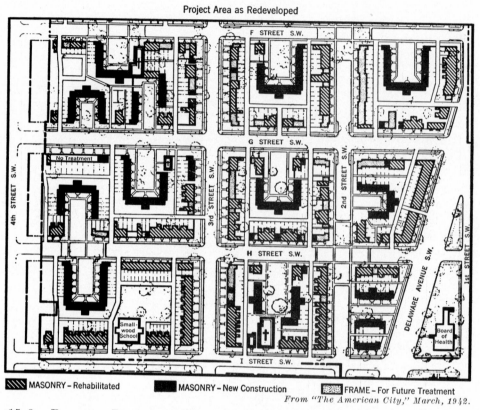

MASONRY – Rehabilitated   MASONRY – New Construction   FRAME – For Future Treatment

From "The American City," March, 1942.

FIGURE 15·6. PROPOSED PROGRESSIVE REDEVELOPMENT OF A BLIGHTED AREA BY USING THE BEST OF EXISTING STRUCTURES IN THE INITIAL STAGES

Illustrated by a study of a "test area" in southwest Washington, D. C., by the Federal Home Loan Bank Board's Neighborhood Conservation Service.

local planning boards, and usually specify some of the financial details of the redeveloping corporation, fixing rents or limiting dividends and sometimes providing for ultimate disposition of the development after a period of years.

The Urban Land Institute in 1947 proposed that Congress enact legislation establishing a Federal Urban Land Commission, the purpose of which would be to encourage private redevelopment. This commission, on petition of the governing bodies representing three-fourths of the population of a metropolitan area, would set up a local commission for that area which

plat, issue bonds, and obtain grants for planning and loans for development from the Federal Urban Land Commission. It could not do any building. On leased lands, both land and improvements would be taxable as usual, but agreements could be made with municipalities on the value for tax purposes, based on the current use value.

One of the more ingenious efforts at reducing rents for redevelopment projects is embodied in the Indiana Redevelopment Act of 1945. This act empowers a Redevelopment Commission duly appointed in a city to levy an assessment on a city-wide ad valorem basis to be used for carrying out redevelopment. By this means cost of interest is eliminated, since redevelopment is put on a pay-as-you-go basis, and the full burden is placed on the present taxpayers. Obviously, such a scheme may meet with considerable opposition on the part of the taxpayers, although in the long run money actually will be saved. The Indiana law limits the rate of assessment to $1 per $1,000 of taxable value for the first two consecutive levying periods, and one-half that rate thereafter. Certainly such a rate is not onerous to the taxpayer, but neither will it provide for much redevelopment. This suggests that perhaps a larger effect could be produced if such funds were used only to make up the required subsidy in land cost which would make private development feasible; in other words, the city might acquire the land by issuing bonds to the extent of its true economic value for the redevelopment purposes intended, make up the rest of the cost by assessment, and lease the land to a redevelopment company at a figure which would cover interest and amortization on the bonds. If an increment tax could be placed on land value, as described in an earlier section of this chapter, the entire proceeds of such a tax might be applied to redevelopment subsidy, as outlined above, thus serving as a double check on blight by discouraging speculative holding of land and by paying for the cost of past speculation in land acquired by the city for development.

Certain efforts aimed at slum clearance are sometimes useful in aiding urban redevelopment. In the city of New York the Tenement House Commissioner has authority to vacate certain multiple dwellings when they consider such buildings to be a nuisance because of being unfit for human habitation. Wherever this power is exercised, the effect is to lower the asking price of the owner for the property, since its earning power is cut off, and it becomes more difficult to hold for eventual sale. In England local authorities can order repairs of dwellings unsuitable for occupancy. Failure to comply may result in condemnation, with award of compensation at the value of the cleared site only. In Holland, in similar cases, the award is made at land value plus the salvage value of the materials.[13]

No single line of attack will succeed in accomplishing the degree of redevelopment which is needed in our cities. The following objectives have been listed by Mabel L. Walker as the more important means toward this end: [14]

1. An adequate city plan.
2. More logical zoning regulations.
3. More effective control of subdivision.
4. Better and more standardized building regulations.
5. Clear and sufficient legal powers for the creation of state and local housing authorities.
6. More effective methods of land assembly at fair prices, and of the exercise of eminent domain for housing purposes.
7. Reform in the system of taxation.
8. Wider use of condemnation for replanning purposes.
9. Improvement of home-financing policies.
10. The creation and rationalization of a home-building industry.
11. Extensive government research in the various aspects of the problem.
12. Government demonstration projects.
13. An intelligent and informed public opinion.

Since the problem of rehabilitation of blighted areas is one of city planning, it is the planner who must interest those in the other fields concerned in the above list, and co-ordinate their efforts toward the goal of a workable and satisfactory solution.

Selected References

A *Handbook on Urban Redevelopment for Cities in the United States,* Federal Housing Administration, Washington, D. C., November, 1941.

A *Realistic Approach to Private Investment in Urban Redevelopment* (a report of the Manhattan Development Committee, New York City), published by *The Architectural Forum,* 1945.

Hearings before the Senate Subcommittee on Housing and Urban Redevelopment of the Special Committee on Postwar Economic Policy and Planning, Parts 6 to 14, Inclusive, United States Senate, 79th Congress, Pursuant to Senate Resolution 102 (78th Congress) and Senate Resolution 33 (79th Congress), Government Printing Office, Washington, D. C., 1945.

[13] As has been pointed out earlier in this chapter, such fixing of compensation would be held unconstitutional in the United States.

[14] Reprinted by permission of the publishers from *Urban Blight and Slums* by Mabel L. Walker, Harvard University Press, Cambridge, Mass., 1938, page 421.

Housing Goals for Chicago, Chicago Plan Commission, 1946.

"Path-finding Study of New York City Reveals Potential Sites for Rehousing," *Information Bulletin* 16, Regional Plan Association, Inc., New York, February 26, 1934.

SANDERS, S. E., and A. J. RABUCK: *New City Patterns,* Reinhold Publishing Corporation, New York, 1946.

WALKER, MABEL L.: *Urban Blight and Slums,* Vol. XII, Harvard City Planning Studies, Harvard University Press, Cambridge, Mass., 1938.

Questions

1. What is a blighted area? To what extent do such areas exist in urban areas?
2. Enumerate the principal causes of blight.
3. Describe the pressures for change as a district developed with one-family dwellings reaches an age of 25 years or more.
4. What is an "increment tax"? How may it control excessive land speculation?
5. List the principal problems to be overcome in the redevelopment of blighted areas.
6. Describe two methods proposed to minimize the amount of development capital required in redevelopment projects.
7. Why has state enabling legislation been deemed necessary to promote urban redevelopment?
8. What forms of federal legislation and agencies have been proposed to aid in redevelopment programs?
9. List some of the objectives, in the field of city planning and administration, which would serve to accomplish the kind and degree of redevelopment needed in our cities.

Part Five

Special Planning Problems

16

THE AIRPORT AND THE CITY PLAN

AIR TRANSPORTATION IS UNIQUE FROM THE PLAN-ning standpoint in that, since the routes of travel do not affect land, the planner's concern is not primarily with the lines of air travel, but with the terminals or stops. Thus planning for air transportation in the community is a problem more of land use than of lines of movement. It is also a problem in co-ordination of transportation facilities, since the airport seldom is, or can be, located near the center of the urban area, and the people and goods which travel by air usually are not near their initial origins or final destinations when they arrive at the airport. The nature of air transportation is such that there are minimum practical trip lengths, since the total time elapsed from initial origin to final destination must be less by air than by other means if the air route is to be used. For example, a traveler from downtown Washington to downtown Philadelphia probably will take the train, with a running time of about 135 minutes, rather than the plane, with a flying time of only 60 minutes, because he will spend about 90 minutes in transferring and traveling to and from the airport if he goes by plane. The distance between the initial origin and final destination is about 140 miles in this instance.

Other features of air transportation are worthy of note. At the end of World War II, the largest commercial planes in use by the airlines in the United States carried some 50 to 55 passengers or six to seven tons of cargo. Experts then foresaw practical plane capacities of 100 to 150 passengers in the not-too-distant future, although there is apparently no theoretical limit to the size of an airplane. However, at these sizes, air operations are more in the nature of bus-line operations, using small units over flexible routes, than of railroad operations, with their long trains carrying varied services over fixed and expensive rights of way. Thus the routing of planes is extremely flexible. Twenty passengers fill a DC-3, one of the very popular commercial transports in 1947, whereupon it can go non-stop, except for refueling, to any place where adequate airport facilities exist. Furthermore, when traffic is sufficient and airport facilities are adequate, flights can be very frequent—a factor of great convenience to the traveler. Because of the speed of the plane, fixed charges on equipment do not bulk as large, relatively, in total costs as those for slower methods of transportation. The Douglas DC-6 transport can cover the 2,500 airline-miles between New York and Los Angeles in about 10 hours' flying time. The fastest railroad trains take about 60 hours to make the same trip. In 1945 planes on scheduled flights averaged well over 500,000 revenue-miles each. At such rates of use, saving a few cents per mile in operating costs may justify the purchase of new equipment. All these factors combine to make air transportation in some ways the most flexible of all forms of transportation.

While the scheduled air carrier is the primary consideration in air transportation, in total miles flown and number of planes it is overshadowed by private and other forms of commercial flying. At the end of 1945 there were about 400 commercial transport planes, which flew some 215,000,000 scheduled domestic revenue-miles in the United States,[1] while in 1941, the last year before World War II, during which civilian aviation activities were curtailed, over 24,000 privately owned planes in

throughout the metropolitan area in such a way as to serve to the maximum extent those who will be using them, and to act as feeders to the main airport or airports without interfering with each other's safe operation.

The Place of Air Transport in the Transportation System

Air transportation has been a significant element in the transportation system in the United States only since the late 1920's, but its growth since then has been meteoric. Table 23 gives significant figures, some of which are

TABLE 23

DOMESTIC AIR-CARRIER OPERATIONS IN THE UNITED STATES, 1926–1945 [a]

	1926	1930	1935	1940	1945
Planes in service	....	....	356	....	400
Route mileage	8,252	29,887	28,267	41,054	51,433
Revenue miles, millions	4.3	32.0	55.4	108.8	215.0
Passengers carried, millions	0.006	0.375	0.7	3.0	7.5
Mail ton-miles, millions	....	....	4.1	10.0	65.0
Express ton-miles, millions	0.001	0.101	1.1	3.5	22.6
Passenger miles, millions	....	84	314	1,147	3,500
Total number of airfields	1,036 [b]	1,782	2,368	2,331	4,026

[a] Figures from *Statistical Handbook of Civil Aviation*, United States Department of Commerce, Civil Aeronautics Administration, Washington, D. C., 1945, pages 22 and 32–34.

[b] 1927.

the United States flew a total of some 346,-303,400 miles.[2] The private planes also require landing facilities, which must be provided for in the master plan.

In order to be properly effective, airport planning should be done on a regional basis. The airport system for the entire metropolitan area must be co-ordinated if adequate facilities are to be provided at an economical cost. One fully adequate, well-located airport for scheduled carriers is better than two, neither of which may be as well located, from the standpoints of convenience, efficiency, and economy. A misdirected "civic booster" spirit sometimes has resulted in such duplication within a single metropolitan area. On the other hand, smaller fields for private flying should be distributed

presented graphically in Figure 16·1. It will be seen that in 1945 route-miles were more than six times the figure for 1926, and revenue-miles were fifty times as great. Passenger-miles flown in 1945 were almost forty-two times as many as they were in 1930.

Perhaps more significant are the ratios of air-passenger revenues to total rail revenues in Pullman accommodations. The Association of American Railroads has estimated that the airlines' share of long-haul passenger transportation by airplane and Pullman car increased from just under 8 per cent in 1937 to just under 18 per cent in 1941.[3] It is a safe guess that this trend will continue for some time. W. A. Patterson, President of United Air Lines, predicted in 1943 that airlines eventually would

[1] *Statistical Handbook of Civil Aviation*, United States Department of Commerce, Civil Aeronautics Administration, Washington, D. C., 1945, page 22.

[2] *Ibid.*, page 87.

[3] *Initial Study of Air Transportation*, Railroad Committee for the Study of Transportation, Association of American Railroads, January, 1944, page 28.

absorb ⅔ of the Pullman, ⅓ of the railroad coach, ⅓ of the interstate bus, ¼ of the railway express, ¼ of the parcel post, and ¹⁄₁₀ of the less-than-carload-lot freight business, representing a growth of 26 times over airline operations in 1940.[4]

steadily to 160,382 in 1945. In that year 70,000 student pilot certificates were issued; this figure is not included in the total number of certificated pilots.[6] The future importance of private flying may be even greater, relatively, than that of commercial flying. A Crowell-

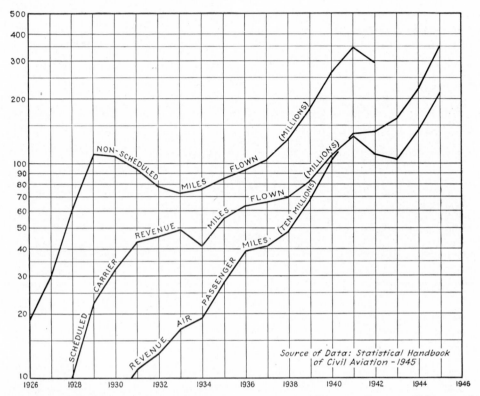

FIGURE 16·1. GROWTH OF AIR TRANSPORTATION IN THE UNITED STATES, 1926 TO 1945

These figures do not include military operations.

The growth of private flying in the United States has been no less spectacular than that of scheduled commercial flying, as is shown in Figure 16·1. There were 2,612 private aircraft in operation in the United States in 1927. This number increased to 10,090 in 1931, decreased to 7,752 in 1934, increased to 24,124 in 1941, decreased during World War II to 21,212 in 1944, and was about 29,000 in 1945.[5] The number of certificated non-military pilots increased from 1,572 in 1927 to 18,594 in 1932, decreased to 13,949 in 1934, and thereafter increased

Collier Survey conducted in 1944 showed the percentages of persons in various age groups desiring to own an airplane to be as follows: [7]

AGE GROUP	PERCENTAGE
18–24	63
25–34	43
35–44	36
45–54	29
Over 55	14

While the desire to own a plane is quite different from actual ownership of one, the higher

[4] *Ibid.*, page 26.
[5] *Statistical Handbook of Civil Aviation*, Civil Aeronautics Administration, United States Department of Commerce, Washington, D. C., 1945, page 87.

[6] *Ibid.*, page 107.
[7] *Airport Plan for Eight Counties of Western New York*, Kenneth Koontz, Niagara Frontier Planning Board, Buffalo, N. Y., 1946, page 2.

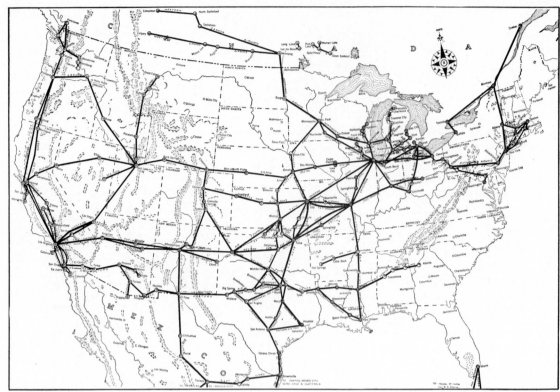

Courtesy, "American Aviation Air Traffic Guide."

Courtesy, Civil Aeronautics Administration.

FIGURE 16·2.   SCHEDULED AIRLINE ROUTES IN THE UNITED STATES IN 1930 AND 1948

Upper view shows passenger lines operating on schedule in 1930; lower view shows routes permanently certificated, March 31, 1948.

percentages in the lower age groups listed above indicate that the potential market for the private plane may be expected to increase for many years. In 1926 1,186 non-military aircraft were produced with a value of $17,694,905; in 1945 10,307 non-military aircraft were produced, having a value of $352,063,597. Small private planes were being manufactured for sale at prices comparable to those of automobiles in 1947. While operation and maintenance costs for an airplane were considerably higher than for an automobile in that year, and the potential market, as compared to that for the automobile, was further limited by the relative difficulty of flying technique, it is to be expected that both these deterrents to private flying will be reduced in importance as time goes by. Military pilot training in World War II was expected further to increase private flying in postwar years.

The commercial practicability of the helicopter, only beginning to be demonstrated at the close of World War II, has opened up further possibilities in air transportation which may be revolutionary. In 1947 the helicopter had a small carrying capacity and was expensive both in initial cost and in operation. All these difficulties, however, may be overcome, at least to a large extent, and the very small landing space required for these aircraft means that they can be operated to and from the heart of a built-up area without the prohibitive investment in landing facilities which is required for the conventional airplane.

Land and water transportation undoubtedly will continue to convey heavy, bulky, and low-unit-value goods, as well as passengers, when trips of less than about 100 miles are involved, for many years to come. Air transportation probably will take an increasing share of the rest of the transportation market. Thus, while the older forms of transportation will not go out like the horse and buggy or wagon, airport capacities may be as much of a problem in the city of tomorrow as street and parking capacities are in today's, unless the development of this new transportation facility receives adequate attention in the planning of the city.

General Airport Requirements

What is written today concerning airport requirements may be out of date tomorrow and almost certainly will be obsolete five years from today. In 1928 standards for a Class A airport, then the best, required minimum runway lengths of 2,500 feet and a clear angle of approach of one on seven. Civil Aeronautics Administration standards for fields to accommodate the largest transports in 1946 called for minimum runway lengths of 5,700 feet and a clear approach angle of one on forty. Larger, faster planes are developed every year. The Douglas DC-7, a 113-passenger transport plane, will require 9,500 feet of runway length for safe take-off and landing. In 1947 successful tests were made on light planes of caster cross-wind landing gears which made it possible to land, regardless of wind direction, on a landing strip of any orientation, thus potentially eliminating the necessity for multiple-runway airports. Helicopter shuttle service for passengers and cargo may greatly reduce the time between the airport and various central points in the city, and permit major landing fields to be located on much cheaper land further out from the centers. And new developments must be expected which are not yet imagined. All these rapidly changing influences make it a requisite that airport plans be brought up to date very frequently.

The recent development of air transportation offers city planning its greatest opportunity and its greatest challenge. It is the first major development since the general acceptance of city planning to affect radically the probable future city pattern. Not only will many new airports be required in urban areas in the next few years, but on the borders of these airports will spring up groups of industries and businesses which benefit particularly by speed of delivery. It is even possible that, when air transportation reaches the stage of development in which it becomes a mass-transportation facility, new "air cities" may develop in areas rich in material resources but formerly inaccessible. A beginning in this direction already has been made in the mountainous sections of South America. If the city

TABLE 24

AIRPORT-PLANNING SIZE STANDARDS AS RECOMMENDED BY THE CIVIL AERONAUTICS ADMINISTRATION IN 1944 [a]

Class	Approximate Minimum Site Area in Acres	Length of Landing Strips in Feet [b]	Width of Usable Landing Strips in Feet	Length of Runways in Feet	Width of Runways in Feet	[c] Number of Landing Strips and Runways to be Determined by Percentage (Given Below) of Winds, Including Calms, [d] Covered by Landing Strip and Runway Alignment	Facilities
I	100	1,800 to 2,700	300	None	None	70%	Drainage Fencing Marking Wind-direction indicator Hangar Basic lighting (optional)
II	160	2,700 to 3,700	500	2,500 to 3,500	150(N) 100(D)	75%	All listed above, plus: Lighting Hangar and shop Fueling Weather information Office space Parking
III	640	3,700 to 4,700	500	3,500 to 4,500	200(I) 150(N)	80%	All listed above, plus: Weather Bureau Two-way radio Visual traffic control
IV	640	4,700 to 5,700	500	4,500 to 5,500	200(I) 150(N)	90%	Instrument approach system (when required) Administration Building Taxiways Aprons
V	800	5,700 and over	500	5,500 and over	200(I) 150(N)	90%	

[a] Based on data in *Airport Design*, Civil Aeronautics Administration, United States Department of Commerce, Washington, D. C., 1944.

[b] At sea level; for higher altitudes longer runways are required.

[c] Should be sufficient in number to permit take-offs and landings to be made within 22½ degrees of true direction for percentage shown of winds four miles per hour and over, based on at least a 10-year Weather Bureau wind record, where possible.

[d] Calms: negligible wind conditions of three miles per hour and under.

(N) Night operation.   (D) Day operation only.   (I) Instrument operation.

planner is to anticipate and plan for all the new problems which are coming with the "air age," he must use his imagination and creative ingenuity to the utmost. By the degree of success or failure which attends the profession's handling of air transportation in the master plan will the practical value of city planning be judged, to a large extent, in the future.

In planning for airports, co-operation with the Civil Aeronautics Administration is essential. This division of the United States Department of Commerce is charged with promotion and development of airways and airports, and is the administrative agency which enforces the regulations of the Civil Aeronautics Board. The CAA at all times has available the latest information on airport standards and requirements, and it is in effect the national airport-planning agency. It maintains as part of its Airports Service an Urban Planning Section for the purpose of rendering consulting service to official planning agencies in the larger metropolitan areas of the United States. Consultation with this Section is the best way of assuring that the plan for airports meets technical requirements.

Flying may be classified according to several general types of activity, such as:

1. *Transport*—including all scheduled passenger, cargo, and feeder line operations.
2. *Private flying.*
3. *Miscellaneous commercial*—including plane sales and service, etc., flight instruction, charter service, plane rental.
4. *Military flying.*

Each type of flying has certain requirements which influence the size, location, and general development of the airport. When the anticipated volume of any one type is sufficiently great, it is desirable to segregate that type in one or more fields functionally designed for its specific use. Such segregation, when warranted, increases the efficiency, convenience, and safety over those of the mixed-operation field.

The CAA has divided airports into five classifications, depending upon size and facilities. The characteristics of each class are shown in Table 24. The application of these classifications, as recommended by the CAA in 1944, is shown in Table 25.

TABLE 25

AIRPORT-DESIGN STANDARDS FOR COMMUNITIES, CITIES, AND METROPOLITAN AREAS, AS RECOMMENDED BY THE CIVIL AERONAUTICS ADMINISTRATION IN 1944 [a]

Type of Community	Planning Classification	Type of Aircraft Which Airport May Safely Accommodate
Small communities not on present or proposed scheduled air-carrier system, and auxiliary airports in larger metropolitan areas to serve non-scheduled private flying activities.	1	Small private-owner type planes. This includes roughly planes up to a gross weight of 4,000 pounds, or with a wing loading (pounds per square foot) times power loading (pounds per horsepower) not exceeding 190.
Larger communities located on present or proposed feeder line airways and having considerable aeronautical activity. General population range 5,000 to 25,000.	2	Larger-size private-owner planes and some small-size transport planes. This represents roughly planes in the gross weight classification between 4,000 and 15,000 pounds, or having a wing loading (pounds per square foot) times power loading (pounds per horsepower) of 190 to 230.
Important cities on feeder line airway systems and many intermediate points on the main line airways. General population range 25,000 to several hundred thousand.	3	Present-day transport planes. Planes in this classification are represented approximately by those between 10,000 and 50,000 pounds gross weight, or by those having a wing loading (pounds per square foot) times power loading (pounds per horsepower) of 230 and over.
The major industrial centers of the nation and important junction points or terminals on the airways system.	4 and 5	Largest planes in use and those planned for the immediate future. This approximately represents planes having a gross weight of 74,000 pounds and over or having a wing loading (pounds per square foot) times power loading (pounds per horsepower) of 230 and over.

[a] Based on data in *Airport Design*, Civil Aeronautics Administration, United States Department of Commerce, Washington, D. C., 1944.

The foregoing classification of airports perhaps is less applicable to preliminary planning than one made by the Regional Plan Association of New York in its plan for a system of airports in the New York Region.[8] The Regional Plan classification of airports divides

[8] "Major Regional Airports for the New Jersey-New York-Connecticut Metropolitan Area," *Regional Plan Bulletin* 68, Regional Plan Association, New York, November, 1946.

them into the following four groups on the basis of use:

1. Transport.
2. Supplementary major.
3. Secondary.
4. Local.

In the final analysis, however, in order to determine the necessary qualifications for a site which is to be selected, the preliminary classification should be translated into the CAA system.

Future Flying Needs

Probably the most difficult problem in airport planning is determining future needs. The relative youth of air transportation, together with the effect of World War II, makes extension of past trends somewhat risky. Nevertheless, some estimate is required of the amount of air travel expected if any effective planning is to be done. The final answer must take into consideration three questions: how many airports are required, of what size, and where located? These questions must be answered for each of the five categories of flying activity—transport, private, miscellaneous, commercial, and military.

The problem may be approached by estimating how many landings and take-offs in each category will have to be accommodated during the peak hour of the peak day, and what combination of fields of the various classes can best handle such a load. The foregoing may, in turn, be approached by estimating the future numbers and types of aircraft to be owned and operated from the area in question, plus an allowance for transients. The usual approach has been to try to prorate the national estimates, making allowance for the peculiarities of climate, terrain, commercial activity, wealth, population, "air-mindedness," and other factors tending to influence the result. In a few cases these analyses have been supplemented by studies of the amounts of traffic of different types which might be generated under various circumstances. Those responsible for planning should be thoroughly familiar with local conditions which will be likely to affect the growth of aviation. The importance of this cannot be overemphasized in the case of airports, since methods of estimating must be suited to the particular locality if the results are to be reliable.

There are comparatively few urban areas in the United States where more than one airport will be required to take care of scheduled air-carrier operations for probably several years to come. Numerically, the smaller plane is a vastly greater problem, and its relative importance probably will increase. *Fortune* estimated in November, 1943, that three years after the end of World War II some 300,000 civilian aircraft might be in operation in the United States, of which only 3,000 would be engaged in scheduled carrier operations. Other estimates range from 400,000 to 500,000 in 1955. Any of these estimates represents a staggering increase over the approximately 29,400 civilian aircraft reported in operation at the end of 1945, and it is probable that at least 99 per cent of these will be smaller planes engaged in non-scheduled operations.

A method of estimating potential private flying has been worked out by the CAA.[9] Briefly, the method comprises tabulations of numbers of families paying rentals over a certain minimum, subdivided into three groups, by census tracts or minor civil divisions, with distinction in rural areas between farm and non-farm families. Various significant factors which tend to increase or decrease the desire for an airplane then are taken into consideration, and the metropolitan area is divided into three or four zones according to the estimated degree of this potential use of private planes. A factor reflecting potential plane ownership, depending on the rental group and the zone in which it is located, is applied to each of the totals found for the three rental groups in each census tract or minor civil division. The result is a total potential plane load for each tract or division. This may be plotted graphically for comparison with existing and potential sites.

[9] *Airport Planning for Urban Areas,* Civil Aeronautics Administration, United States Department of Commerce, Washington, D. C., June 1, 1945, pages 39–47.

The capacity of a field for private planes does not increase directly as its size. While a 100-acre field can provide ground and air space for 100 small aircraft, a single field to accommodate 200 airplanes of the same type might have to be 400 acres or more in extent. The CAA concluded that, as of 1945, the optimum size for an airport for small planes was about 160 acres. This approximates the area on which a good Class I or Class II airport can be built, and such fields can accommodate about 100 aircraft.[10]

In addition to scheduled commercial flights and private flying, there are the activities of miscellaneous commercial flying and military flying to be considered in evaluating future needs. The question of potential military need will have to be taken up with the various military forces, and in most cases will not bulk large in the total airport plan. Miscellaneous commercial activities, consisting of manufacturers' display and sales rooms, demonstration, flight instruction, plane overhaul and repairs, and non-scheduled commercial traffic (incompatible with the activities at either the major airport or the small private fields), will require fields of their own of CAA Class II or better. The CAA suggests a ratio of one field of this type for every five to 15 private fields.

After future airport needs have been estimated, existing airports should be surveyed to determine their relationship to these future needs. It should be determined which of the existing airports can be expanded, if desirable, and the present and potential capacities of existing fields should be ascertained in detail. Meteorological records of existing fields may be of great value in attempting to select future sites and in evaluating the present and potential usefulness of existing fields.

Transportation to and from the Airport

Since airports seldom can be located in the hearts of urban areas, the problem of transportation to airports is of considerable importance. It probably is safe to say that this factor is

[10] *Ibid.,* page 5.

one of the principal deterrents to air travel and shipment. In the case of the private airport, there is relatively little difficulty, since the owners of private planes usually prefer to drive to the field in their own cars, and the number of persons using such a facility is small. The transport field, however, presents a different picture. Not only are there considerable numbers of passengers to be taken to and from the field, but employees and cargo must be considered. The transport fields for the eleven largest metropolitan districts of the United States, in which in 1940 lived over one-quarter of the total population, averaged about 10 miles and 50 minutes by limousine or taxicab from the downtown areas of the respective central cities.

In 1946 the American Transit Association made a survey of various leading transit companies in the United States in an effort to determine practices, trends, and opinions on transit service to airports. More than 100 replies were received to the questionnaires sent out. The evidence was overwhelming that the people who ride airplanes are not prospective customers for mass transit to and from the airports. The most consistent source of patronage of mass-transit facilities to airports was found to be the employees working at the airports or in near-by activities. In most cases it was found that, unless there was considerable patronage as a result of other activities near the airport, or unless the airport was a stop on a line which passed by, transit service could not be furnished on a self-supporting basis.

Like the passenger traffic to and from the transport airport, cargo traffic also is relatively small in volume and in lots. It is improbable that air shipments in the next quarter of a century will change in nature, although total volumes may be expected to increase greatly. The type of cargo carried by plane therefore will best be transported by truck to and from the airport.

Since passengers seem likely to be carried by limousine, taxi, or private car, and cargo by truck, the general problem of transportation to and from the transport airport is reduced to that of adequate highway connections. It is desirable for the airport to be located close to an express highway leading to the center of the city. Willow Run Airport is about 24 miles from downtown Detroit, and about five-sixths of the distance is by express highway. The limousine time for this run is 60 to 70 minutes. Detroit's Municipal Airport, only six miles from the downtown area, is 35 to 45 minutes away, using the city streets. Were an express highway available connecting the downtown area with the Detroit Municipal Airport, the trip probably would take no more than 15 minutes.

In the larger metropolitan districts, where volumes of air passengers and cargo are large, the problem of speedy and economical transfer of passengers and cargo between the airport and the point of origin or destination is very difficult. Several limousine terminals at different locations within the central area may be desirable, and facilities for sorting and dispatch of air cargo require careful planning. The one greatest advantage of air transportation is speed. In 1947 the newest-model transport planes cruised at over 300 miles per hour. At this rate, one minute saved on the ground is worth five miles of air distance.

Development of helicopter shuttle service between downtown terminals and outlying airports may prove to be an important factor in speeding up transfer between these points. A helicopter cruising at 60 miles per hour could reduce time in transfer to a quarter or a fifth of the time required by limousine. With common limousine runs of 30 minutes to an hour, this would mean 25 to 45 minutes saved at each end of the trip by air.

Zoning and Other Controls

If the great investment made in airports is to be protected, the heights of structures surrounding them must be regulated. Figure 16·3 shows obstruction height limitations for areas surrounding airports, as recommended by the CAA in 1946. The flat angles required in the approach zones have resulted as airplane speeds have increased and instrument landing-control devices for use under conditions of poor visibility have been developed.

Charles S. Rhyne has listed eight possible methods of controlling heights in areas surrounding airports.[11] They are:

1. Voluntary action by owners of property surrounding the airport.
2. Purchase of required land outside of airport, using eminent domain, if necessary.
3. Acquisition of air space rights over required areas outside airport, using eminent domain, if necessary.
4. Condemnation of hazards by exercise of police power.
5. Zoning regulation of heights.
6. Use of commerce power by the federal government.
7. Use of war power by the federal government.
8. Use of postal power by the federal government.

While voluntary action by property owners has been reported, in a few locations, to be effective as a means of controlling heights in areas surrounding airports, certainly such action is not sufficiently dependable as a protection of the large investment required to construct a modern airport. Outright purchase of the required land outside the airport usually will be an expensive process, often prohibitively so. In some cases it may be possible to acquire such land and resell it or lease it with restrictions on the height and use to which it may be put, thereby recouping at least a large part of the cost, but the initial investment may still be excessive. In effect, such a process almost amounts to the purchase of air space rights, which also may prove too expensive.

Condemnation, under the police power, of hazards to air navigation in areas surrounding airports has proved useful principally in "spite" cases, since the courts have been properly reluctant to condemn under this power unless malice is shown. Obviously, there are many instances of hazards in which no such spite or malice is intended, so that this power is at best only a partial solution to the problem. Use of the commerce or postal powers of the federal government might be considered an encroachment of states' rights and probably would be impracticable. In practice there has been some indirect federal control through the insistence of the CAA on sufficient protection

[11] *Airports and the Courts,* by Charles S. Rhyne, National Institute of Municipal Law Officers, Washington, D. C., 1944, page 165.

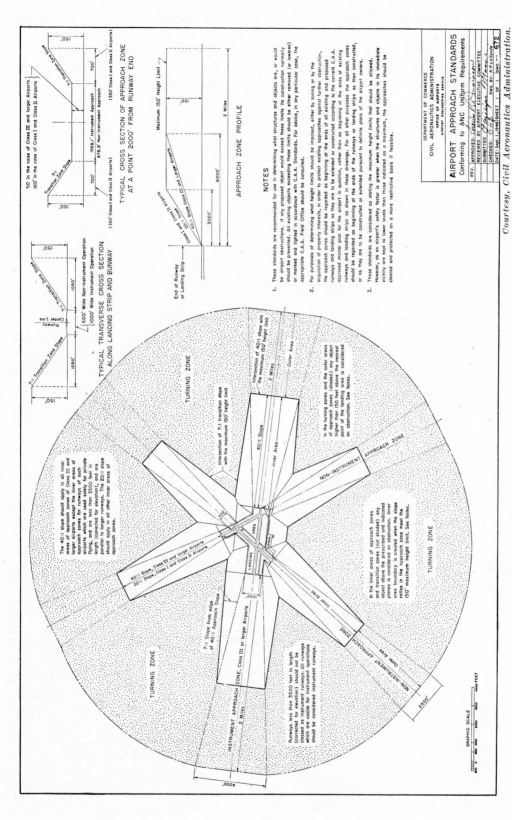

FIGURE 16·3. AIRPORT APPROACH STANDARDS MEETING REQUIREMENTS ESTABLISHED BY AN ARMY, NAVY, AND CIVILIAN COMMITTEE

Courtesy, Civil Aeronautics Administration.

against excessive heights around airports before federal money is advanced for construction. Use of the war power of the federal government probably would be condoned only in time of emergency, and even then practical difficulties would arise.

The use of airport zoning seems to be becoming the most widely used approach to the problem of height control in areas surrounding airports. In 1944 some 15 states had passed enabling legislation for this type of ordinance, and Rhyne stated in 1944 that "in the more than 15 years during which airport zoning ordinances have been in effect throughout the nation, not one court contest has been instituted to contest the validity of any city ordinance on this subject."[12] But in the following year an airport zoning ordinance of the city of Newark was set aside by a New Jersey court on the grounds that it would take private property without due process of law and without just compensation.[13]

Airport zoning, like all zoning, has as its legal basis the promotion of safety, comfort, convenience, and general welfare of the community, and may regulate only to the extent that it is not confiscatory. It may be possible to restrict heights by zoning to as low as 40 feet, or even 30 feet, but probably seldom less. Figure 16·3 shows a required slope for instrument runway approach zones of 1 on 40, and the CAA prefers a slope of 1 on 50. Even at the steeper figure, a height of 40 feet above the runway is not reached for a distance of 1,600 feet beyond its end. If the area is assumed to be level with the runways, this would mean that, for an approach slope of 1 on 20, an area of over 12 acres on each end of each runway would have to be controlled by some means other than zoning, and that for an instrument approach slope of 1 on 40, the area at each end of each runway would be about 55 acres. Control in these areas probably will have to be effected either by outright purchase of the land or by purchase of air rights, and at such low heights there probably will be little difference in cost between the two methods.

12 *Ibid.*, page 176.
13 Yara Engineering Corp. *v.* City of Newark, 40 Atl. 2d, 559 Sup. Ct. (N. J.), Jan. 8, 1945.

Some uses and practices within certain distances of airports may also create hazards. In particular, where instrument approach controls are to be used, ground-made electrical disturbances may interfere with their proper operation. It may be that airport zoning can be broadened to include certain use prohibitions as well as height limitations, thereby solving this problem.

Site Selection and General Plan

In planning airport locations, the following considerations must be favorable:

1. Suitability and size of site.
2. Approaches.
3. Relationship to other flying fields.
4. Relationship to aids to navigation.
5. Relationship to population to be served.
6. Relationship to plan of community.

The ideal airport site from the standpoint of topography is the top of a very gentle slope. This minimizes the effect of obstacles in the area surrounding the airport and promotes easy

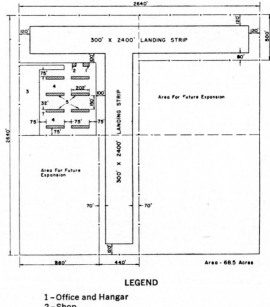

LEGEND
1 – Office and Hangar
2 – Shop
3 – Parking Area – Auto
4 – Apron
5 – Multiple Unit Hangars – Capacity 6 Planes Each

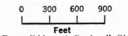

From "Airport Design," Civil Aeronautics Administration, April 1, 1944.

FIGURE 16·4. SUITABLE DESIGN FOR CLASS I AIRPORT

drainage. A site on a slight hilltop also usually has the meteorological advantages of less fog and more wind, the latter factor making for shorter runs on take-off and landing. The area required will depend on the anticipated traffic using the field and the number and directions of runways needed, as explained in Table

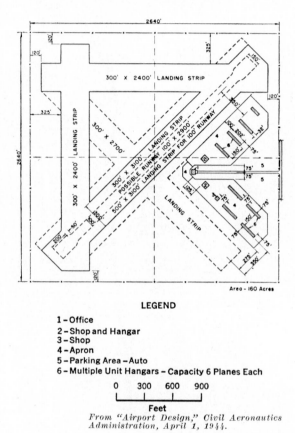

LEGEND

1 – Office
2 – Shop and Hangar
3 – Shop
4 – Apron
5 – Parking Area – Auto
6 – Multiple Unit Hangars – Capacity 6 Planes Each

0 300 600 900
Feet

From "Airport Design," Civil Aeronautics Administration, April 1, 1944.

FIGURE 16·5. SUITABLE DESIGN FOR CLASS II AIRPORT

24. Minimum areas listed in that table assume a square site with dimensions sufficient to allow required minimum runway lengths in any direction. Typical designs for airports of various classes, as recommended by the CAA, are shown in Figures 16·4, 16·5, and 16·6. However, it must be remembered that each airport is a separate design problem in itself and must be "custom made" to fit the conditions of its own particular site, traffic, and meteorology. To avoid early obsolescence in this rapidly advancing form of transportation, each new airport must represent an advance and improvement in design over what has been done before.

A fully satisfactory site for an airport must be so located that its approaches will be clear of hazards to navigation. In effect, this means that nothing over 150 feet above the level of the runways should be within two miles of the outer ends of any runway, and that within the inner areas of the approach zones, lower height tolerations are maximums, as shown in Figure 16·3. In cases where an airport can be so located as to be surrounded by agricultural land, the cost of protection against future hazards may be materially reduced. Many agricultural uses can be made of land with as little as 10 feet or less of overhead clearance, with little or no loss or inconvenience to the owner.

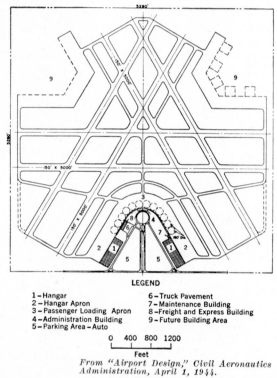

LEGEND

1 – Hangar
2 – Hangar Apron
3 – Passenger Loading Apron
4 – Administration Building
5 – Parking Area – Auto
6 – Truck Pavement
7 – Maintenance Building
8 – Freight and Express Building
9 – Future Building Area

0 400 800 1200
Feet

From "Airport Design," Civil Aeronautics Administration, April 1, 1944.

FIGURE 16·6. SUITABLE DESIGN FOR CLASS IV MAJOR AIR TERMINAL

Air-traffic turning zones are recommended by the CAA to consist of circles centered on the airport, with the following radii:

CLASS OF AIRPORT	RADIUS IN MILES
I	1
II	2
III	3
IV	4

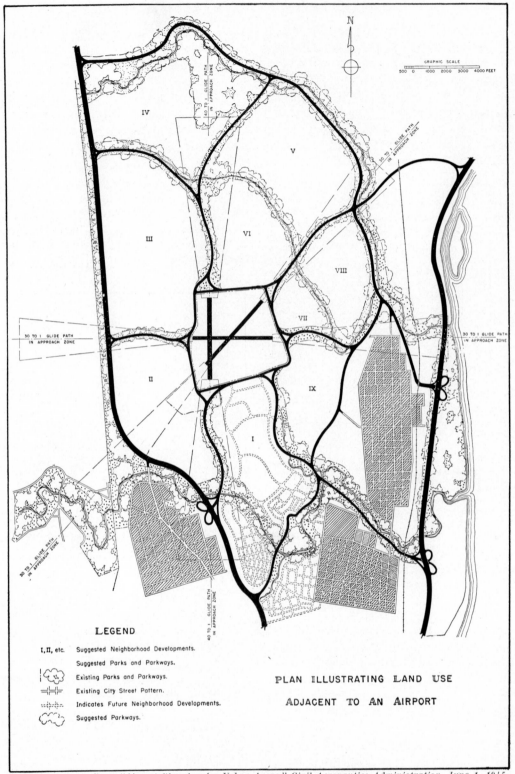

LEGEND

I, II, etc.   Suggested Neighborhood Developments.

               Suggested Parks and Parkways.

               Existing Parks and Parkways.

               Existing City Street Pattern.

               Indicates Future Neighborhood Developments.

               Suggested Parkways.

PLAN ILLUSTRATING LAND USE

ADJACENT TO AN AIRPORT

From "Airport Planning for Urban Areas," Civil Aeronautics Administration, June 1, 1945.

FIGURE 16·7.   PLAN ILLUSTRATING AN AIRPORT TIED IN WITH A CITY MASTER PLAN

Note that orientation of runways minimizes the effect of approach zones on heights of buildings in the area surrounding the airport by locating the approaches over the park system.

This area is required for airplanes circling the field preparatory to landing, and the turning zones for any two fields should not overlap. An additional limitation on proximity is that, if two fields are to use instrument approaches on parallel runways simultaneously, the fields should be at least 10 miles apart, and if the runways are in line with each other, that distance should be doubled.

airport, this means a location near the center of population of the area to be served, if such a site can be found, and if not, one which can be reached rapidly from that center. The private fields should be located in or near the areas in which live the heavier concentrations of potential plane owners, as determined by the survey described in an earlier section of this chapter.

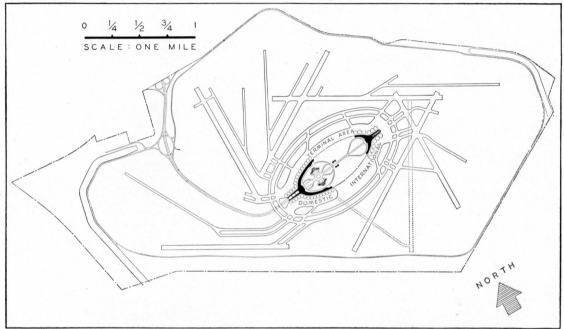

Courtesy, Port of New York Authority.

FIGURE 16·8.   GENERAL PLAN OF NEW YORK INTERNATIONAL AIRPORT ON THE EDGE OF JAMAICA BAY IN THE BOROUGH OF QUEENS, CITY OF NEW YORK

Initial operation of this airport was started July 1, 1948.   It was the most elaborate air terminal yet planned at that time.

Most long-distance flying is done within the limits of well-defined airways which are established, regulated, and equipped with aids to navigation by the federal government. Since the use of these air lanes will increase, airports should be so located as to avoid unnecessary congestion of the airways. This applies particularly to fields for private flying. However, it is also important that some airports, at least, be located close by these airways for convenience and as emergency landing fields.

Obviously, it is desirable that airports be located as close as possible to the population which they are to serve. For the transport

Finally, airports must be located as a part of the master plan for the area. (See Figure 16·7.) Their relationship to other means of transportation already has been discussed. There are other considerations, however, such as the sometimes vociferous objections of home owners to the noise, dust, and vehicular traffic which accompany an airport. Flying enthusiasts minimize these objections, but while it probably is true that people living near airports will ultimately adjust themselves to such conditions, there often are protests from residential groups today which are of serious concern to the planner. The size of an airport makes it a block to future development, and may cause dislocation of the street or highway system if the site is not carefully selected.

In planning for airports it is particularly important that the possibility of eventual need for expansion be considered. Sites selected should be capable of expansion, and the development of immediately surrounding areas should be controlled in so far as is practicable to keep future land acquisition from being too expensive. It may sometimes be possible to achieve this end by incorporating the airport within a park area. This has the additional advantage of protecting the inner portions of runway approach zones against obstacles to air navigation. Such an arrangement may be accomplished with an actual net gain in park area by developing unneeded portions of the airport as part of the park. In Ontario, California, where the site selected for the municipal airport was a large vineyard, instead of leveling off the entire area, as is customary practice, only the areas actually required for landing strips and other essential facilities were disturbed. As a result, the city receives a considerable income from the grape crop, which does not interfere with the operation of the airport. The possibilities of some such type of airport development are well worth investigating, since airport costs are so high as frequently to necessitate public subsidy unless additional sources of revenue can be found.

The CAA has outlined the considerations, other than potential plane load, which should govern airport-site selection, as follows: [14]

1. *Terrain.* The area must be generally level, free from major obstacles such as hills, topography producing adverse air currents.
2. *Meteorology.* A minimum degree of fog, smoke, smog, gusty or shifty winds, uneven precipitation, heavy snow with sudden thaw.
3. *Proximity to air centers for possible users.*
   a. Time-distance from residential areas.
   b. Convenience for majority of communities.
   c. Usefulness to significant satellite communities.
   d. Possible joint operation with neighboring community.
   e. Time-distance from center of city or town.

[14] *Airport Planning for Urban Areas,* Civil Aeronautics Administration, United States Department of Commerce, Washington, D. C., June 1, 1945, page 49.

4. *Supplement transportation.*
   a. Proximity to radial and circumferential activities. Taxi, bus, or other transit services available in the area.
   b. Closeness to railroad station.
5. *Land use.*
   a. Prospects of higher than airport use.
   b. Possibility of depreciation of area by airport use.
   c. Possibility of increased land values by airport use.
   d. Blocking of normal growth of a section of a city, township, or community.
   e. Excessive loss in tax returns to the city, county, or township.
6. *Protection.*
   a. Possibility of local zoning to protect approaches and expansion.
   b. Possibility of local zoning for appropriate land use.
   c. Possibility of zoning aid from adjacent communities.
   d. Exercise of eminent domain.
7. *Area cost differentials.*
   a. Land.
   b. Natural resources.
   c. Drainage and grading.
   d. Other construction.
8. *Intergovernmental relations between independent jurisdictions.* Co-operation and planning of the airport program.
9. *Utilities.* Water, sewers, power, and communications.

Program for Progressive Development

Proposals in the master plan for new streets or new parks often can be carried out by stages, each step forming a useful part as it is acquired and developed. On the other hand, a considerable area is required for a useful airport, and until this minimum is secured, whatever parts of it may have been acquired already are of no use for airport purposes. If even a small portion of a potential airport site is developed for some other use, the cost of acquisition may thereafter be so high as to preclude subsequent development as an airfield. Since this is the case, and since airports are certain to be an increasingly important part of the land use pattern, it is particularly important that a definite program of action be undertaken to assure that the airport plan be realized.

The following is quoted from the CAA publication *Airport Planning for Urban Areas:* [15]

[15] *Ibid.,* pages 51 and 53.

The comprehensive plan of airports . . . is only the first step toward the community's objective. It is an over-all pattern of airports for the entire metropolitan area. Each airport in the pattern will require engineering study and detailed design before being constructed; each site will have to be acquired; and the necessary funds will have to be available as each step toward the plan's realization is to be taken.

Even though many of the smaller fields eventually are planned for development on privately owned ground, the public interest will be concerned in several ways and will compel the attention and action of local or state governments. . . .

An essential part of the carrying out of any general plan is the preparation of a long-range program and capital budget. This, too, is usually a function of the local administration. The estimates of need used in arriving at the over-all, ultimate plan may be examined and broken down to show the expected air traffic loads and the anticipated airport requirements during the first year and each succeeding year for a five- or 10-year period. Then a program may be developed which will contemplate land acquisition, construction, and maintenance—each at the proper time and as the needs materialize. Suitable available airport sites frequently will be so scarce that their acquisition quite a while in advance of actual construction will be advisable and will usually pay dividends in lower total cost. If the estimates of need later are found to be too high, other uses for the land usually will easily be found and the community will not incur financial loss.

A program of specific action one year ahead, a more general five-year program, and a broad program for 10 years in advance can be projected from the estimates of need. . . . Although this projected program may be either too ambitious or inadequate for each yearly cycle, it will at least provide a steering device in which adjustments can be made as conditions freeze or change.

The program for airport development will have to be revised constantly as new developments in air transportation and its place in the plan materialize, and it will have to be vigorously pursued if the full benefits of airport planning are to be realized.

Selected References

Airports of Tomorrow, Report of the Regional Airport Conference on Its Plan for Development of an Airport System for the New York Metropolitan Region, Regional Plan Association, Inc., New York, 1947.

FROESCH, CHARLES, and WALTER PROKOSCH: *Airport Planning*, John Wiley & Sons, New York, 1946.

HUBBARD, HENRY V., MILLER MCCLINTOCK, and FRANK B. WILLIAMS: *Airports—Their Location, Administration, and Legal Basis*, Vol. I, Harvard City Planning Studies, Harvard University Press, Cambridge, Mass., 1930.

RHYME, CHARLES S.: *Airports and the Courts*, National Institute of Municipal Law Officers, Washington, D. C., 1944.

United States Department of Commerce, Civil Aeronautics Administration, Washington, D. C.: *Airport Design*, 1944; *Airport Planning for Urban Areas*, June 1, 1945; *Small Airports*, September 1, 1945; *Statistical Handbook of Civil Aviation*, 1945 to date.

Questions

1. What are some of the factors contributing to the flexibility of air transportation?
2. For what types of services is air transportation best adapted?
3. What agency determines the standards for airport design? How many classes of airports does it provide for?
4. What types of aircraft can be accommodated on each class of airport?
5. How would a community go about estimating its future airport requirements?
6. List the types of special landing fields that might be needed in a large city.
7. What types of transportation are required to and from major airports?
8. What clearances are necessary on approaches to airport runways?
9. What are the principal methods of controlling structures in approach zones to airport runways?
10. What considerations should govern the selection of an airport site?

17

MOTOR-VEHICLE PARKING

BEFORE THE LATE 1920's THE PROBLEM OF AUTO-motive transportation was thought of almost exclusively in terms of streets and highways, that is, the movement of vehicles. Of course, there were garages in which automobiles were stored, but this storage was provided principally near the residences of the owners at the origins of automobile trips. There were not many automobiles, nor were they extensively used for shopping and business purposes, and parking space at the curb was adequate in all but the most congested parts of the largest cities for those who did drive to business or to shop. In 1925 just under 20 million motor vehicles were registered in the United States, and an estimated 200 billion passenger-miles were traveled by motor vehicle. In 1940 the respective figures had increased to slightly over 32 million and about 500 billion.

As the automobile has come into its own as an important means of transportation, it has become apparent that there must be terminals for automobiles at their destinations as well as at their sources. With the end of World War II the termination of gasoline rationing and the resumption of production of new automobiles made the problem of parking in downtown urban areas one of great urgency. Not only was there need for parking space vastly in excess of existing curb and offstreet capacities, but also the extent of parking on the public streets was seriously limiting the capacity of those streets for the movement of vehicles. In order to relieve this congestion, rigid enforcement of curb-parking prohibitions on certain streets in the downtown areas of Philadelphia was begun in January, 1946, and in similar

areas of New York in October of the same year. This device was used successfully in Chicago in the late twenties, simultaneously with the establishment of water-front parking areas, and strict enforcement of parking bans had been tried previously to 1946 in New York. However, such enforcement had formerly been relaxed after a few weeks, and parking violations in New York City soon became as common as ever.

Such prohibitions are at best only partial palliatives of the traffic and parking problem. An automobile is fully useful only if it can be parked at a location reasonably close to the destination of the user. Offstreet parking facilities in the central areas of both Philadelphia and New York were not adequate at the time these bans were put into effect, and the only result was a decrease in the use of automobiles as a means of reaching these sections. There are those who argue that such a result is desirable and proper, since mass transportation is both a cheaper and a more efficient means of travel to and from central business districts. That mass transportation is cheaper and more efficient is undeniable, but it is neither as comfortable nor as convenient as the private automobile. The solution is not that simple.

If people cannot drive to the larger urban shopping centers, they may drive elsewhere to shop. To the extent that this happens, business in the larger centers will fall off, business centers will become decentralized, and property values in the large but inaccessible centers will depreciate. The values of business properties are largely dependent on their accessibility, and business properties in the central areas of our cities furnish a very large proportion of the total tax base. Indicative of the decentralization trend is the fact that several large department stores in New York, Los Angeles, and other cities have opened branch stores in suburban communities. With these facts in mind it seems reasonable to expend considerable effort and funds to preserve these values by developing adequate parking space in established central areas.

General Requirements of Terminals for Automobiles

The amount of parking space which should be provided in any particular area depends upon varying conditions of land use, both as to type and density. Obviously a stadium or theatre will require a much larger amount of space than a warehouse covering the same area, and a skyscraper office building draws many more people than a three- or four-story loft building. Furthermore, the travel habits of the community affect the quantities required. In 1940 ratios of population to vehicle registration in cities of over 100,000 persons varied from 2.77 persons per vehicle in Los Angeles, and 3.05 in Dayton and Flint, to 6.6 persons per vehicle in Philadelphia, 7.15 in Boston, and 8.1 in the city of New York. The Eno Foundation for Highway Traffic Control found that in 1940 the percentages of persons entering the central districts of cities of over 500,000 by automobile ranged from 56.8 per cent in Cleveland to 30.3 per cent in Chicago and 14.2 per cent in New York, while in cities of from 100,000 to 500,000 the figures varied from 78.5 per cent in Houston to 60.3 per cent in Youngstown. The same authority reports the following averages: for eight typical cities under 100,000, 81.2 per cent; for six typical cities of 100,000 to 500,000, 69.1 per cent; and for ten typical cities of over 500,000, 41.1 per cent.[1] The reasons for such different ratios are not simple. Such factors as

[1] *The Parking Problem—A Library Research*, The Eno Foundation for Highway Traffic Control, Inc., September, 1942. For more detailed figures see Table 6 in Chapter 7, "The Local Transit System," Volume I.

adequacy and cost of suburban rail service, convenience of rail terminal facilities, convenience and cost of local mass-transportation systems, adequacy of local street systems and regional through-highway networks, and amount, convenience, and cost of local parking facilities all enter into the particular local situations.

An increasing amount of research is being done to determine quantitative standards for parking space. It should be emphasized that various "standards" which are determined in one way and another are neither constant nor universally applicable. Furthermore, who can say how many people would drive into the central area of any large established urban center, provided there were good express highways of unlimited capacity leading into the area and unlimited free parking space available there? It is obviously impossible to make any direct test of what would happen under these conditions. Nevertheless, some indication of the conclusions of various students of the problem is in order. For theatres, the ratio of one parking space for every two seats has been held desirable. David D. Bohannon has recommended three square feet of total parking space for every square foot of floor space in shopping centers. In 1942 the Eno Foundation proposed 0.73 of a parking space per foot of business frontage. J. C. Nichols, Chairman of the Community Builders' Council of the Urban Land Institute, suggested in 1945 a ratio of 1½ to three square feet of parking space per square foot of floor space in shopping centers. The Federal Housing Administration recommended in 1946 that in community shopping centers there should be from 200 to 250 car spaces per 1,000 persons living in the area served, or a ratio of two-thirds of the total business land area in such a center.

There also are qualitative questions to be considered. The shopper may want to park anywhere from 15 minutes to three hours during the day, whereas those who drive to work require space for eight or nine hours. The theatre load is heavy at night, but lasts only three to four hours. The short-time parker is not willing to travel as far from his car to his ultimate destination as the all-day parker. In a survey made in New York City by the Regional Plan Association in 1941 [2] it was found that almost 96 per cent of the curb parkers walked to their destinations, as compared to 83 per cent of the offstreet parkers, while the remainder used some form of public transportation. This survey also showed that the walking time from parking place to destination varied as follows:

WALKING TIME IN MINUTES	PERCENTAGE OF CURB PARKERS	PERCENTAGE OF OFFSTREET PARKERS
0– 3	56	43
4– 7	25	42
8–12	10	13
Over 12	9	2

The foregoing figures are presented only as an example of the findings in one city, and cannot be used elsewhere except as a very general guide. A reliable answer to the parking requirements in any particular area can be reached only by a thorough survey of the locality in question.

The Parking Survey

Where a small suburban shopping center is being considered, it is probable that the automobile carries the overwhelming majority of the people who come there during an average day. However, in a large urban center where mass-transportation facilities are highly developed and traffic congestion is a matter of miles instead of blocks, the entire problem becomes more complex. A survey which attempts to determine with accuracy the parking requirements of such an area is likely to be an expensive process and to require a considerable degree of organization. In outlining here the processes which may be used to survey parking requirements, a complex center will be considered rather than a simple one. In considering a smaller area, it will be readily apparent which of the studies suggested herein may be omitted or only generally considered.

Certain background data will be required for all cases. First, it must be determined what

[2] *Traffic and Parking Study—A Plan for Improvement of Conditions in the Central Business Areas of New York City,* Regional Plan Association, Inc., December, 1942.

area—local only, city-wide, or regional—the center in question serves. Population and motor-vehicle registration trends in that area should be analysed. Data on automobile traffic flow and the numbers of passengers carried on mass-transportation facilities serving the business area should be secured and presented as flow diagrams. Existing parking facilities, both at the curb and offstreet, should be mapped; over-all dimensions, capacities, and rates charged should be listed. Graphic presentations of existing offstreet parking facilities in the central business district of Los Angeles and in midtown Manhattan, New York City, are shown in Figures 17·1 and 17·2. Focal points of traffic in the central area, such as terminals (railway, bus, and air), large stores, office buildings and factories, and such places of assembly as arenas, stadiums, exhibition halls, and theatres, should be plotted. In general, these should provide, as many of them have done, their own separate parking facilities.

A cordon count of all persons entering and leaving the central area in a typical business day is very helpful in studying parking and other related planning problems. This count should be broken down by method and time of entry, and from these figures the proportions using private automobiles may be determined, and the accumulated number of persons and automobiles in the central area at any given time established. The use of ingenuity and sound sampling methods in making such counts will reduce the necessary work considerably. In many instances earlier partial counts can be used by making a complete control count at one or a few places.

An important method of securing information concerning the travel habits and preferences of persons entering the central area is by questioning shoppers, workers, etc., in the area. This is a sampling technique, and so must be carefully planned to assure an adequate and representative sample. Questionnaire cards with return postage may be distributed, or interviewers may be used. The latter method is probably better, but is also much more expensive. However, the information thus obtained is of utmost importance,

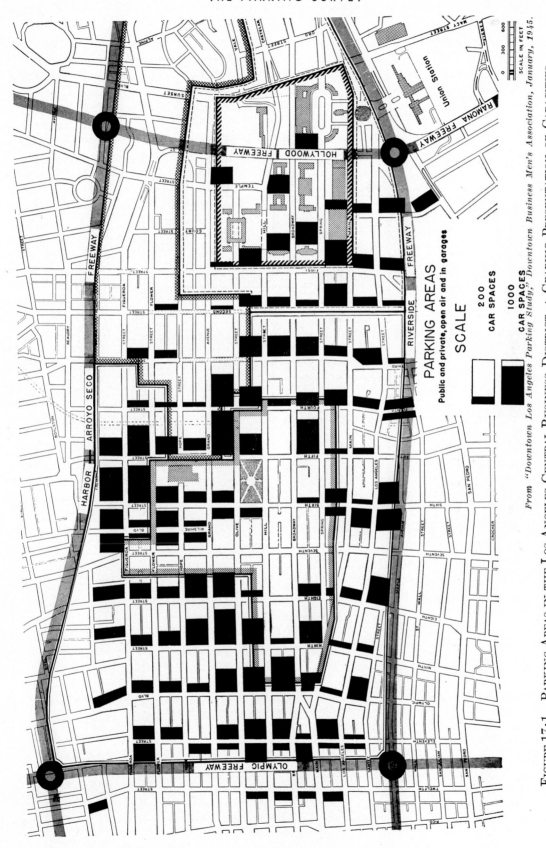

From "Downtown Los Angeles Parking Study," Downtown Business Men's Association, January, 1945.

FIGURE 17-1. PARKING AREAS IN THE LOS ANGELES CENTRAL BUSINESS DISTRICT, A GRAPHIC PRESENTATION OF CAPACITIES

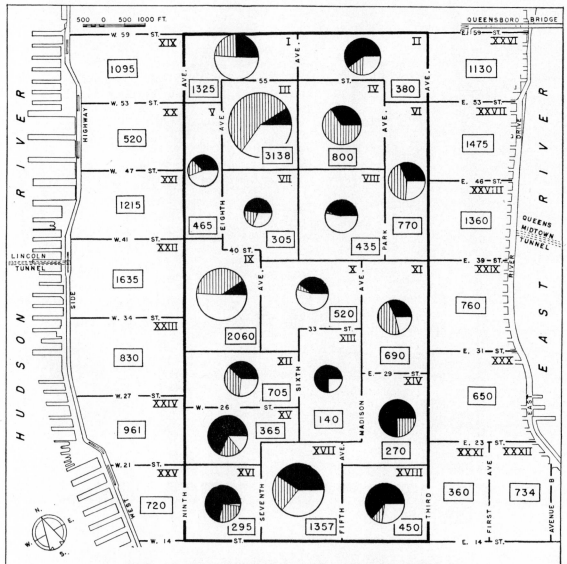

CAR SPACES AVAILABLE FOR TRANSIENTS
MIDTOWN MANHATTAN DISTRICT
BETWEEN THE HOURS OF 1 P.M. AND 5 P.M. BY SUB-DISTRICTS
OCTOBER, 1941

LEGEND
BETWEEN 14 ᵀᴴ AND 59 ᵀᴴ STREETS, THIRD AND NINTH AVENUES: ◣ AT CURBS ; ⬛ IN GARAGES; △ IN PARKING LOTS ;
AREAS OF CIRCLES ARE PROPORTIONAL TO TOTAL CAR SPACES AVAILABLE
FIGURES IN RECTANGLES INDICATE CAR SPACES ON OFF-STREET FACILITIES ONLY

SOURCE OF INFORMATION:
METROPOLITAN GARAGE BOARD OF TRADE
HYDE AND G.W. BROMLEY ATLASES OF MANHATTAN　　REGIONAL PLAN ASSOCIATION, INC., NEW YORK CITY
FIELD SURVEY　　　　　　　　　　　　　　　TRAFFIC AND PARKING STUDY—CENTRAL BUSINESS AREA

Courtesy, Regional Plan Association, Inc.

FIGURE 17·2

since it is the only way of determining preferences as opposed to practices. By questioning those entering the central area by all means, it can be determined how many would use automobiles under various conditions which would encourage or discourage driving in, and to what extent.

10. Other factors affecting frequency of trip by automobile into central district.

Again, either personal interviews or return-postage questionnaires distributed to drivers of parked cars may be employed. A card used by the Regional Plan Association in its survey in New York City is shown in Figure 17·3.

1. AFTER PARKING CAR, WHERE DID YOU GO? (check which) shop ☐ dine ☐ home ☐ other .... business ☐ amusement ☐ ☐ (fill in or check)

....
(location described by nearest street corner)   (borough)

2. HOW DID YOU GO FROM PARKING PLACE TO DESTINATION ABOVE? (check as many as needed)
Subway or "El" ☐ walk ☐ bus ☐ taxi ☐ trolley ☐ **HOW LONG DID IT TAKE?** .... minutes

3. HOW LONG DID YOU PARK HERE? From .... AM PM to .... AM PM

4. HOW DO YOU PAY IN LOT OR GARAGE? (check which) by the visit ☐ weekly ☐ monthly ☐ amount charged.............................

5. HOW MANY TIMES DO YOU DRIVE YOUR CAR TO THIS PART OF THE CITY?
............per week; ....per month; or ....per year

6. STARTED FROM ....at ....AM PM
(nearest street corner if in Greater New York)   (city, town, village or borough of New York City)   (state)

7. ROUTE TAKEN ENTERING AND THROUGH DOWNTOWN AREAS................................
(bridge, tunnel, ferry, if used)

....
(parkways, highways, avenues or streets)

8. IF PARKING FACILITIES WERE PROVIDED AT REASONABLE RATES, (a) **WOULD YOU DRIVE INTO THIS SAME AREA MORE OFTEN?** Yes ☐ No ☐ **HOW OFTEN?** ....per week; or ....per month
(b) **WOULD YOU HAVE PARKED LONGER?** Yes ☐ No ☐ From .... AM PM to .... AM PM
(c) (Curb Parkers only) **WHAT RATES WOULD YOU BE WILLING TO PAY FOR PARKING?**
............per hour ....per day
(DO NOT WRITE BELOW THIS LINE)

Date			Street Location	Origin	Destination	Parking	Crossing	Route
Gar.	Lot	Curb	....					

FIGURE 17·3. QUESTIONNAIRE USED BY REGIONAL PLAN ASSOCIATION IN PARKING SURVEY OF DECEMBER, 1940–JANUARY, 1941, NEW YORK CITY

It is also important to determine the practices and preferences of those who already come into the central district by automobile. The type of information needed may include all or part of the following:

1. Origin of person questioned.
2. Destination of person questioned.
3. Route used in driving and trip time.
4. Location and type (curb, lot, or garage) of parking space.
5. Length of time parked and fee paid, if any.
6. Method of reaching destination from parking place, and trip time.
7. Frequency with which car is driven into central district.
8. Number of passengers carried.
9. Effect of parking charges on frequency of trip by automobile into central district.

Location and duration of curb parking may be checked by a field survey in which license numbers of parked cars are noted periodically, with times.

Correlation of the collected information should show present parking requirements from the standpoints of where and when parking space is needed and how much, with a breakdown showing how various charges for parking would affect this demand. It should also indicate how modification of various other factors would affect the demand for parking space, and what probable future demand may be expected. The total picture desired is one of theoretical demand, uncomplicated by practical problems of supply. The next step is to find out to what extent this demand can be met.

Cost of Curb-parking Space

The question of the cost of parking space is too often taken as a simpler problem than it actually is. The average driver is prone to consider only his apparent out-of-pocket cost; thus, if he parks at the curb, it is free parking unless there is a parking meter, in which case the cost usually is nominal. This simply is not the situation; the community pays for every curb-side parking space. It is admittedly difficult to arrive at an accurate estimate of the cost of curb parking because of several assumptions required, but such an estimate must be made if the facts of the problem are to be obtained. The first question arises in trying to determine the value of the land at the curb which is used for parking. It cannot fairly be taken at the front-foot value of abutting property, because the street is what gives this property value. But it seems reasonable to start with the premise that a line of parked cars in effect means one less line of moving traffic on the street. If the full width of the street between curbs is to be used for traffic, either the cars must be parked elsewhere, or the street must be widened eight feet on each side to allow for parking.

Let us, then, assume that a street is to be widened eight feet on each side in order to provide parking space, and assign the cost of such widening to the cars parked at the curb. Table 26 presents an analysis under three assumed conditions, chosen so as to represent those which might occur in a large city, a small city, and a suburban village, respectively. It indicates that each car parked at the curb may cost the municipality from about two-thirds of a cent (in a small village) to 20 cents or more (in a large city) for each hour parked.

Lest the more expensive figure for cost of parking space at the curb as presented above be thought too high, two independent figures from other sources are given. In 1933 the Committee on City Traffic of the American Road Builders' Association estimated that the cost

TABLE 26

AN ANALYSIS OF THE COST IN DOLLARS OF CURB-PARKING SPACE IN A DOWNTOWN BUSINESS AREA

Cost Item	Large City	Small City	Sub-urban Village
Assumed land value per front foot	3,000	500	150.00
Assumed building value per front foot	3,000	300	....
Land cost per front foot at 5 per cent of total [a]	150	25	7.50
Building cost per front foot at 15 per cent of total	450 [b]	45 [b]	None [c]
Total cost of eight-foot depth per front foot	600	70	7.50
Cost of acquisition per car space at 20 feet per car space	12,000	1,400	150.00
Cost of street improvements per car space [d]	200	200	200
Total cost per car space	12,200	1,600	350
Annual charges per car space			
Interest on investment at two per cent	244	32	7.00
Amortization of building cost and street-improvement cost at five per cent	460	55	10.00
Maintenance	8	8	8.00
Total annual cost per car space	712	95	25.00
Daily cost per car space (300 days per year)	2.37	0.32	0.08
Hourly cost per car space (12 hours per day)	0.20	0.027	0.0067

[a] Assuming a lot depth of 100 feet and that the 92 feet left after widening would, in accordance with the Hoffman-Neill depth rule, be worth 95 per cent of the original value.

[b] Assuming that existing buildings come out to property line.

[c] Assuming that existing buildings are set back at least eight feet from property line.

[d] Assumed at $1.25 per square foot.

to New York City of parking an automobile on Fifth Avenue (obviously an exceptional case) was $142 per month, or 45 cents per hour under the assumptions in Table 26. The Eno Foundation for Highway Traffic Control reported in 1942 that in connection with a street-widening program in Pittsburgh it was found that the capital cost of a parking space at the curb was $12,932, or about the same as the theoretical example for a large city.

Cost of Offstreet Parking

In considering the cost of offstreet parking facilities, there are four factors other than design efficiency which are of importance: the cost of acquiring the site, the ratio of site cost to development cost, the expense of financing, and operating costs. These factors are somewhat interrelated, as will be shown in the discussions that follow.

Site cost is made up of cost of land plus cost of existing improvements. It is minimized in the case of garages by a multi-level use of the land. The location of the land affects the price, both through varying values from block to block and because land at the rear of lots is vastly less expensive than that which has street frontage. For example, if it is assumed that

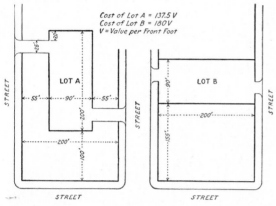

FIGURE 17·4. PLAN SHOWING ADVANTAGE OF INTERIOR OVER STREET FRONTAGE LOCATION FOR A PARKING LOT

the two alternative parking lots shown diagrammatically in Figure 17·4 are in the same block, the land for lot A, including the entrances, is worth only 77 per cent as much as the land for lot B, but both lots will accommodate the same number of cars.[3] In the case of lot A the more valuable frontage can be used for other purposes which may produce higher land rentals. This principle can be applied to either parking lots or garages; an example of its application to garages is shown in Figure 17·5, where the more valuable corner frontage on the ground floor of a garage has been used for a store.

The second factor which influences the cost of offstreet parking is the ratio of site cost to development cost, or, in other words, the question of whether merely a lot is developed or several stories of garages are built. A garage

[3] Applying the Hoffman-Neill depth rule, one of the standard rules used by tax assessors in calculating land values for lots of different depths.

of two or more floors results in distributing the land cost over as many floors as the garage has. If cars are parked on an open roof, as is customary in the deck-type ramp garage with open wall construction (hereinafter referred to as an open ramp garage), the cost of the land is spread over an additional floor. Likewise, the use of the roof will spread the development cost over one more floor than is available in the standard type of enclosed garage.

Figure 17·6 shows the total site and development costs for a parking lot, for open ramp garages of various story heights with parking on the roof, and for enclosed ramp garages—in each case expressed as a function of the cost

Courtesy, Public Roads Administration.

FIGURE 17·5. PARKING GARAGE WITH BUSINESS USE ON THE GROUND FLOOR

of the site and the type of parking facility. The total site and development costs are expressed in dollars per square foot of gross parking area, which would be the area of the lot and any street connections for a parking lot, the gross floor area for an enclosed garage, and the gross floor area plus the roof area for an open ramp garage. The cost of the site is expressed in dollars per square foot of land covered. For a parking lot or a garage built up solidly over the entire lot, this would be the cost per square foot of the lot. But if the floors of the garage cover, on the average, only ¾ of the lot, it would be ⅓ times the square-foot cost of the lot; if they cover only ⅔ of the lot, it would be ½ times the square foot cost of the lot; and so on.

ciation that, to accommodate passenger cars, "clearance between floors and supporting beams or joists for floors above the first floor need not exceed 7.5 feet, with probably nine or 10 feet on the first floor, where there may be office space and perhaps certain services." [5]

The resulting development costs are those shown at zero site value on the diagram. They decrease quite regularly with the number of

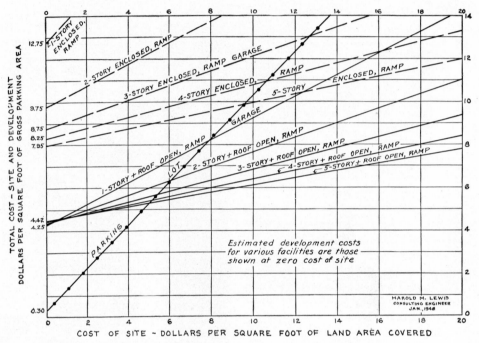

FIGURE 17·6. RELATION OF SITE COST TO TOTAL COST FOR VARIOUS TYPES OF OFFSTREET PARKING
FACILITIES

The development, or construction, costs of garages are based on a unit cost of 50 cents per cubic foot for open ramp garages and 80 cents per cubic foot for enclosed ramp garages.[4] The cubage is based on a 12-foot height between first- and second-floor levels, a nine-foot height between upper floor levels, and allowances of two feet below the ground floor for foundations and three feet above the roof for the cost of a parapet wall and other incidental roof costs. These story heights are based on the recommendation of the American Automobile Asso-

floors for enclosed garages. For open garages, however, the relative savings from roof parking and from lower unit-construction costs for taller buildings tend to keep the development costs per square foot of gross parking area quite uniform regardless of the number of stories, the figures being as follows:

NUMBER OF STORIES IN BUILDING	COST IN DOLLARS
1	4.25
2	4.33
3	4.36
4	4.40
5	4.42

[4] These costs are taken as fairly typical of 1947 construction costs in an average American city; in New York City and vicinity, corresponding costs reached about 80 cents and $1.20 per cubic foot in 1947.

[5] *Parking Manual,* American Automobile Association, 1946, page 128.

It appears from Figure 17·6 that, on the basis of the assumed development costs (which will vary widely in different parts of the country and from year to year), a parking lot is the most economical development per square foot of gross parking area on land costing not over $5.10 per square foot, if compared with costs for a four-story open ramp garage, and $6 per square foot, if compared with costs for a two-story open ramp garage, in each case with roof parking. On land costing $8 per square foot, total site and development costs per square foot of gross parking area would be about $6 for a four-story open garage with roof parking, as compared with about $8.25 for a one-story open garage with roof parking and $11.40 for an enclosed three-story garage. On land costing $12 per square foot, the total site and development costs per square foot of gross parking area would be about the same for a five-story enclosed garage as for a one-story-and-roof open ramp garage.

Ramp garages with more than five parking floors have not proved feasible for self-service parking. Enclosed garages are considerably more expensive than open garages but will be justified in some instances by other considerations. The number of floors to be constructed, in either case, will depend largely upon the capacity required and the floor area which will permit an efficient layout.

The third factor which affects the cost of all offstreet parking facilities is the expense of financing. This factor is discussed further in a later section of this chapter, but two points are important here: interest rates may vary from one per cent to as much as eight per cent, depending on who is financing the lot and how; and amortization may run as high as 10 per cent, depending on the value of any buildings which have to be removed to make the site usable and the value of the structures, if any, which are built on the site as part of the parking facility. This can best be demonstrated by examples. Table 27 shows the calculation of annual carrying charges per car space for four facilities (designated W, X, Y, and Z), each of which is assumed to cost $2,000 per car space, but in each of which this cost is distributed differently between raw land, existing

structures to be demolished, and improvements. Alternative carrying charges are shown under public financing and private financing.

TABLE 27

STATISTICS FOR FOUR PARKING FACILITIES, SHOWING HOW CARRYING CHARGES IN DOLLARS PER CAR SPACE WILL VARY WITH SITE AND DEVELOPMENT COSTS AND METHOD OF FINANCING

Cost Item	Parking Lot		Garage	
	W	X	Y	Z
Capital investment (assumed)				
Cost of raw land	1,900	1,000	1,400	900
Cost of existing structures on site	0	900	0	500
Cost of improvements constructed	100	100	600	600
Total cost per car space	2,000	2,000	2,000	2,000
Annual carrying charges with public financing (first 20 years)				
Land only—amortized in 100 years at two per cent interest	44.09	23.20	32.48	20.88
Structures and improvements, existing and proposed—amortized in 20 years at two per cent interest	6.12	61.16	36.69	67.27
Total annual carrying charges	50.21	84.36	69.17	88.15
Annual carrying charges at private rates (first 10 years)				
Land only—amortized in 100 years at five per cent	95.73	50.38	70.54	45.34
Structures, existing and proposed—amortized in 10 years at eight per cent interest	14.90	149.03	89.42	163.93
Total annual carrying charges, with tax exemption	110.63	199.41	159.96	209.27
Taxes at 3.5 per cent on 100 per cent of land value and 75 per cent of improvement value	69.13	37.63	64.75	47.25
Total annual carrying charges, without tax exemption	179.76	237.04	224.71	256.52

It has been assumed that private capital could, in each instance, secure mortgage money at five per cent only to the extent of the value of the raw land, and that the equity would have to be amortized in 10 years to attract investment at eight per cent. A comparison of the total annual carrying charges shows that those for lot X are substantially greater than those for lot W, whether they are publicly or privately financed. A similar, but much smaller, difference is found in corresponding figures for garage Z and those for garage Y. This difference results from the fact that, for lot X and garage Z, existing improvements on the site must be acquired and demolished, but the value of such improvements are destroyed and, in effect, become a part of the total improvement cost of the new facility and must bear the same rates of interest and amortization as the latter. Total carrying charges with private financing are shown both with and without tax exemption, as the tax situation may be handled in

Separate figures are given for various densities of parking (as indicated by the number of square feet per car space) to show the effect of this factor on the number of employees required. An extremely high density, represented by an allowance of only 145 square feet per car, is the condition existing in a parking lot such

TABLE 28

OPERATING COSTS FOR ENCLOSED GARAGES AND PARKING LOTS OF 200-CAR CAPACITY, UNDER VARIOUS PARKING DENSITIES

(Based on estimated 1947 costs)

	Square Feet per Car Space	Number of Employees, 3 Shifts	Annual Payroll Costs in Dollars			Operating Costs per Car Space in Dollars			
						Per Year			Total per Day [b]
			Employees [a]	Supervision	Total	Payroll	Others	Total	
Garages	165	15	39,000	4,000	43,000	215	15 [c]	230	0.767
	200	12	31,200	3,600	34,800	174	15 [c]	189	0.630
	300 [d]	6	15,600	3,200	18,800	94	15 [c]	109	0.363
Parking lots	145	15	39,000	4,000	43,000	215	6 [e]	221	0.737
	200	10	26,000	3,600	29,600	148	6 [e]	154	0.513
	275 [d]	6	15,600	3,200	18,800	94	6 [e]	100	0.333
	325 [f]	0	0	3,000	3,000	15	6 [e]	21	0.07

[a] At $46.50 a week, plus 7.5 per cent for social security, compensation, etc.
[b] Based on a 300-day year.
[c] Including $7 for electricity, $5 for heating, $0.50 for telephone, and $2.50 for advertising and supplies.
[d] Driver parks own car, fee collected by attendant.
[e] Including $3 for electricity, $0.50 for telephone, and $2.50 for advertising and supplies.
[f] Driver parks own car, no fee collected.

different ways. The annual charges of the publicly financed facilities run from about 42 per cent to 45 per cent of those for the privately financed facilities with tax exemption. This is not intended as an argument for public ownership, except to point out that, with municipal credit backing the financing of offstreet facilities, the element of risk in lending is vastly reduced and, with that, the cost of financing.

The last of the four factors, other than design efficiency, which have an influence on the cost of offstreet parking facilities is operating costs. These are shown for a 200-car garage or parking lot in Table 28, where they are broken down into payroll and other costs.

as the one pictured in Figure 17·9. Obviously such a situation not only requires an excessive number of attendants to park and shift cars, but also is undesirable from other standpoints, such as frequent damage to cars, slow delivery, and inability to lock a car. The lowest density shown is represented by an allowance of 325 square feet per car space, the approximate area per car required in a parking lot of the type illustrated in Figure 17·8. In this type of parking lot drivers park and get their own cars, which may be locked when they are left, since every space is accessible at all times.

The chief significance of Table 28 is shown most clearly by comparing payroll costs per car space per year with other operating costs. For a densely used garage payroll costs are over 14 times all other operating costs, whereas in the self-parking garage payroll costs are just over six times as much as all other operating

quired from each car space if the project is to be made self-supporting. Both the number of cars that will be served and the fees that must be charged will be affected by the expected daily average turnover, which may run from

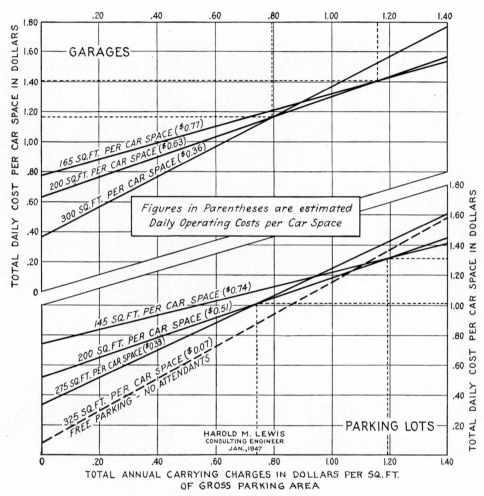

FIGURE 17·7. EFFECT OF OPERATING DENSITY ON TOTAL DAILY COST PER CAR SPACE FOR PARKING LOTS AND GARAGES

costs. The contrast is equally startling for parking lots, where the ratios of payroll to other operating costs are almost 36 to one for the dense lot, as against not quite 16 to one for the self-service lot with fees collected, and only 2½ to one for the free lot.

A combination of the four cost factors discussed above will give the total costs for any specified offstreet parking facility. These can best be expressed as the total cost per car space per day, which will be the total income re-

less than one up to about four, with 2.5 a reasonable figure for a retail district in an average city.

It has been shown that the operating costs for any facility will vary considerably with the density at which that facility is operated. The density will vary inversely as the square feet per car space, the ratio used in these calculations. Figure 17·7 shows how the relationship between total costs per car space and annual carrying charges per square foot of site will vary under different types of operation as represented by different ratios of square feet per car space. Separate diagrams are shown for parking lots and garages, using in each case figures for square feet per car space that range from maximum crowding to generous space allowances permitting driver-parking and rapid entrance and exit.

year. The broken lines indicate the points at which such changes will take place. These diagrams can also be used to show, for any annual carrying charge, what daily income per car space would be required under different operating densities.

FIGURE 17·8. A WELL-DESIGNED PARKING LOT

Each car can be moved without interference with other cars. Attractive landscaping is provided.

lowances permitting driver-parking and rapid entrance and exit.

It is evident from these diagrams that, if a fee is to be charged for the use of a parking lot, a low-density, customer-parking operation (275 square feet per car space) will be most economical when carrying charges are not over $0.74 per square foot per year; likewise a garage can best be run on low-density, customer-parking operation (300 square feet per car space) when carrying charges are not over $0.80 per

There were probably only a few places in the United States where it was possible, even with a favorable turnover, to collect more than $1.00 per car space per day on the basis of 1947 costs, unless some combination of both daytime and overnight use was feasible. With this practical ceiling on parking rates taken as typical, the following calculations are presented as illustrating how a problem in offstreet parking could be worked out by use of the factors described above.

PROBLEM: It is desired to determine what might be paid, under two different operating densities, for sites for four-, three-, and two-story open ramp garages with roof parking, in an area where there is an expected income of $1.00 per car space per day, based on a 300-day year. The land cost, but not the cost of any existing improvements to be demolished, is to be tax exempt.

CALCULATIONS:

Based on operating densities, in square foot per car space, of:	*200*	*300*
Daily income per car space	$1.00	$1.00
Deduct operating costs, no heat (Table 28)	0.613	0.346
Balance available for daily carrying charge per car space	0.387	0.654
Available for annual carrying charge per square foot (×300 ÷ density)	0.581	0.654

Deduct interest and amortization of eight per cent of construction costs per square foot of gross parking area (costs used in Figure 17·6), assuming 5 per cent interest and amortization in 20 years:

$0.352 for a four-story garage		
0.349 " " three- " "		
0.346 " " two- " "		

giving a balance available for carrying charges on site cost per square foot of gross parking area, as follows:

With four-story garage	0.229	0.302
" three- " "	0.232	0.305
" two- " "	0.235	0.308

Reducing these figures to the basis of square feet of land area covered, by multiplying by number of parking floors, gives:

With four-story garage (five parking floors)	1.145	1.510
With three-story garage (four parking floors)	0.928	1.220
With two-story garage (three parking floors)	0.705	0.924

CONCLUSIONS: With these amounts available for financing site acquisitions, it is found that the land costs which might be afforded in each case would be as follows:

Based on operating densities, in square foot per car space, of:	*200*	*300*
A vacant site requiring annual charges of 5.04 per cent, assuming five per cent interest and amortization in 100 years and that the building covered the entire lot, could be acquired at the following costs per square foot of site:		

For four-story garage	$22.70	$29.95
" three- " "	18.40	24.20
" two- " "	13.98	18.31

If the site has existing improvements on it worth one-half the land value and these are to be amortized in 20 years and the land cost in 100 years, in each case with five per cent interest, the land, excluding improvements, must be acquired at not more than the following costs per square foot of site:

For four-story garage	12.67	16.70
" three- " "	10.25	13.50
" two- " "	7.83	10.21

It is indicated that in each case self-service parking at a density of 300 square foot per car space would prove more profitable than attendant parking at 200 square foot per car space, and would be justified on vacant land costing $29.95 per square foot for a four-story garage and $18.31 per square foot for a two-story garage. If buildings costing half as much as the land must be acquired and demolished, only about 56 per cent as much could be afforded for land, or $16.70 for a four-story building and $10.21 for a two-story building.

Location of Parking Facilities

The first factor to be considered in preparing plans for parking facilities is location. A thorough-going attack on the parking problem of any community will include studies outlined in the earlier section of this chapter on the parking survey. These studies should show, as specifically as possible, the ultimate destinations of automobile users. Parking facilities should be located near these destinations. As the distance from parking space to destination increases, the utility of the parking space decreases, and with that the fee that may be charged. Furthermore, the distance which parkers are willing to walk will vary with the size of the locality served and the established habits of motor-vehicle users in that locality. Although in a small suburban shopping center parking space should probably be provided within 400 to 500 feet of the stores to be served, a distance of 750 feet has been used as a standard for urban conditions. In New York City, where conditions are obviously exceptional, an engineering committee reporting to the City Planning Commission in 1946 stated in connection with a proposal for parking garages in

Manhattan that "the average driver might use the facilities of a public garage for offstreet parking for over an hour if his walk to the garage did not exceed 1,600 feet." [6] Although this distance might satisfy an all-day parker,

demand for offstreet facilities, rather than in locations where demand was great, but land prices were higher. In large cities with great traffic congestion in their central areas, some schemes for peripheral parking lots with spe-

Courtesy, American Automobile Association.

FIGURE 17·9.   EXAMPLE OF AN UNPLANNED AND OVERCROWDED PARKING LOT

previous surveys showed that it would be considered excessive by the average shopper.

It is the opinion of some planners who have studied the problem that one reason for the financial failure of many privately constructed garages is that they have been located where land costs were low, and where there was little

[6] *Selected Measures for the Partial Relief of Traffic Congestion in New York City,* Report of Engineering Committee on New York City Traffic, November 14, 1946.

cial bus service to central areas have been tried.

For example, the Baltimore Transit Company established in 1946 a perimeter parking lot with shuttle bus service into the downtown area (Figure 17·10). A 25-cent ticket entitled a driver to all-day parking and bus transportation to and from downtown. Non-parkers could use the shuttle buses for five cents; there were no transfers. The service was reported popular. In Chicago, shuttle buses were operating in 1946 for a 10-cent fare between the central business district and a previously almost unused parking lot at Soldiers' Field. In November, 1947, New York City established an experimental free-parking lot at Flushing Meadow Park in the borough of Queens, using part of a former parking area for the World's Fair. It is bordered by a rapid-transit line on which additional express service to Manhattan was provided.

Courtesy, Public Roads Administration.

FIGURE 17·10. A PERIMETER PARKING LOT ON THE EDGE OF BALTIMORE, OPERATED BY THE BALTIMORE TRANSIT COMPANY

The peripheral lot with shuttle service is not, however, a solution to the problem, but more of a palliative, inasmuch as it serves principally the relatively long-time parkers, and then at considerable loss of convenience.

Another consideration in the location of parking facilities is their effect on traffic in the areas they serve. In the downtown areas in which parking facilities are most urgently needed traffic usually is congested. Parking facilities should be so located as to take vehicles off the streets before they enter the most congested area, in so far as is possible. This means in effect a ringing of the core of the central area with parking facilities. There should be easy access from main traffic arteries to offstreet parking facilities to prevent overloading of the local street system in the vicinity by traffic to and from the parking space. In this connection both the size and the design of the parking facility must be considered. The effect of a 1,000-car garage disgorging 75 to 90 per cent of its capacity into one narrow street during the evening rush hour could be paralyzing to traffic. Furthermore, entrances and exits to parking lots and garages should be at the maximum possible distance from a street intersection, or congestion will result. Figure 17·11 shows a proposal for parking lots to serve the business uses in a large suburban village.

Detailed Design

The conventional commercial parking lot is an eyesore, but this condition need not exist. A minimum number of restrained signs and the use of trees, hedges, walls, and differences of level can make the lot a place of beauty instead. The parking lot shown in Figure 17·12 is in the Country Club District of Kansas City. The photograph is taken from well above normal eye level. The level of the lot is such that the cars are below eye level for pedestrians on the sidewalk, and the wall is higher than the tops of the cars in the lot. Figure 17·13 shows another attractive parking lot in connection with a local shopping center. Open borders of a parking lot should have a planting strip, at least five feet in width, for hedges, trees, grass, flowers, or shrubs, and within the lot there should be additional planting areas. Walks are desirable within the lot to separate pedestrian and vehicular traffic.

In the arrangement of parking spaces within the lot, certain standards must be considered. In 1941 over three-quarters of all cars sold were 17 feet 6 inches or less in length and 6 feet 3 inches or less in width. Only eight models (all expensive cars, with small sales volume) out of 29 of the more common American makes needed an outside diameter more than 48 feet clear in which to turn, and all would turn in a 60-foot clear space. Figure 17·14 shows desirable dimensions and clearances for cars 6 feet 3 inches wide by 17 feet 6 inches long, which will turn in an outside diameter of 48 feet, parked in a single motion in berths 8 feet 6 inches wide, for several different angles of parking. These diagrams are designed for self-service parking, because it was determined in the previous sec-

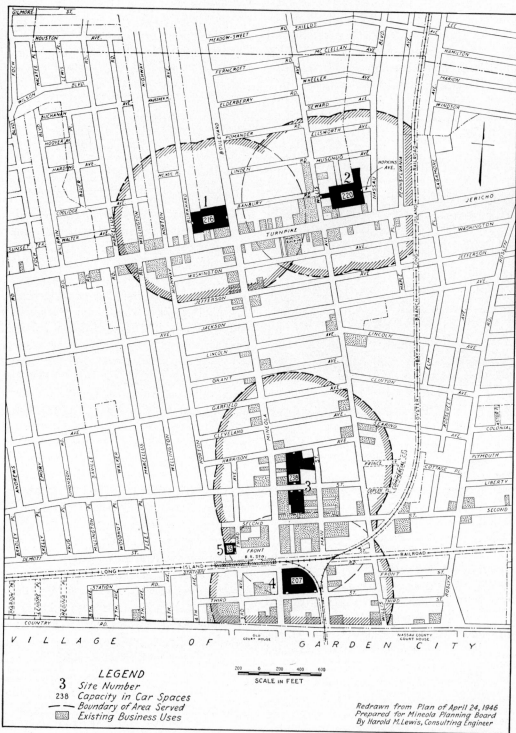

FIGURE 17·11. MASTER PLAN FOR MUNICIPAL PARKING LOTS IN THE VILLAGE OF MINEOLA, NEW YORK

FIGURE 17·12.   AN ATTRACTIVE PARKING LOT IN THE COUNTRY CLUB DISTRICT OF KANSAS CITY, MISSOURI

FIGURE 17·13.   OFFSTREET PARKING AT A LOCAL SHOPPING CENTER

A development in Arlington, Virginia, at the corner of Columbia Pike and Glebe Road.

tion of this chapter that this type of parking is more economical in most cases than attendant parking, for which smaller clearances are permissible. Since the average driver is not too expert at backing his car into a confined

that 16 feet was taken as the practical minimum aisle width which would permit two cars to pass, provided the aisle was to be operated one-way. With two-way operation this minimum should be increased to 20 feet.

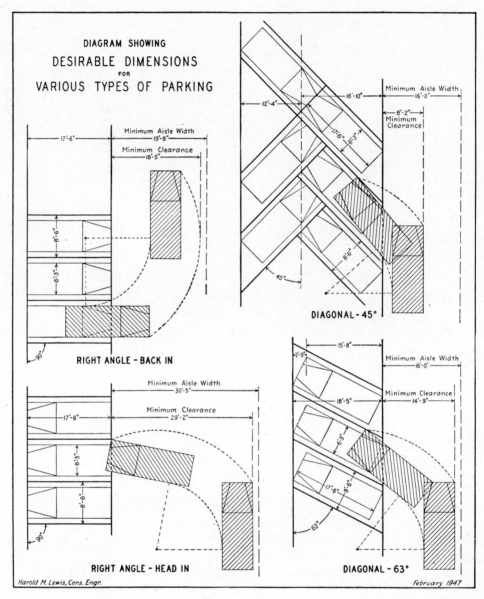

FIGURE 17·14

space, all the diagrams but one are for head-in parking, but 90-degree back-in parking also is shown because of its high spatial efficiency. In designing practical minimum aisle widths, an operating margin of 1 foot 3 inches was allowed over the minimum clearance dimension, except

With two lines of parked cars flanking a 16-foot aisle, the theoretical requirement in number of square feet of lot area per car is: 232 for 90° back-in parking; 278 for 90° head-in parking; 251 for 63° parking; and 298 for 45° parking. On this basis 90° back-in parking is most efficient. Of all the possible angles of head-in parking, about 63° is the most efficient, as it permits a maximum use of the minimum aisle width. At angles over 63° the aisle requirement per car increases faster than the dead space per parking space decreases, while at angles of less than 63° there is no additional

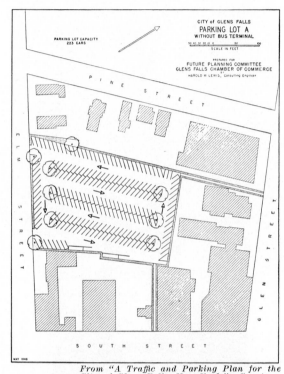

From "A Traffic and Parking Plan for the City of Glens Falls, New York." Courtesy, Glens Falls Chamber of Commerce.

FIGURE 17·15. LAYOUT FOR A LARGE PARKING LOT ON A REGULARLY SHAPED SITE

economy in aisle space per car, but the dead space per parking space increases.

In actual design, however, the most efficient angle will depend more on the dimensions of the lot than on any theoretical determination. When the sum of the widths of the lines of parked cars and access aisles equals the total width of the lot, with every access aisle serving two lines of parked cars, the most efficient over-all layout will be secured, in spite of the use of angles of parking other than 63°. It is also important that the lines of parked cars be not too short, since access aisles at the ends of a row of cars are wasted space as far as that row of cars is concerned. The length of the

row has an additional effect when diagonal parking is used, in that the angle causes additional dead space at the ends of the row, this space being independent of the length of the row. In general, the larger the lot and the more regular its shape, the higher is the efficiency to which it may be designed.

Figures 17·15 and 17·16 show designs for parking lots on two different sites. Both use berth dimensions of eight feet by 17 feet per car. The lot shown in Figure 17·15 is on a large site, and utilizes 60° parking except on the ends; aisle widths are 19 feet; excluding the pedestrian access walks, actual lot area per

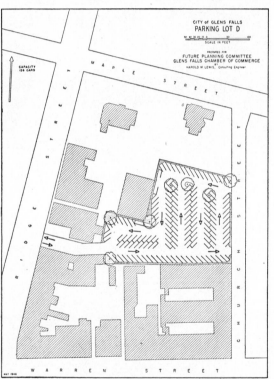

From "A Traffic and Parking Plan for the City of Glens Falls, New York." Courtesy, Glens Falls Chamber of Commerce.

FIGURE 17·16. LAYOUT FOR A SMALL PARKING LOT ON AN IRREGULAR SITE

car space is 310 square feet. The lot shown in Figure 17·16 is on a small site and utilizes 45° parking throughout; aisle widths are 16 feet; excluding the access drive, actual lot area per car space is 339 square feet. Theoretical area per car space, using berth dimensions of 8 feet by 17 feet and figuring a row of parked cars on either side of the access aisle as in the analysis above, would be 252 square feet for 60° parking and 276 square feet for 45° parking. The waste space per car then is 59 square feet in Figure 17·15 and 64 square feet in Figure 17·16 over the respective theoretical figures. This demonstrates the loss in efficiency caused by the smaller dimensions and irregular shape of the lot in Figure 17·16.

The parking garage has been the object of considerable study and experimentation. Vari-

Longley Photo, Cincinnati, Ohio.

FIGURE 17·17. RECEIVING ENTRANCE TO CAREW TOWER GARAGE IN CINCINNATI

The cars are handled by a mechanical device to and from elevators.

ous mechanical devices have been designed to permit a high number of cars to be parked on a small piece of land, without sacrificing accessibility. One of these, which employs a mechanical device for moving cars to and from elevators, is illustrated in Figure 17·17. Two similar garages, called Kent Automatic Garages, were built in New York City in 1930 at a cost of $6.65 per square foot of floor area. They would probably have cost about $15 per square foot in 1947, the year on which other costs discussed herein have been based. Other designs include a tower-elevator type similar to a flattened ferris wheel and a turntable arrangement. A brief examination of such devices will show that 165 square feet per car is about the minimum floor area which can be achieved, owing to the necessary minimum dimensions of elevators and the space required for the machinery. In addition, the operating

and maintenance costs of such garages are high. For these reasons it is doubtful that such schemes are economically feasible, as has been shown in the discussions earlier in this chapter. A simple forked lift developed about 1946 to raise a car to upper-level parking berths is illustrated in Figure 17·18.

The more conventional types of parking garage may be classified by the means of getting from floor to floor—that is, ramp or elevator—and by the type of construction—whether open or closed. The elevator type of garage is most suitable when the total lot area is small because the space required for an elevator is very much less than that required for any system of ramps. However, the use of an elevator requires an operator, and delivery of cars is slow. The

Photo by David C. Guilbert, Spokane, Washington. Courtesy, American Automobile Association.

FIGURE 17·18. DEMONSTRATION OF A PORTABLE MULTIPLE DECK, USING A FORKED LIFT FOR PLACING CARS ON THE UPPER DECKS

elevator-type garage probably is not suitable for offstreet parking in central areas where there may be either a high turnover of cars or peak hours for entrance and discharge. On the other hand, one ramp can handle almost as many cars in one direction as one lane of a street, and where the lot area is sufficient, the ramp type of garage will operate most efficiently.

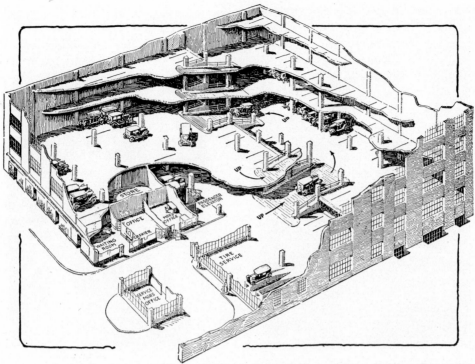

Courtesy, d'Humy Motoramp System, Ramp Buildings Corporation.

FIGURE 17·19. DESIGN FOR A RAMP GARAGE WITH STAGGERED FLOOR LEVELS

The necessity for allowing space for getting from floor to floor reduces the design efficiency of the parking garage as compared to that of the parking lot. Furthermore, wall space and waste space caused by necessary columns will equal or exceed the amount of space allowed for planting in a lot of the same size. The lowest area per car which can be achieved in a ramp-type garage, using 90° back-in parking, berths 8 feet by 17½ feet and aisles 18 feet 8 inches wide to permit one-movement parking for self-service operation, is about 275 square feet, and this only on a lot of ideal dimensions. This figure can be achieved in a staggered-floor type of design, such as is shown in Figure 17·19, or in a continuous-ramp design, such as is shown in Figure 17·20. The more conventional types of garage design will require 300 or more square feet per car for self-service parking with the minimum berth and aisle dimensions mentioned above.

The economies in construction cost of the open garage (see Figure 17·21) over the conventional closed type are obvious. Probably the principal disadvantage of this type of ga-

rage is that it cannot be heated. However, while this might be considered an objectionable feature in a garage to be used for permanent

Courtesy, American Automobile Association.

FIGURE 17·20. A CONTINUOUS-RAMP DESIGN FOR A PARKING GARAGE

storage in cold climates, it probably is not important if the garage is to furnish parking space in a business district, inasmuch as the same criticism applies to curb or lot parking.

Courtesy, Public Roads Administration.

FIGURE 17·21. A MODERN OPEN-WALL RAMP GARAGE

Illustrated by the S and H Parking Center on Eye Street, N.W., near 16th Street, Washington, D. C.

Combinations of garages with buildings of other types, or locating garages in such a way as to permit other use of the same land area,

Courtesy, Macy's, New York.

FIGURE 17·22. MACY'S BRANCH STORE AT JA-MAICA IN THE BOROUGH OF QUEENS, NEW YORK CITY, SHOWING PARKING ON THE ROOF

can result in reductions in land costs which may be worth while in areas of high land value. (See Figures 17·5 and 17·22.) A garage was built under a centrally located park in San Francisco

(see Figure 17·23), a similar proposal was advanced in 1946 for Newark, and an underground garage is proposed in connection with the municipal auditorium in Kansas City. It is possible to construct a single building running through a block with a garage located in the center. The more valuable street frontages may be used on the ground floor for stores and on the upper floors for offices, while the less valuable land in the interior, where it is difficult to get natural light from the lower floors, is used for automobile storage. Such a plan was carried out in Cincinnati, where the Netherland-Plaza Hotel, the Carew Tower Garage (Figure 17·17), a department store, and offices are all housed in a single building. Designs of this type increase the over-all efficiency of the use of the land, permitting full ground coverage with outside exposures for all offices and convenient parking space for tenants and customers.

Before leaving the subject of the design of parking facilities, some brief discussion of curb parking is in order. In general, parallel parking is preferable on streets, since this type inter-

Courtesy, San Francisco Chamber of Commerce.

FIGURE 17·23. UNION SQUARE GARAGE IN SAN FRANCISCO

A multiple-deck garage constructed beneath a public park.

feres least with moving traffic in the adjacent lane. Where the street is very wide, or where through and local traffic are separated by malls and the service street is of sufficient width, diagonal or vertical parking may be permissible. However, an angle of more than about 45° with the curb will result in obstructing more than one lane of moving traffic, as is shown in Figure 17·14. Furthermore, it is difficult for the driver to see when it is clear behind him and safe to back out of his space, and he probably will back almost straight out, which will result in his obstructing two moving lanes rather than one, even at 45°.

Financing Offstreet Parking

The various methods of paying for offstreet parking facilities may be outlined as follows:

A. Private construction and operation.
   1. As a business venture for profit from fees.
   2. As a service in connection with another business or businesses and paid for by:
      a. Fees.
      b. Credits on fees on the basis of patronage of the other business.
      c. Charging expenses to advertising or good will.
      d. Any combination of *a*, *b*, and/or *c*.
B. Public construction and operation paid for by:
   1. Parking fees.
   2. Appropriation of general public funds or general assessment in the tax levy.
   3. Municipal bond issue.
   4. Assessment on benefited property.
   5. A special authority, self-sustaining through fees, perhaps supplemented by some form of municipal subsidy.
   6. A combination of two or more of these methods.
C. Combinations of *A* and *B*, such as public construction and private operation.
D. *A* or *C* above, with public subsidy by real estate or other tax exemption.

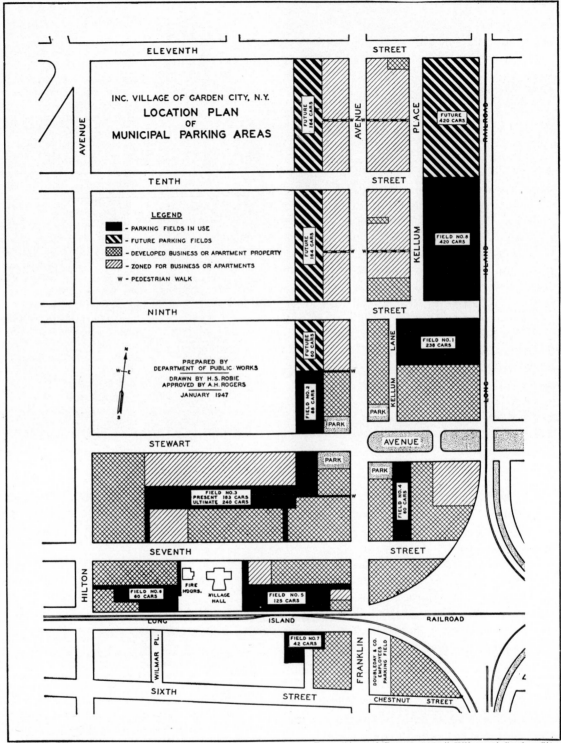

From "Annual Report, 1947," Village of Garden City.

FIGURE 17·24. A COMPREHENSIVE SYSTEM OF PARKING LOTS TO SERVE THE BUSINESS AREA OF THE
VILLAGE OF GARDEN CITY, NEW YORK

The lots were financed by assessing land and acquisition costs against business and apartment properties
directly abutting, and by paying improvement costs from municipal funds.

Past experience has indicated that private capital is not sufficiently interested in this form of investment to solve the parking problem voluntarily, although all the various means outlined in *A* above have been and are in use in many communities.

Control by Zoning Ordinances

As various types of buildings in themselves draw large numbers of vehicles which require parking space, some communities have adopted zoning ordinances which require that specified minimum amounts of offstreet parking space, depending on the use and size of the building, be provided when such a building is constructed. In August, 1946, reports from 586 of the 1,060 cities in the United States having populations of more than 10,000 in 1940 showed 70 cities, or 12 per cent, having zoning ordinances requiring such parking space (or offstreet loading space).[7] The types of regulations then in effect or proposed varied considerably, as shown by the figures at the top of the next column.

The standard size of each berth required varied from 200 to 300 square feet. In many cases the provisions were applicable only to buildings which exceeded a minimum specified size, such as a restaurant seating 100 persons or a hospital with beds for 50 patients.

Such requirements will help to solve the parking problem, but unless their provisions are retroactive—a procedure still of questionable legality—it will be a great many years before offstreet parking space will be adequate. Furthermore, on the small lots which predominate in the already built-up central areas of most cities it is impractical and inefficient to try to provide parking space, and in certain locations offstreet parking is actually undesirable because of the traffic congestion which such a facility may cause. The difficulty of small lots may be overcome by allowing parking space to

[7] "Zoning Applied to Parking," by Charles S. Le-Craw, Jr., and Wilbur S. Smith, *Traffic Quarterly*, Vol. I, No. 1, The Eno Foundation for Highway Traffic Control, Saugatuck, Conn., January, 1947, page 11. See also "Automobile Parking in Central Business Districts," *Technical Bulletin* 6, Urban Land Institute, July, 1946.

Type of Building	One Parking Berth Required for Each of the Following Units:
Theatre or auditorium	Each two seats to each 10 seats.
Hotel	Each sleeping room to each three sleeping rooms; the first 20 sleeping rooms and each four above 20.
Restaurant	Each four seats to each five seats; each 50 square feet of floor area for patron use.
Hospital, sanatorium	Each 300 square feet of floor area of sleeping rooms to each 1,000 square feet of total floor area.
Office building	Each 400 square foot of floor area of one-story building and each 750 square feet of upper floor area to each 500 square feet of gross floor area for buildings of 7,500 square feet or more of gross floor area.
Retail store	Parking area equal to total floor area (equivalent to berth for each 200 square feet of floor area) to berth for each 800 square feet of floor area.

be provided within a certain distance of the building, but this still does not solve the problem of organization of space from a traffic standpoint.

A Public Responsibility

The planning of parking facilities certainly is a public responsibility, and the point of view that the construction of offstreet parking facilities is a proper field for municipal action is gaining more widespread acceptance. Among the principal arguments in favor of this course are:

1. Parking is part of the highway and traffic problem—long recognized as a public responsibility.
2. Private development has not provided sufficient offstreet parking facilities in areas where they are most needed.
3. In many locations where more parking space is badly needed, the power of eminent domain would be required to assemble property of sufficient size for economically efficient facilities.
4. Offstreet parking facilities can be financed much more cheaply by municipalities than by private interests.

In December, 1945, the Urban Land Institute reported 12 states having legislation enabling municipalities to provide parking facilities by one means or another. The rapid spread of this type of legislation to other states is to be expected.

Offstreet Loading Space for Trucks

A problem related to the parking of passenger automobiles is the parking of motor trucks for

Courtesy, "New York Sun."

FIGURE 17·25. TRAFFIC BLOCKED BY TRUCKS LOADING AND UNLOADING AT THE CURBS

As illustrated by 36th Street in Manhattan's garment district, New York City. Vehicles in center lane were barely moving at 3:55 P.M.

loading or unloading of merchandise or freight. This problem is different in that such an operation must take place at the site where the truck's load is to be picked up or delivered or at a joint offstreet loading platform connected by some other means of conveyance with such site.

In portions of the central areas of many cities the loading and unloading of trucks while standing on public roadways cause as much or more traffic congestion than automobile parking. This is particularly true in light manufacturing districts and wholesale market areas. The conditions shown in Figure 17·25 are typical of many cities. The solution is more difficult than that of the automobile parking problem because there is no practical alternative means of short-haul distribution of freight, whereas mass-transportation facilities offer an alternative to the automobile rider.

Where truck loading has caused acute congestion at critical points, some cities have tried loading prohibitions during peak hours. This obviously is a temporary resort and not a satisfactory solution to the problem. Offstreet loading space is a necessity. This has been recognized by many progressive builders who have included offstreet loading facilities in the design of business and industrial buildings in every sizable community. The provisions range from space for a single truck to back into a recessed loading platform, in a small structure, to elaborate basement or ground-floor designs which will accommodate from 40 trucks at one time, as in Rockefeller Center in New York City, to 70 trucks, as in Macy's department store in the same city. There is a substantial saving in handling costs when goods can be loaded directly into trucks from platforms at truck-bed height, rather than stacked on the sidewalk, lifted into the truck, and manhandled to their position therein.

As in the parking of passenger cars, zoning ordinances may be used to make mandatory the provision of adequate offstreet truck-loading and unloading space accessory to buildings which are served by a considerable number of trucks. There were in 1946 a good many examples of such provisions for new buildings, some of which are as follows:

1. One berth of 250 square feet for each 25,000 square feet of building space or fraction in excess of 5,000 square feet in buildings used for manufacture, storage, or goods display, or for a department store, hotel, or hospital (New York City).
2. One berth 10 feet by 25 feet for each 20,000 square feet or fraction thereof in excess of 3,000

square feet of building-floor use or for every 20,000 square feet or fraction thereof in excess of 3,000 square feet of land use for certain specified manufacturing and business uses (Detroit).

3. One berth of 200 square feet for each 8,000 square feet of gross floor area devoted to lofts, department stores, retail and wholesale food markets or stores, warehouses, or supply houses (Plainfield, New Jersey).

4. One berth for each 2,000 square feet of lot area and, if the building has a gross floor area of more than 80,000 square feet, one additional berth for each additional 40,000 square feet or fraction thereof above 10,000 square feet in hospitals, institutions, hotels, commercial or industrial buildings (Los Angeles).

5. In several ordinances, particularly for smaller communities, offstreet loading space is required for manufacturing or commercial buildings over a specified size, but the amount of such space is to be determined by the zoning board of appeals.

To provide loading space for trucks at buildings already constructed there are two methods: (1) requirement of provision of space within a period of time through the zoning ordinance, and (2) use or construction of rear alleys in commercial areas, to be used for loading. Police generally are opposed to rear alleys as hard to patrol, and frequently the cost of acquisition of rights of way through the centers of blocks is prohibitive.

Various authorities, including the Regional Plan Association and Nathan Cherniack, have recommended the amendment of zoning ordinances to require certain types of existing commercial and industrial buildings to provide offstreet truck-loading and unloading space, according to a sliding scale based on gross floor area, within a period of five to 10 years.[8]

Selected References

A Parking Survey of the Providence Central Business District, 1945, by the State Highway Planning Survey in co-operation with the Federal Public Roads Administration, State of Rhode Island Department of Public Works, Providence.

[8] See "A Statement of the Parking Problem," by Nathan Cherniack, Economist, the Port of New York Authority, *American Planning and Civic Annual,* 1945, pages 122–138, and *Traffic and Parking Study,* Regional Plan Association, Inc., December, 1942, pages 40–44.

A Traffic and Parking Plan for the City of Glens Falls (prepared by Harold M. Lewis, Consulting Engineer), Glens Falls Future Planning Committee, Glens Falls Chamber of Commerce, Glens Falls, N. Y., September, 1946.

"Automobile Parking in Central Business Districts," *Technical Bulletin* 6, Urban Land Institute, Washington, D. C., July, 1946.

Downtown Los Angeles Parking Study, Downtown Business Men's Association, Los Angeles, January, 1945.

MICKLE, D. GRANT: "Solutions to Local Parking Problems" (reprinted from *Proceedings of 30th Annual Michigan Highway Conference,* February 29, 1944), Automotive Safety Foundation, Washington, D. C.

Offstreet Parking Study for the City of Anaheim, City Planning Commission, Anaheim, Calif., 1945.

Parking Manual—How to Solve Community Parking Problems, American Automobile Association, Washington, D. C., 1946.

Parking Study of the Pittsburgh Central Business District, prepared by the Pittsburgh Regional Planning Association for the Allegheny Conference on Community Development, Pittsburgh, Pa., 1945–1946.

Selected Measures for the Partial Relief of Traffic Congestion in New York City (report of Engineering Committee on New York City Traffic) and *City Planning Commission Recommendations on Traffic Report,* City Planning Commission, City of New York, November 14, 1946.

SMITH, WILBUR S., and CHARLES S. LeCRAW: *Parking,* The Eno Foundation for Highway Traffic Control, Saugatuck, Conn., December, 1946.

The Parking Problem—a Library Research, The Eno Foundation for Highway Traffic Control, Saugatuck, Conn., September, 1942.

Traffic and Parking Study—a Plan for Improvement of Conditions in the Central Business Districts of New York City, Regional Plan Association, Inc., New York, December, 1942.

Questions

1. Why cannot parking bans solve the parking problem in downtown areas?
2. What variations are found, in cities of different population ranges, in the percentages of persons entering central districts who come by automobile?
3. What standards have been suggested to determine the amount of parking space needed in shopping centers?
4. Describe the kind of information that should be gathered in a parking survey of a typical business and retail center.
5. What kind of questions might be included on a questionnaire distributed to automobile parkers?

6. How could one compute the cost of curbside parking space? How will such a figure vary with the size of the city?
7. What are the principal factors affecting the cost of offstreet parking facilities?
8. Discuss the relative merits of municipal versus privately owned offstreet parking facilities.
9. About how many square feet of gross lot area are required to permit customer parking in a parking lot? How many square feet of gross floor area to permit customer parking in a garage?
10. What considerations affect the selection of sites for parking facilities to serve business areas?
11. What features should be incorporated in the design of a parking lot?
12. List the various methods of financing offstreet parking facilities.
13. How may zoning be employed to aid in solving the parking problem? Describe typical requirements that have been used.
14. What steps have been taken to require provision of offstreet space for the loading and unloading of trucks?

18

DECENTRALIZATION OF INDUSTRY AND RESIDENCE

CENSUS FIGURES OFFER CONVINCING PROOF that both population and industry are moving from the central cities to the outskirts of the major metropolitan and manufacturing areas. In 1937 the eight industrial areas with the largest numbers of wage earners engaged in manufacturing were defined by the United States Census as consisting of 40 counties including and surrounding 11 central cities. Their importance in the industrial economy of the country is shown by the fact that the total number of wage earners engaged in manufacturing within these areas in that year amounted to just over 35 per cent of the total so employed in the United States, whereas their total population in 1940 was about 19,100,000, or only 14.5 per cent of the population of the United States.

In 1919 the 11 central cities had accounted for almost 85 per cent of the manufacturing wage earners in these same 40 counties, but in 1937 their share had fallen to just under 60 per cent. During this period the number of wage earners in the central cities decreased from 2,045,789 to 1,808,692, while in the surrounding areas it increased from 365,403 to 1,218,465. Most of this increase occurred during the decade from 1919 to 1929, when many new industrial plants chose sites on the edges of, rather than within, the cities. During the succeeding eight years, 1929 to 1937, the number of manufacturing wage earners in these 11 central cities declined 4.8 per cent, while the number within those parts of their industrial areas lying outside the cities increased by 9.7 per cent.[1] The conclusion is inescapable that

certain types of industry are moving out of the central cities in these eight major industrial areas.

TABLE 29

PERCENTAGE DISTRIBUTION OF MANUFACTURING WAGE EARNERS FOR THE UNITED STATES BY CITY GROUPS, BASED ON THE 1939 DECENNIAL CENSUS: 1899–1937 [a]

Cities by Population Groups	Average Number of Wage Earners for the Year as Percentage of Total Wage Earners in the United States			
	1937	1929	1919	1899
I. Cities of 500,000 or over	23.2	24.9	25.1	27.3
II. Cities from 100,000 to 499,999	17.8	18.9	19.6 [b]	17.9 [b]
III. Cities from 25,000 to 99,999	18.0	17.4 [b]	17.2 [b]	15.3 [b]
IV. Remainder	41.0	38.8	38.1	39.5 [b]
United States	100.0	100.0	100.0	100.0

[a] Based on population figures, as enumerated in the report for the nearest decennial census year and wage-earner figures adjusted for comparative purposes.
[b] Partially estimated.

The figures in Table 29, taken from a co-operative study made by the United States Department of Commerce and the United States Department of Agriculture, indicate a similar trend in the United States as a whole.[2] It appears that the part played in total manufacturing employment by the largest class of cities has been declining since 1899, that the share of the second class has been declining since 1919, and that the share of all places with less than 100,000 population has been increasing since 1919.

The reasons why manufacturers locate in outer areas rather than in the central cities are various. Many manufacturing concerns which were originally located in large and growing

[1] Basic figures from *Changes in Distribution of Manufacturing Wage Earners, 1899–1939,* United States Departments of Commerce and Agriculture, Government Printing Office, Washington, D. C., 1942.

[2] *Ibid.,* page 46.

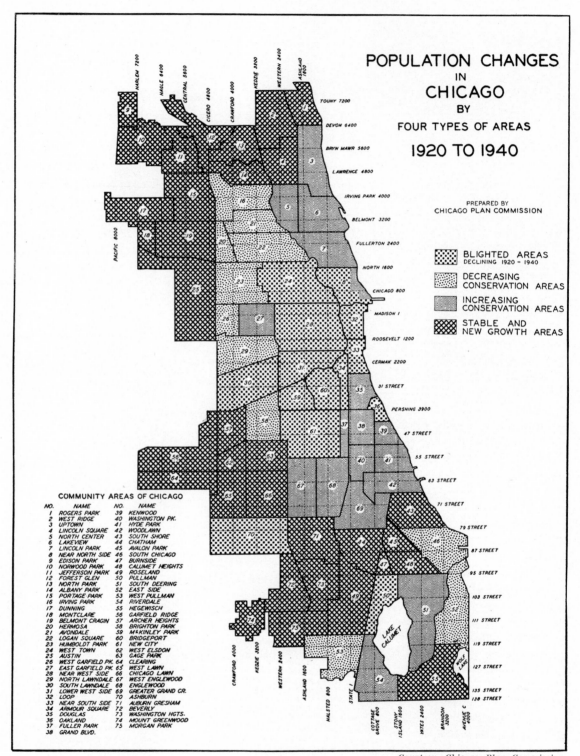

FIGURE 18·1

Courtesy, Chicago Plan Commission.

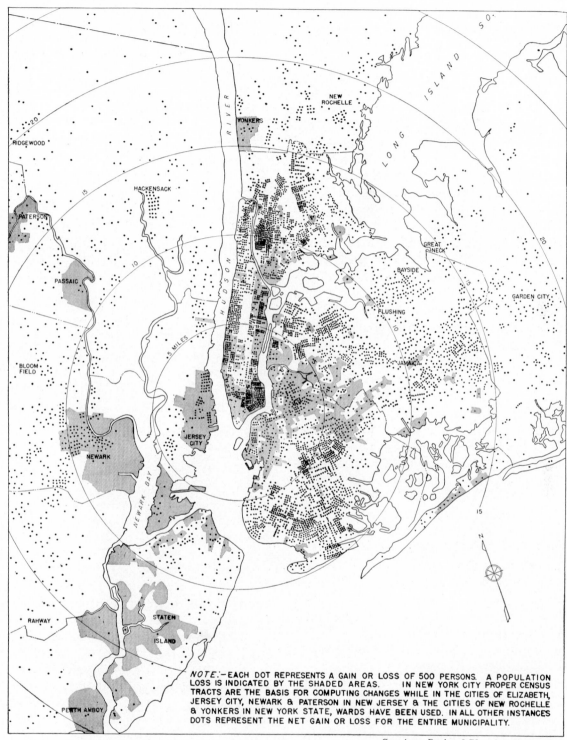

NOTE:—EACH DOT REPRESENTS A GAIN OR LOSS OF 500 PERSONS. A POPULATION
LOSS IS INDICATED BY THE SHADED AREAS. IN NEW YORK CITY PROPER CENSUS
TRACTS ARE THE BASIS FOR COMPUTING CHANGES WHILE IN THE CITIES OF ELIZABETH,
JERSEY CITY, NEWARK & PATERSON IN NEW JERSEY & THE CITIES OF NEW ROCHELLE
& YONKERS IN NEW YORK STATE, WARDS HAVE BEEN USED. IN ALL OTHER INSTANCES
DOTS REPRESENT THE NET GAIN OR LOSS FOR THE ENTIRE MUNICIPALITY.

Courtesy, Regional Plan Association, Inc.

FIGURE 18·2. CHANGES IN POPULATION DISTRIBUTION IN THE NEW YORK REGION, 1925 TO 1940

cities, influenced no doubt by the prospect of an adequate supply of labor, have found it impossible to expand with increasing business. They have found themselves hemmed in by a rigid and inflexible street system which, if they expanded their plant beyond the original city block or blocks on which they first located, would divide the plant into several separate units when there should be but one, render it impossible to extend their railway tracks, and increase the cost of operation. The situation becoming intolerable, they have concluded to scrap the buildings and such equipment as could not be removed and go farther out where there is no street system to hem them in. In some cases, high tax rates in the central city have encouraged this outward movement.

The extent of the outward movement of residence becomes fully apparent only when a more detailed study is made of central cities and their surrounding areas. This is necessary, as there have been large vacant areas at the peripheries, but within the boundaries, of the larger cities in the United States. These peripheral vacant areas have been developing while the central districts lost population. Figure 18·1 illustrates this process in the city of Chicago, where a large area in the center of the city lost population as most of the outlying sections gained in the two decades from 1920 to 1940. Similar symptoms in the New York region are shown in Figure 18·2 by changes in population distribution between 1925 and 1940.

At the time of writing, statistics were not yet available on the effect of World War II on the outward movement of industry and population. However, in every section of the United States huge war factories were built in suburban and even rural areas. These war factories have, to a large extent, been converted to peacetime production and will continue to be operated. Also, with the end of the war the construction of housing on a considerable scale began again, mostly in the outlying sections of the metropolitan areas. Both these developments undoubtedly have accelerated the already demonstrated outward movement.

Decentralization versus Concentration

The concepts of concentration and decentralization should be carefully considered before one is damned and the other praised without restraint. All community groupings are centers, and all urban growth is a form of centralization. There are desirable characteristics to certain degrees of concentration, which are the most basic reasons for the existence of urban areas.

Concentration does not necessarily bring congestion, and decentralization to areas poorly planned may not result in improvement. The skyscraper is efficient if it has enough space around it and can be conveniently reached. Small communities may develop slum areas as objectionable as those in their larger neighbors. It is the well-planned community, whether it be a central business district or a newly developed suburb, that can have a healthy growth that will result in permanent values. . . .[3]

There are certain types of business, such as banking, theatres, professional offices, and some kinds of industry, where concentration will probably continue. The banking center seems least subject to change, and even in the older European cities has remained in the same locality throughout the centuries and increased in size as the cities have grown. The industries which gain from concentration are those which have great seasonal changes in the amount of labor they employ and which profit from convenient access to local markets, for example, the manufacture of jewelry or women's dress goods.[4]

However, an undesirable degree of centralization can be and has been reached in many of the large urban centers of the United States. Such overconcentration results in lack of convenience to the residents in requiring excessively long trips from home to place of work, shopping, or amusement; it necessitates vast investments in highway and transit facilities which otherwise would not be required; it usually causes considerable congestion of all kinds of traffic; and it often results in land speculation and large areas of blight (see Chapter 13, page 1, and Chapter 15, pages 35 to 37). Not the least of the bad effects of excessive centralization is the overcrowding of land which so often follows the resulting high land values. Insufficient open space and lack of light and air

[3] *City Planning—Why and How,* by Harold MacLean Lewis, Longmans Green and Company, New York, 1939, page 37.

[4] *Ibid.,* pages 34–36.

as a result of excessive coverage of land with buildings make the downtown areas of the large cities poor places in which to live.

An indiscriminate process of so-called "decentralization" is of little benefit in alleviating these conditions. Wide diffusion of industry, business, and residence probably would result in neither convenience, efficiency, nor amenity. What is required is, rather, a recentralization of uses into subcenters more or less near the main center. The Regional Plan of New York and Its Environs recommended the following:

First: Diffused recentralization of industry with the objects of lessening the density of congested centers and of creating new centers.
Second: Diffusion of residence into compact residential neighborhoods throughout the whole urban region, integrated with the industrial sections so as to reduce distances between homes and places of work.
Third: Subcentralization of business so arranged as to provide the maximum of convenience to residents.[5]

It went on to say that the recentralization processes were referred to in the above order "because industry (including major business or commercial activities) should be regarded as preceding residence, while residence has to be established before retail business, in the course of development." [6]

Problems of Industrial Districts

When one thinks of Pittsburgh, it is in terms of iron and steel and the smoke and grime that always accompany their production. Sheffield suggests cutlery; Manchester, cotton goods; Lyons, silk; Essen, ordnance and steel forgings; Grand Rapids, furniture; Minneapolis, flour; Omaha and Kansas City, packing houses and stockyards. The larger cities have such varied industries that we think only of the great value of their manufactured products and do not identify them with any particular output, yet different parts of these cities are as closely identified with certain industries and activities

[5] *The Graphic Regional Plan,* Vol. I, Regional Plan of New York and Its Environs, New York, 1929, page 149.
[6] *Ibid.,* page 150.

as are the smaller towns with their one chief product.

While certain fundamental principles should control the planning of industrial districts or towns, even though they lack the distinctive label of iron, cotton goods, furniture, flour, or some other product, there are special needs which must be taken into account in working out their plans. Facilities for the expeditious and economical receipt, handling, and shipment of raw materials and manufactured products must be provided in order that these costs may be reduced to a minimum and a greater proportion of the value of the output may go to the labor which creates it. It follows that ample facilities for movement by rail or water or both must be made possible. The workers should be able to reach their places of employment quickly and comfortably and should be assured decent and wholesome dwellings, in order that they may render efficient service. Provision must be made for their homes in as close proximity to the plants as will permit such conditions to be realized, while the place set apart for these homes can usually be so chosen that the prevailing winds will carry the smoke, fumes, and gases away from rather than towards them. A mill and factory population will create a considerable amount of general business which should be carried on even more economically than that of the fashionable shopping districts; it will have the same need of entertainment and recreation as will that of exclusively residential towns and districts. While these facilities may be on a less pretentious scale, the needs of such a population are proportionately great, and ample provision should be made for them.

Although lack of planning has been a conspicuous characteristic of the average city, it has nowhere been so marked as in the industrial town. The person, firm, or corporation establishing a new plant is quite certain to give very careful consideration to the suitability of the site, the transportation facilities, room for expansion, and the probability of an adequate supply of labor, but little thought appears to have been given to the place where, or the manner in which, the operatives are to live. Many towns offer inducements of various kinds to manufacturers to establish plants in them, these sometimes being in the form of free sites or exemption from taxation for a term of years, and such towns realize that every new plant will bring additional population and increased business. How the newcomers are to live is usually a matter of indifference. It is expected that they will make more business for existing shops, and the suggestion that they should be well housed in a separate quarter convenient to their work and should have there shops to supply their household needs and places of amusement suited to their resources is strongly resented by already established businesses.

The mere establishment of factories in suburban areas without provision for housing the workers and the necessary adjuncts to such housing may cause as many problems as are present in central locations. Sometimes factory employees are unable to find homes in the vicinity of their work, owing to the high class of the development. Such unusual conditions existed in the neighborhood of Cincinnati. A number of large manufacturing plants located in suburbs outside the city limits. These suburbs had attractive sites, and the working conditions were exceedingly favorable, but during the decade or more after their establishment little was done to provide homes for their operatives. Some houses and flats designed to be within the means of factory workers were erected, but the real estate men and builders found that there was more profit in building houses of a better class to accommodate Cincinnati business men who wished to live in the suburbs. Meanwhile nearly half the employees of these plants had their homes in the tenement districts of Cincinnati and traveled to their work in the suburbs every morning and back every night, while about five per cent were said to live across the Ohio River in Kentucky. This was the anomalous condition of an industrial suburb which became an attractive residential district for those in no way connected with the industries about which these suburbs were built.

Writers and speakers on city planning and housing frequently draw rather startling contrasts between the worst conditions which can be found in industrial towns of their own country and the best which has been done in other countries. They like to show pictures of the most distressing living conditions in Pittsburgh and Fall River side by side with those of the workmen's cottages at Essen (see Figures 13·9 to 13·12, pages 11 and 12), and give the impression that the manufacturing towns in the United States are examples of hopelessly bad planning and utter indifference on the part of employers to the manner in which their workmen live, whereas similar towns in other countries are models of what ought to be. The facts are frequently bad enough. The housing is often desperately bad, and statements that employees frequently elect to live in the most crowded and unwholesome quarters available to save a small sum in rent, even though their pay would enable them to secure better accommodations, are probably based upon facts. Corporations and individuals who have tried to promote good living conditions and an attractive environment for their employees and have endeavored, by well-intended and apparently reasonable regulations, to insure the maintenance of these standards have encountered resentment at what was thought to be too much paternalism or an interference with the freedom of their workmen. A notable instance of this feeling is afforded by Pullman, Illinois, established by the Pullman Company about 60 years ago. The failure of this experiment was undoubtedly due to the fact that the model town which was created was founded upon paternalism. The company was autocratic in its control of the living conditions of its employees, and, while it exercised a benevolent despotism, it could not win the confidence and co-operation of the men. The dream of its founder was shattered by the great strike which occurred within the decade after the establishment of the town.

Between this control by the employer, whose interest in the employee is sincere, though not wholly unselfish, and exploitation by the real estate developer, whose interest ceases when his last lot has been sold, there seems but one other course, that is, co-operative ownership and control by the employees themselves. This has been most successful in Great Britain and Germany, where the workers have been able to secure large funds at very low rates of interest, the state itself often supplying the money. This has not yet been done in the United States, but it may be possible for such co-operative enterprises to be carried out through the aid of building and loan associations, which have been very successful in this country and which are unlikely to arouse the suspicion or distrust of the workmen.[7]

How is the industrial town or district to be saved from the kind of development which, with a few conspicuous exceptions, has characterized most of them? It seems quite clear that the trouble has been due to the exploitation of the land by speculators who have been intent on getting out as quickly as possible with a handsome profit. Where the industrial corporation has itself attempted to control the development of the town as well as the plant, either it has become an exploiter of the land itself, or, if it has made an earnest effort to create an attractive town and wholesome surroundings for its employees, the workers have distrusted its motives or have resented the paternalistic spirit in which its plans were carried out. Proprietary towns, dependent for their existence upon a single industry, are likely to be seriously affected by the development of ill will on the part of the citizen-workmen toward the individual or corporation which not only established the town but tries to administer its affairs. Permanent success is more likely if the planning of the town, the regulation of the use of property, and the entire conduct of the public business are left to some duly constituted authority, if there is one, whose jurisdiction covers the territory within which the development is located, or, even if the entire business is turned over to some agency in which the individual or corporate proprietor is known to have no financial interest. Many such enterprises have been established within the limits of municipal corporations which have manifested little interest in the orderly development of the part of the town in which they are located and have shown little capacity to solve the problems of planning

[7] For a step in this direction confined to housing, see example of projects of Amalgamated Clothing Workers Union, pages 25–26.

and administration. There have been so many examples of the heavy penalties which such towns have had to pay for their indifference or incompetence and a few such conspicuous instances of the great value of foresight in planning and administration that there has been an awakening as to their responsibilities and opportunities.

In Birmingham, England, is found one of the best instances of the exercise of wise control by the municipal corporation itself of its industrial development. Birmingham's corporate limits were so extended as to take in outlying industrial towns, some of which had already been started in an admirable manner; but the city did not confine itself to extending its territory. It set about the improvement of the older parts of the city, the better placing of its public buildings, the improvement of its transit system, the provision of adequate water supply and drainage, and the betterment of housing conditions. No one man or group of men or no great corporation brought these changes about, but the city itself did. Able leadership there was, of course; Joseph Chamberlain, in the establishment of wise municipal policies, and J. S. Nettlefold, in an aggressive movement for improved housing, rendered splendid service. Moreover, the citizens found these things worth while and took advantage of the opportunities which were afforded by the British Town Planning Act of 1909 to improve existing conditions further and insure orderly growth.

The Industrial Town

It occasionally happens that an industrial plant is established in a location so remote from any existing city that a new town must be provided to furnish homes for its employees. An opportunity is thus presented to plan in a rational manner for the development of the entire town: the plant itself with adequate shipping and handling facilities; homes for the operatives and for the principal officers, superintendents, and technical experts; shops, places of recreation and amusement, schools, and buildings for the administrative business of the new town and in fact for every phase of urban life. In the feverish haste to get things started, and to offset by earnings the interest on capital outlay, little thought is commonly bestowed upon anything but the productive plant, the town being left to grow for itself or to be exploited by real estate speculators who see the probability or the certainty of a great increase in land values.

Instances of the extraordinary advance in land values following the establishment of an industrial center are given by Graham Romeyn Taylor in his book *Satellite Cities*, which graphically describes the physical and social conditions which have grown up about industrial plants.[8] One example is the land purchased by the Corn Products Refining Company in the city of Chicago in 1879 for $147,-000. When the plant of this company was removed to a site further out of the city in 1908, an offer of $2,500,000 for the property was refused. Another case is that of the Pullman Company, which stated in 1893 that the time was near at hand when the $30,000,000 capital stock of the company would be covered by the value of the 3,500 acres of land on which the town of Pullman was built. This company, however, was not permitted to reap the complete advantage of this enormous increase in land values because the Supreme Court of Illinois decided that its charter did not authorize it to engage in the real estate business or to hold any real estate beyond that required for its manufacturing business, and it was obliged to abandon the rôle of real estate operator.

When the United States Steel Corporation created Gary, Indiana, it built a thoroughly modern plant so arranged as to reduce the cost of production to a minimum. The company was obliged to provide a town in which its officers and operatives might live, and there was much comment at the time as to the thoroughness with which the construction work connected with the establishment of the new town was done. It may be that the corporation did not realize what a big thing it was doing and how important a city it was founding. At any rate, the opportunity to establish a compre-

hensive plan was not availed of. The company laid out and kept control of one limited section and refused to profit by increased values at the expense of its employees. The growth of Gary has been spectacular. In the spring of 1906 the site was simply a level stretch of land with a few scrub oaks and an occasional pond or swamp. Within three years a great steel plant and harbor had been constructed, and a town of 12,000 inhabitants had grown up with 15 miles of paved streets, a sewer system, water, gas, an electric lighting plant, banks, hotels, newspapers, schools, and churches. In 1912 this community had grown to more than 25,000; in 1920 its population had reached 55,378, and in 1940 a total of 111,719. The real estate speculators saw and were quite prompt to avail themselves of their chance, and a series of scattered and unrelated developments were undertaken. Figure 18·3 shows very plainly what happened, and how an admirable opportunity was lost to plan and build a real city which might have been one of the most notable of its kind.

It does not follow that the United States Steel Corporation did not make an effort to establish a town in which its employees could find decent and sanitary homes. It *did* make such an effort, and it was not simply intent upon the earliest possible dividends; it had at heart the best interests of the men in its service, but it did not go far enough in planning the original town. In the design of the plant the greatest foresight and ingenuity were exercised in order to render the handling of material as economical and expeditious as possible. Every shop and other building was so located that spur tracks could be run into or alongside of it, with such curves as would reduce to the lowest limit the tractive force required to move cars. Wherever there was an opportunity for a short-cut, it was availed of.

In the plan for the town, however, no such foresight appears to have been displayed. The employees, in going from their homes to their work and back, have no direct routes which they can follow, and the facility of movement, so well provided in laying out the plant, was entirely overlooked so far as the conduct of the miscellaneous business of the town was con-

[8] Some of the statistical information in the following pages has been taken from Taylor's book.

cerned. The land company, a subsidiary of the United States Steel Corporation, which laid out the first subdivision, attempted to plan the town, but with indifferent success. Although in designing the plant the best expert advice was secured, it did not occur to the company to retain the services of a city planning expert to work out the plan for the town. Since the latter part of 1920, however, Gary has had a City

school plant as a social as well as an educational agency.

That this corporation realizes what might have been but was not done at Gary appears evident from the course followed by one of its subsidiary companies in the establishment of another industrial town on the outskirts of Duluth. Here a town plan has been evolved to accommodate the workers in the steel mills and

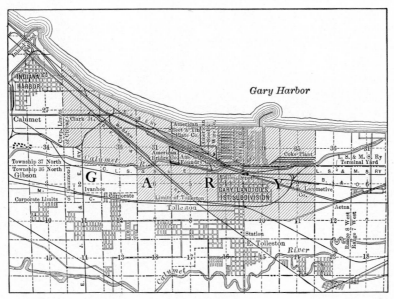

FIGURE 18·3. PLAN OF GARY, INDIANA, THE INDUSTRIAL TOWN ESTABLISHED BY THE UNITED STATES STEEL CORPORATION

Plan Commission which has been making studies preparatory to a correction of some of the earlier mistakes. And yet the original town possesses some excellent features. Building lines from 20 to 35 feet back of the street lines have been established for all but the chief business streets, several parks have been created, and some of the public and semi-public buildings have been effectively grouped. It is to be regretted that occupation of the entire lake front by the steel plant has made it impossible to provide any water-front park for the use of the people. But Gary has done some notable things. Her school system, under the original direction of William A. Wirt, has become known throughout the educational world as the "Gary plan," and is being adopted elsewhere as one which will permit the most effective use of the

cement plant which have been built; the general features of this plan are shown by Figures 18·4 and 18·5. Originally the town was totally owned by the company, but about 1944 it was sold to a real estate firm which in turn sold many of the houses to individuals.

Where a new town is established outside the limits of or remote from an existing municipal corporation, the problem of securing and maintaining the values of a planned community may be even more difficult than in cases where an undeveloped portion of an incorporated area is used. Even if an intelligent plan has been established, the administration of the town's public business and the regulation of its further development cannot be safely entrusted to its citizens, among whom there will be no men trained in municipal affairs. Leaders will come

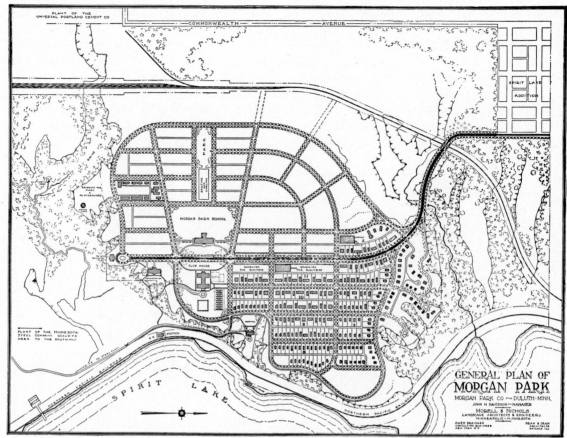

From "Urban Planning and Land Policies," National Resources Committee, 1939.

FIGURE 18·4

to the front, but they will scarcely be capable of dealing wisely with the intricate problems which will present themselves for solution. If

Courtesy, Owen Brainard.

FIGURE 18·5. WORKERS' HOUSES IN MORGAN PARK, AN INDUSTRIAL TOWN NEAR DULUTH

a capable, strong, and experienced municipal business manager is ever needed, it is in a case like this; but there is no body of citizens less likely to appreciate the advantages of such a method of conducting public business or less willing to submit themselves to such a system than the population of a newly established industrial community.[9]

There have been several examples of successful planned industrial towns in this country.[10] Among the oldest is Hopedale, near Milford, Massachusetts, which was established in 1841 as a Christian Socialist community. Taken over in 1856 by the Draper Corporation to house workers in a cotton machine plant, it was then extended, and further additions were made in 1915. In 1935 the population of Hopedale

[9] See Chapter 13 for a discussion of the problem of management of planned communities and a description of existing examples (pages 7 to 14).

[10] For a full list and descriptions of several, see *Urban Planning and Land Policies*, Part I, National Resources Committee, Government Printing Office, Washington, D. C., 1939.

was about 3,070 persons. The company owns most of the land within the corporate limits and has successfully controlled development, result-

lage and has since been developed with little interruption and in close conformity with the original plan. The Kohler Company is the

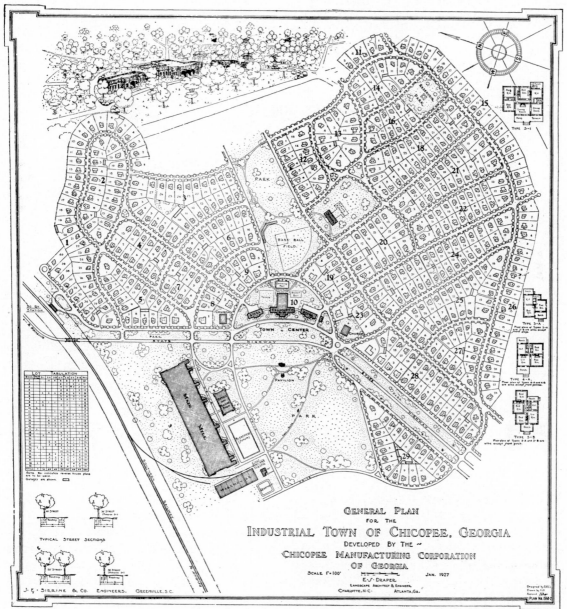

From "Urban Planning and Land Policies," National Resources Committee, 1939.

FIGURE 18·6

ing in the maintenance, in general, of the character and individuality which gave Hopedale the reputation of a model industrial town.[11]

Kohler, Wisconsin, was planned in 1916 by the Kohler Company as a model industrial vil-

[11] *Ibid.*, pages 30–32.

one industry in the town. It is a community of home owners, most of the houses having been built by a non-profit development corporation organized by the company. Detached dwellings predominate, and an active community life is fostered by a large and varied number of clubs and organizations. Kohler is incorporated and had a population of 1,789 in 1940.[12]

In 1927 the Chicopee Manufacturing Company, a subsidiary of the Johnson & Johnson Company, established the industrial town of Chicopee, about 4 miles from Gainesville, Georgia (see Figure 18·6). The population of Chicopee in 1936 was about 1,025 persons, but

city ultimately is to contain some 25,000 persons, the primary industry being a farm tractor factory. A perspective drawing of the proposed city is shown in Figure 18·7. Four residential neighborhoods are to have church, recreation, and education facilities, with the population housed in three-story and eight-story apartments and bachelor dormitories at a net density

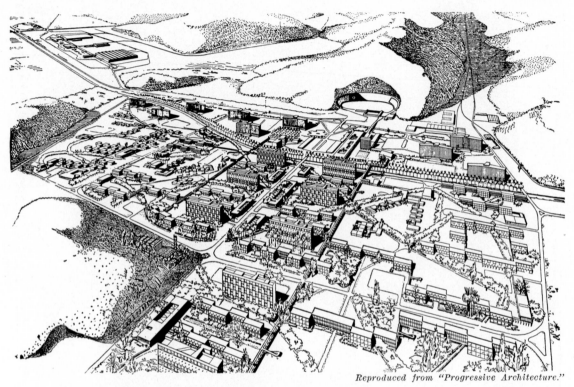

Reproduced from "Progressive Architecture."

FIGURE 18·7. PERSPECTIVE DRAWING OF CIDADE DOS MOTORES NEAR RIO DE JANEIRO, BRAZIL

the community was not yet fully developed. About 4,000 acres of land owned and farmed by the company completely protect the town from undesirable growth at its periphery, except across the railroad at the northwest boundary, where the poor development which has taken place has demonstrated the value of an adequate buffer. Chicopee is completely owned and operated by the corporation.[13]

In the spring of 1947 construction was started on an industrial satellite city to be known as Cidade dos Motores, located about 25 miles from Rio de Janeiro. The site consists of some 12,000 acres of reclaimed swamp land, and the

of 100 persons per acre. Automobile circulation is to be confined to the peripheries of the neighborhoods, with interior circulation entirely by bicycle paths and covered walks. An elaborate and spacious business and civic center is planned (see center background of Figure 18·7) to include a stadium and swimming pool, and the factory district is located at some distance from the rest of the city (see extreme upper left of Figure 18·7). The two neighborhoods adjacent to the civic center were scheduled for initial construction, with the entire city expected to be completed about 1957.[14]

[12] *Ibid.,* pages 39–41.
[13] *Ibid.,* pages 24–27.

[14] A detailed description of this plan may be found in *Progressive Architecture—Pencil Points,* September, 1946, Reinhold Publishing Corporation, New York.

The English Garden City Movement

The origin of what is called the garden city movement is commonly attributed to the publication in England in 1902 of a book by Ebenezer Howard, *Garden Cities of To-morrow*, which appears to have been prompted by discussions in England and other countries of the used for the display of goods and for leisurely shopping, while their protection from the weather would afford a ready refuge for those using the park and recreation ground in case of storm. Beyond this arcade Howard suggested five circular roadways upon which residences would be located, the central of the five having the extraordinary width of 420 feet.

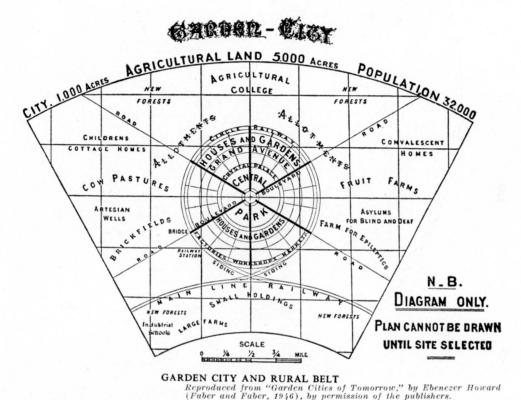

GARDEN CITY AND RURAL BELT
*Reproduced from "Garden Cities of Tomorrow," by Ebenezer Howard
(Faber and Faber, 1946), by permission of the publishers.*

FIGURE 18·8. SCHEMATIC DIAGRAM OF EBENEZER HOWARD'S GARDEN CITY UNIT

seriousness of the problems presented by the rush of population to the cities and the depletion of the country districts. Howard described a fanciful garden city laid out on a tract of some 6,000 acres of agricultural land worth about $200 an acre. At its center he proposed a circular garden covering about five acres, and fronting on this garden a group of public buildings, such as the town hall, library, museum, theatre, concert hall, and hospital. Outside of this he proposed a zone of park and recreation fields covering about 145 acres, and encircling this what he called a "crystal palace," which was simply a ring of glass arcades broken only by the radiating streets, these arcades being

Outside this residential zone he proposed to place the factories, warehouses, dairies, and farms with a railroad encircling the town and connecting with the tracks of a trunk line. Six radiating streets were to lead directly from the central garden to the outer limits of the proposed town, each of them 120 feet in width. This town was designed to accommodate 30,000 people.

Howard urged that, while there always must be some main center of population, efforts should be made to keep this center down to 60,000 persons or less, and that as the number of people in the urban district grows, growth should be from new subordinate centers, each restricted if possible to about 30,000 persons and connected by an adequate radial railway with an encircling railroad around the main town and another connecting the inner edges of the subordinate centers or those nearest the main center. (See Figures 18·8 and 18·9.)

nity." Howard's concept was that of a self-sufficient community of maximum utility, convenience, and amenity, in which the advantages of urban living were to be secured to the greatest extent while retaining as many as possible of the best features of rural life. His approach

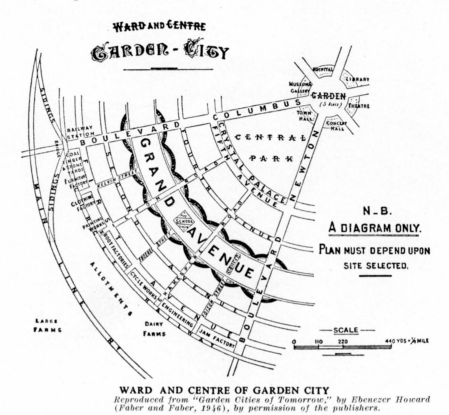

WARD AND CENTRE OF GARDEN CITY
Reproduced from "Garden Cities of Tomorrow," by Ebenezer Howard (Faber and Faber, 1946), by permission of the publishers.

FIGURE 18·9. SCHEMATIC DIAGRAM OF NEIGHBORHOOD IN GARDEN CITY AS CONCEIVED BY EBENEZER HOWARD

Note that neighborhood principles were anticipated here even to the approximate population of 5,000, although such principles were not formerly described for another quarter of a century.

The term "garden city" has come to be loosely used, until today it means little more than any urban community with generous provision of open space and regard for amenities. Howard's use of the term implied much more. The Garden Cities and Town Planning Association, in consultation with him, adopted the following short definition: "A garden city is a town designed for healthy living and industry; of a size that makes possible a full measure of social life, but not larger; surrounded by a rural belt; the whole of the land being in public ownership or held in trust for the commu-

was that of the social philosopher rather than the designer. An examination of the short book in which he explained his plan [15] is well worth the while of the student of planning for its exceptionally clear and thorough analysis of planned recentralization.

The first garden city company was formed in 1903 and purchased a 3,818-acre tract (later

[15] *Garden Cities of Tomorrow*, by Ebenezer Howard, introduction by F. J. Osborn, Faber and Faber, London, 1946. This is a republication of Howard's original book, published in 1902 by S. Sonnenschein & Co., London.

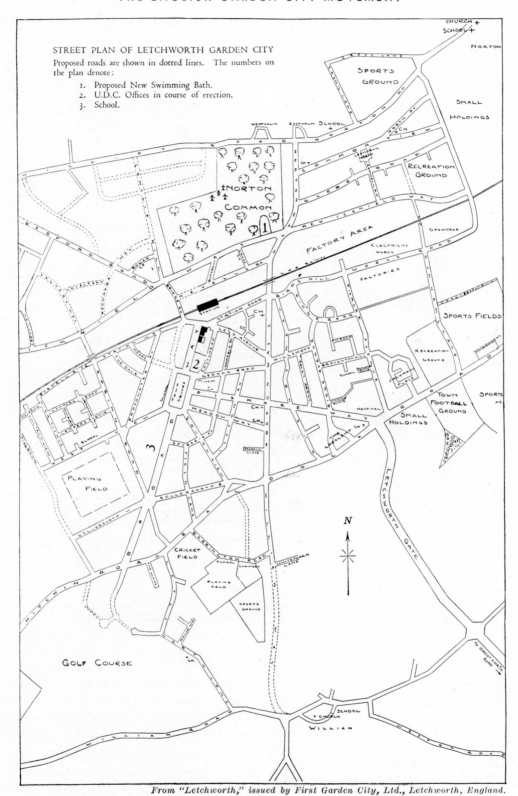

STREET PLAN OF LETCHWORTH GARDEN CITY
Proposed roads are shown in dotted lines.   The numbers on
the plan denote:

1. Proposed New Swimming Bath.
2. U.D.C. Offices in course of erection.
3. School.

From "Letchworth," issued by First Garden City, Ltd., Letchworth, England.

FIGURE 18·10

expanded to 4,562 acres) about 34 miles from London, on which Letchworth was established. Figure 18·10 shows the plan of the town proper, which covers about 1,600 acres, the balance of the area being reserved for an agricultural green

third complete, having a population of about 17,000 persons.[16] That it is a true satellite town is proved by the fact that some 85 per cent of its working population in 1945 found employment within the town.[17] In 1946 it was

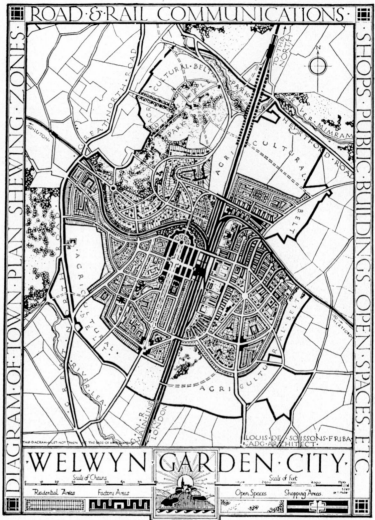

From "City Planning—Housing," by Werner Hegemann, Vol. 3. Courtesy, Architectural Book Publishing Co., Inc.

FIGURE 18·11

belt. In 1946 Letchworth was about half developed, and housed a population of approximately 22,000 persons.[16] As a result of Howard's efforts, in 1919 a second garden city was established at Welwyn on a site of about 2,400 acres located 17 miles from London. (See Figures 18·11 and 18·12.) Welwyn is about one-

reported that a "large number of inquiries for industrial sites [at Welwyn] are in hand— more than enough to complete the development of the whole industrial area."[18] Although

[16] "Britain to Build New Satellite Towns," by John F. Eccles, in *The American City*, June, 1946, page 74.

[17] *Garden Cities of Tomorrow*, introduction by F. J. Osborn, Faber and Faber, London, 1946, page 14.

[18] *Town and Country Planning*, Summer, 1946, The Town and Country Planning Association, London, England, page 75.

neither Letchworth nor Welwyn has been fully developed as yet, both are financially sound and may be considered successful garden cities.

New Residential Suburbs

While Letchworth and Welwyn are the only two English "garden cities," as the term has

of Ebenezer Howard, although there have been attempts to accomplish some of his aims. These attempts logically divide into three classifications: the satellite towns, such as Mariemont in Ohio, Radburn in New Jersey, and the community near Olympia Fields, Illinois; the "Greenbelt" towns of the United States Resettlement Administration; and the "garden

Courtesy, British Information Services.

FIGURE 18·12.   AIR VIEW OF CENTER OF WELWYN GARDEN CITY

Built between 1919 and 1939, 23 miles out of London.   Factories can be seen in the background beyond the railway station; in the foreground shops and houses are located among trees and open spaces.

been strictly defined, there are many more developments in which are embodied the same principles, including the low densities for housing, without an attempt to establish self-contained satellite cities. Such developments generally have been referred to as "garden suburbs." Among the more outstanding of these in England are Hampstead Garden Suburb, Alkrington Estate, and Knebworth Estate.

In the United States no development has completely followed the garden city principles

suburbs," such as Billerica Garden Suburb in Massachusetts and Garden City on Long Island, New York. None of these classifications can be said to have been completely successful in this country. Billerica Garden Suburb never developed as planned, owing to changes in plans by the railroad company which had intended to locate shops near by. However, both Mariemont and Radburn have functioned with limited success as garden suburbs rather than satellite towns, owing to their failure to attract industry. It remains to be seen whether the same fate awaits the community planned near Olympia Fields, Illinois.

Mariemont, Ohio, was established in 1923 with the financial backing of a public-spirited woman of large means. The area of 485 acres lies about 10 miles east of the central business

as of 1936 there were only some 1,600 residents. The principal reason for this explains the failure of Mariemont as a satellite community; the town was built before industries were secured, and very little industry has located there. Thus Mariemont was forced to become a residential suburb, and since its location is not

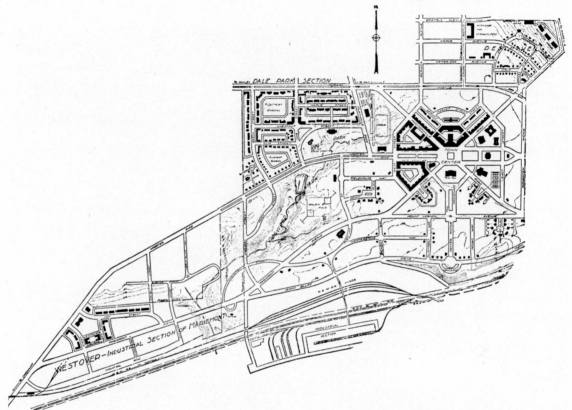

From "Urban Planning and Land Policies," National Resources Committee, 1939.

FIGURE 18·13. MARIEMONT, OHIO, AS PLANNED AND SHOWING EXTENT OF DEVELOPMENT IN 1936

district of Cincinnati. The town was planned as a more or less self-sufficient community, something over 60 acres being set aside as an industrial district. Figure 18·13 shows John Nolen's plan and the extent to which development had taken place in 1936. A line of bluffs between the residential portion of Mariemont and the railroad forms a natural boundary on the south, but no further peripheral protection has been provided except that of Dogwood Park on a portion of the southwest boundary. Another weakness of the plan is the routing of through traffic through its center. The plan provides for a population of about 10,000, but

favorable to this use, its development has been confined to a higher-income group than was originally intended.

Probably the new community in the United States most widely reputed among planners is Radburn, New Jersey, located 10 miles west of the George Washington Bridge to Manhattan. Figure 18·14 shows the original design, which follows the principles of neighborhood planning and uses the superblock with short cul-de-sac streets and interior parks with pedestrian ways and recreational features. Radburn was intended as a self-contained community of 25,000 persons, with 127 of its approximately

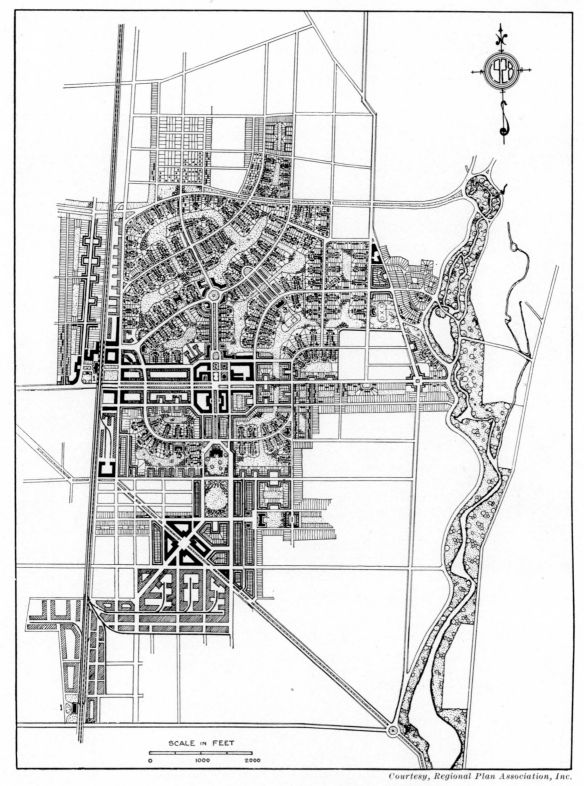

FIGURE 18·14. RADBURN, NEW JERSEY, AS PLANNED

1,600 acres set aside for industrial uses. Its development, begun in 1929, was prematurely halted two years later by the economic depression, and the promoting company went through reorganization in 1936. A large part of two

ficulties, and the use of cul-de-sac streets to the extent planned has been questioned by some authorities.

The population of Radburn was about 1,450 persons in 1936. The only establishment in its

FIGURE 18·15. AIR VIEW OF RADBURN, NEW JERSEY, AS OF 1933

Shopping center is in left central portion of the picture, with one apartment group to the right thereof; a school, intended to serve four superblocks, appears at the upper right.

of the proposed superblocks was completed by 1933 in accordance with the original plan (Figure 18·15). The large areas set aside for parks led to small individual lots with the houses rather close together, but provided a low density based on total land area.

Most of the later subdivision and construction in Radburn has been along conventional lines. The original layout was found to limit house planning and to increase subdivision dif-

industrial area in 1947 was a warehouse. Although the town is connected with New York City both by bus over the George Washington Bridge and by rail to the Jersey City ferries to lower Manhattan, its competitive position as a commuting suburb is not very good, although its working population consists almost entirely of commuters.

As of the spring of 1947, the most recent proposal for a satellite town in the United States was that of American Community Builders, which had started construction on 2,300 acres of rolling land near Olympia Fields, about 30 miles south of downtown Chicago. Figure 18·16 shows the tentative plan for the town, which of single-family units selling at $7,000 to $10,-000. (See Figure 18·17 and also Figure 11·47, Volume I.)

The development being located on a railroad, about 55 minutes' ride from the Chicago

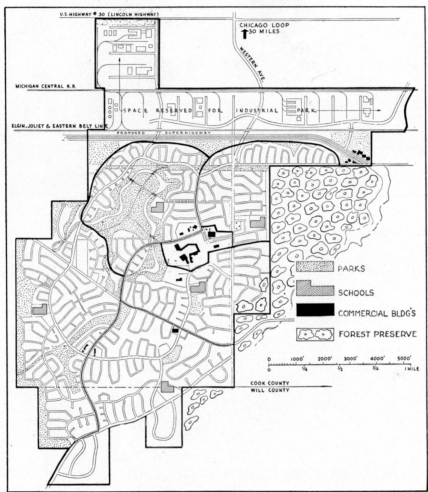

Courtesy, American Community Builders, Inc.

FIGURE 18·16. TENTATIVE PLAN FOR A SATELLITE TOWN NEAR OLYMPIA FIELDS, ILLINOIS, LOCATED 30 MILES SOUTH OF THE CITY OF CHICAGO

was to house 25,000 persons in five neighborhoods, with a central business area, an industrial area of about 475 acres, generous areas in park, and a considerable forest preserve. Church sites were to be reserved. A town hall was planned, and entertainment facilities were to include bowling alleys, theatres, playgrounds, a swimming pool, and picnic areas in the forest preserve. With financing by the FHA, the initial program called for 3,000 family units of duplex and group housing, and later a program

"Loop," it was intended as a commuting suburb as well as a self-contained community. However, the time and costs involved for commuters seem somewhat excessive for competition with more conveniently located housing in times when the shortage may be less acute than in 1947. The eventual development of this community will be of interest to planners.

The so-called "Greenbelt" towns were designed and built by the Suburban Division of the Resettlement Administration between 1933

Loebl, Schlossman & Bennett, Architects & Engineers.
Courtesy, American Community Builders, Inc.

FIGURE 18·17.   ARCHITECT'S RENDERING OF GROUP HOUSING FOR SATELLITE TOWN NEAR OLYMPIA
FIELDS, ILLINOIS

Showing grouping of buildings around a landscaped court.

From "The American City," August, 1936."

FIGURE 18·18.   PLAN OF GREENDALE, WISCONSIN, ONE OF THE THREE GARDEN SUBURBS DEVEL-
OPED BY THE RESETTLEMENT ADMINISTRATION

Courtesy, Doubleday & Co., Inc.

FIGURE 18·19. A BOOK-PUBLISHING PLANT LOCATED IN A SUBURBAN COMMUNITY

The Doubleday & Company plant in the village of Garden City, New York. Upper view is a general air view of the plant, showing parking lots for employees in the foreground and background. Lower view shows entrance to the main building.

and 1937 to function as garden suburbs for families of modest incomes, with an effort to "integrate both the physical plans and the economies of the rural area and the suburban community." [19] The plan of Greendale, Wisconsin, situated southwest of Milwaukee, is shown in Figure 18·18 and is typical of the three developments constructed by this agency. The other two are Greenbelt, Maryland, between Washington and Baltimore, and Greenhills, north of Cincinnati, Ohio. George Herbert Gray has written of them that they

. . . departed from the original conception and from the traditional garden *city* idea in that they had no sustaining industries within the towns and provided housing for but one income group—in the Maryland project the group was mostly modestly salaried white-collar federal workers from Washington. They departed from the tried and proved precedent of English garden *suburbs* in being at a considerable distance from the places of employment (whether measured by time or expense). In these two items, i.e., location and type of population, they were also in violation of generally accepted principles of city planning. Topographically they were well planned, but introduced no new features either of planning or of housing. Being emergency measures, partly in the interest of re-employing the idle in both white-collar and blue-jean groups, costs were excessive and had to be greatly written down to put the property on a sound financial operation basis.[20]

An example of the garden type suburb in the United States which is considerably older than Ebenezer Howard's statement of principles is Garden City, a village on Long Island about 20 miles east of Manhattan. It was established by Alexander T. Stewart in 1869. Garden City was exclusively a residential town and was laid out about a central park well planted with trees and shrubbery, in which were located the railway station and a casino or club house. The streets were broad, and the plan was rigidly rectangular; it was a community of tenants only, the founder and, after his death, his estate, retaining complete ownership of all the lands and buildings. The plan originally included some homes for workingmen which were little more than wooden barracks of the most unattractive sort. These have fortunately disappeared, and where they stood is now the attractive plant of Doubleday & Company, publishers (Figure 18·19).

Since 1895, the owners of the Garden City property have offered residence plots and houses for sale, while contiguous to it there have been several developments of a similar kind by other owners. The rectangular plan was adhered to in most of the latter developments, but in one an agreeable variation was made by the introduction of a few curved streets and diagonals in accordance with a design by Charles W. Leavitt. The original Garden City and the more recent additions still retain their character as residential communities of New York commuters, and have none of the copartnership or paternal characteristics of the garden cities of Europe.

Postwar Decentralization in England

The concern in England over the continuing spread of large urban areas at their suburban fringe, which inspired Ebenezer Howard's garden city concept, continued to grow after his ideas were published, but the process might have gone on indefinitely had it not been for the damage done to the cities by World War II. With the determination to prevent the replacement of the demolished congested areas by redevelopment with the same or equal congestion came the need to house elsewhere those displaced. Rather than allow the suburban spread to continue, it was decided to build new self-contained garden cities, separated from the existing urban centers by permanent open areas, the idea advocated by Howard a half-century earlier. With the passage of the New Towns Act of 1946,[21] the decentralization of the large urban areas in England was made public policy, and a program was begun.

Under this act, the Minister of Town and Country Planning might, after consultation with the local authorities concerned, designate an area as the site of a new town and establish a corporation to develop this town. The

[19] From the official description of the function of the Suburban Division of the Resettlement Administration.

[20] *Housing and Citizenship*, by George Herbert Gray, Reinhold Publishing Corporation, New York, 1946, page 237.

[21] This act is discussed further in Chapter 20, "City Planning Legislation," page 146.

corporation was authorized to undertake any activity necessary for the purpose of the new town, including the acquisition of land by compulsion, if necessary; to hold, manage, and dispose of land and other property; to carry out building and other operations; and to provide utility and other public services. Development plans had to be approved by the Ministry, which was required to consult with local authorities before giving approval.

The new towns were to be at least 15 miles from existing urban centers, except in the London area, where 25 miles was considered a desirable minimum. Over-all densities of the new towns were to be roughly 12 persons per acre, and the peripheral belt was to be about three-quarters of a mile wide. Thirty to fifty thousand persons were suggested as the normal population range, except in exceptional cases, where a lower limit of 20,000 and a higher limit of 60,000 to 80,000 were allowed. All the necessary public services, such as transport, health, and education, were to be organized in advance of the eventual population, and facilities for industry, commerce, and town administration were to be included. Stores were to be provided at the ratio of one for each 100 to 150 persons, to be let at progressive rentals proportional to the population. Total capital cost was estimated at 27 to 36 million pounds for a town of 50,000 persons.

As of early 1947, plans for one new town, Stevenage, were completed (see Figure 18·20), and those for four more—Harlow, Hemel Hempstead, Crawley, and Kilbride—were in preparation. John F. Eccles, managing director of Welwyn, stated that Great Britain might see a dozen such new towns by 1966.[22]

In this planned program for the decentralization of urban areas, Great Britain is making the first large-scale, comprehensive, positive move which has been undertaken to correct the evils of overconcentration. British concepts of property rights have undergone great changes in the past century, the culmination of which process has made this new approach possible (see Chapter 20, pages 145 to 147). While the degree of

[22] "Britain to Build New Satellite Towns," by John F. Eccles, *The American City*, June, 1946, page 74.

success attained in this program may hasten or deter future programs of this sort in Great Britain and elsewhere, it is probable that the British are again spearheading an important

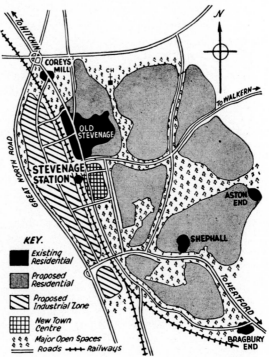

From "The American City," April, 1947.

FIGURE 18·20. DIAGRAMMATIC PLAN FOR STEVENAGE, HERTFORDSHIRE, ENGLAND

new movement which will become accepted practice in future generations. The development of this program and analysis of its successes and failures will be of the greatest interest to planners everywhere.

Selected References

Barlow Report: *Report of Royal Commission on Distribution of Industrial Population,* H.M. Stationery Office, London, 1940.

Changes in Distribution of Manufacturing Wage Earners, 1899–1939, United States Departments of Commerce and Agriculture, Government Printing Office, Washington, D. C., 1942.

Greenbelt Towns, Resettlement Administration, Government Printing Office, Washington, D. C., 1936.

HOWARD, EBENEZER: *Garden Cities of Tomorrow* (introduction by F. J. Osborn, and with an introductory essay by Lewis Mumford), Faber and Faber, London, 1946.

MUMFORD, LEWIS: *Social Foundations of Postwar Building,* Faber and Faber, London, 1943.

OSBORN, F. J.: *Green-belt Cities: The British Contribution,* Faber and Faber, London, 1946.

PURDOM, C. B.: *The Building of Satellite Towns,* J. M. Dent, London, 1925. Deals with Letchworth and Welwyn Garden Cities up to 1925.

"Urban Expansion—Fifteen Years of Development in the New York Region," *Information Bulletin* 63, Regional Plan Association, Inc., New York, November 27, 1944.

Urban Planning and Land Policies, Part I, National Resources Committee, Government Printing Office, Washington, D. C., 1939. (Describes newly established towns and communities in the United States)

WARREN, HERBERT, and W. R. DAVIDGE: *Decentralization of Population and Industry,* P. S. King and Company, London, 1930.

Questions

1. What trends toward decentralization of industry are revealed by United States Census figures?
2. Give examples of extensive decentralization of residence.
3. What types of business and industry tend to decentralize? What types will probably continue to centralize?
4. What special physical considerations should govern the planning of industrial districts?
5. What jurisdictional problems have arisen in the establishment of industrial communities centered around a single industry?
6. Describe the good features and the defects of the original plan of the industrial town of Gary.
7. Describe good examples of more recent industrial towns established on new sites.
8. What are the principal features of a "garden city" as conceived by Ebenezer Howard? To what extent have his proposals been carried out in Great Britain?
9. What attempts have been made to establish satellite towns in the United States? How successful have these been?
10. Give examples of successful "garden suburbs," as distinct from "garden cities."
11. In what way did the "Greenbelt towns" of the Resettlement Administration depart from their original conception?
12. What steps has Great Britain taken since World War II to decentralize industry through the establishment of new towns?

19

PLANNING FOR THE URBAN REGION

IT SHOULD BE OBVIOUS THAT A PLAN FOR THE future development of a city, or a new portion of a city, will have fallen short of completion if it does not take into account the environs. Yet in most of the city planning which has been done, studies and the resulting plans stop abruptly at the city line. In some cases this may have been due to lack of foresight on the part of the planner or failure to appreciate the fact that the area beyond the arbitrary line now forming the city boundary would some day become a part of the greater city and that the plans of these outlying districts would ultimately have to be corrected and adjusted to new conditions. More frequently it is due to lack of proper authority, to small units of administration, or to overlapping authority on the part of a number of bodies or boards having concurrent jurisdiction.

The need for such an outward extension of city plans has been most obvious in metropolitan areas. In several such areas planning of this kind is now in effect, and the progress made will be described later in this chapter. The term "regional planning" is often used as synonymous with "metropolitan planning," but was also employed by the National Resources Committee to describe large-scale planning embracing main drainage areas, such as the Tennessee Valley, and involving many interstate problems. Such planning, as well as state planning, is devoted largely to the conservation of natural resources, flood control, and broad economic and governmental problems. These two types of planning—large-scale regional and

state—thus deal little with urban planning, and no attempt will be made to discuss them in this volume.

Need for Planning Beyond City Borders

Before describing the process of planning for the urban region and methods of carrying out such plans, it is well to analyze the general problems involved. Certain definite physical needs require the extension of a city plan into the environs of the city. In addition, there are administrative and jurisdictional needs to be met.

In the United States, where centers of population were originally established at points remote from each other, these centers were connected by roads which have since developed into important and reasonably direct arteries of traffic, such as those connecting New York with Boston, Albany, and Philadelphia, the length of these roads being respectively about 230, 150, and 100 miles. The original highways were crudely located and constructed. The road surface was little more than the native soil, the tractive force required in proportion to the load was very great, and the gradients were necessarily light and were secured, not by cutting down hills and filling up valleys, but by detours, short or long, as the topography required.

Since the introduction of self-propelled vehicles, with their greatly increased radius of action, the loss of time, energy, and money caused by lack of directness in these main high-

117

ways has been more apparent. Any intelligent plan for their improvement and extension must include the correction of alignment in the existing roads and provision for more direct routes between important centers. The degree of directness which is practicable will depend upon the gradients, which are controlled by the topography, and upon the desirability of slight departures from a generally direct course between focal points in order to give subordinate centers of population convenient access to the main arteries.

Every large city, particularly a port city, serves as the business and trade center for not only the central city but also adjoining communities. Its terminals must, therefore, be accessible to those communities, and its transportation routes by rail and highway and its facilities for the movement of passengers (described in Chapter 7, "The Local Transit System," Volume I) must be laid out with that in mind. Such routes must, therefore, extend beyond the city line. The street system of every town, whether large or small, should be articulated with the highways, not only of neighboring towns, but with those of the next larger political unit, the county; and these in turn with those of adjacent counties, the main roads of which should form a complete system of state highways. The chief highway joining two towns should form a direct connection with the most important traffic thoroughfares of each. Frequently this is not the case; the main, and sometimes the only adequate, road connecting the towns leads at either end into narrow, tortuous, and shabby streets which must be traversed in order to reach the business or administrative center. Under such conditions the impression gained of either town will be unfortunate.

The pleasure, comfort, and convenience of going from one town to the other will be greatly increased if the approach in each case is through a dignified, well-improved street, constantly increasing in importance and interest until the climax is reached at a well-designed and convenient focal point, whether it be a civic center, the business district, a railway terminal, or the water front.

In some cases city streets are given a generous width up to the corporate limits, where they connect with important and heavily traveled roads. Their width, however, is abruptly reduced at the boundary, notwithstanding the fact that the city is almost certain to extend its limits, at which time these roads will become city streets and their widening will be necessary. Such outlying roads should be gradually increased in width as they approach a city; the cost of doing so will be slight if it is done in time.

The purpose of a road leading from a city into the surrounding country is not solely that of reaching some objective point in the shortest possible time and by the most direct route. Many of the French roads were laid out "from steeple to steeple" or from one point to another in perfectly straight lines over ridges and across valleys with little regard for easy grades. Such roads, while originally located with a view to military strategy, are now used predominantly for passenger-car and general automobile traffic. With the great speed of motor vehicles a slightly greater distance is of little or no importance, particularly when by lengthening the roads somewhat the grades will be improved and they can be made in every way more attractive.

Cities commonly confine their park areas within their corporate limits, but in selecting such reservations the environs of the city should be considered. Some of the most valuable and useful pleasure grounds could profitably be acquired long before the city limits are expanded to include them, and even though they remain permanently outside the city limits, the people will use them if they are made accessible by transit lines. The extent to which cities have acquired lands outside their boundaries has been discussed and illustrated in Chapter 10, "Parks and Recreation Facilities," Volume I.[1]

In many instances residential development has spilled over city lines into unplanned areas, resulting in developments with low standards of planning and in land speculation leading

[1] See Figure 10·1, Volume I, showing public parks and reservations in the Paris and Berlin regions.

to premature subdivision of acreage property into building lots. The problems which such practices may create and the methods for con-

portation and cheap fares, those who work for small pay are no longer obliged to live where they work or immediately adjacent thereto.

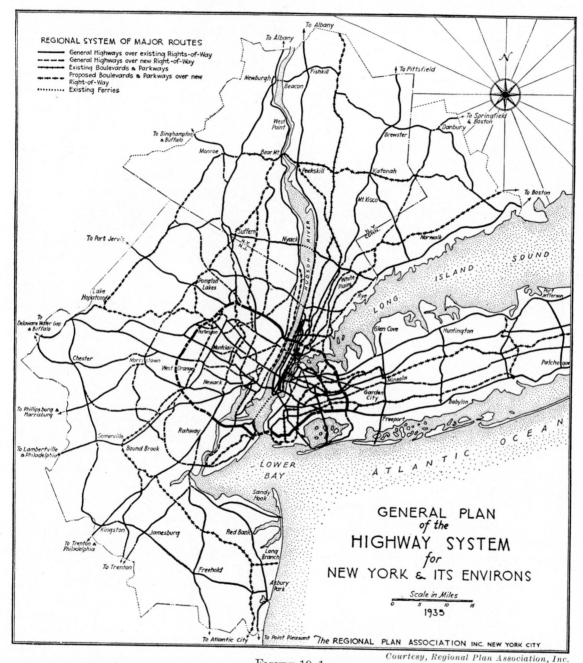

FIGURE 19·1

Courtesy, Regional Plan Association, Inc.

trolling such subdivisions will be discussed in Chapter 21 (see pages 150 to 154). Such suburban developments have been encouraged by the fact that, with improved methods of trans-

Cheap and quick transportation has enabled workers to seek healthy homes for their families in districts which are still essentially rural. To provide houses for them many unrelated developments have been made on the outskirts of all great cities. Where the cities themselves have acquired large areas of land outside their corporate limits, as have many of the German towns, the sightly and sanitary development of cheap residential property can be insured; but without such ownership there is an obvious necessity of granting greater powers than are now possessed by most cities for the control and development of the surrounding territory, or of setting up adequate machinery for metropolitan and regional planning.

The unsightly approaches to growing American towns are proverbial. Cheap and hideous groups of houses are much in evidence in their suburbs. This is in marked contrast with the manner in which the towns of continental Europe move solidly outward into the surrounding country, one block at a time. The building stops abruptly, and beyond the last developed block is open country, so that the cities appear more compact. Their superficial area is less, and the density of population per acre appears to be greater than in British and American cities. The development of these rural districts outside the built-up territory was not, however, left to chance, especially in the German cities. Long before any building was done, the street system was planned after the most careful study, limitations of building heights and the proportion of the lots which might be built upon were determined, and the highways by which the city was to be connected with the neighboring towns which might some day be a portion of it, and with others more distant, were definitely located.

Where a city, but not the surrounding unincorporated areas, has been zoned, the way is open for a fringe of cheaper development, with low standards of light and air, to spring up around its borders. A function of regional planning should be to encourage and assist bordering communities to give adequate protection, through zoning, to such areas.

Jurisdictional difficulties within an urban region may arise from a disposition on the part of the smaller towns to resent an intrusion into their territory as an infringement of their independence and their jealously guarded autonomy. As an example, in and about London the London County Council, the various local councils, the Board of Trade, and the ministries of Health and Transport all have a certain amount of jurisdiction over and responsibility for the development of an adequate system of highways within the different municipalities and roads connecting various centers of population. Each locality is jealous of its own powers, and there is a disposition on its part to consider as conclusive its own views of what may be needed in the way of interurban highways; the larger aspect of the problem—that of tying together the entire highway system of a thickly settled portion of a country—is likely to be lost sight of. It was said that, before World War I, there were within 15 miles of Charing Cross ninety local road authorities acting independently of each other, and that a main road in 20 miles might pass through territory controlled by ten different highway authorities. Concerted action under such circumstances was manifestly very difficult, if not impossible, and little progress was being made toward supplying main roads between the city and its environs. Now, with a regional highway scheme laid down by the County of London Plan of 1943,[2] adequate routes are more possible of achievement. (See Figure 19·2.)

Jurisdictional problems can seldom be solved as effectively through the co-operation of different administrative units as they would be if a metropolitan planning district were created and some board or commission were given power to make and impose upon the smaller municipalities within its limits a plan which would treat the entire district as a whole. Such a policy is not infrequently followed in the development of comprehensive plans for systems of water supply, sewerage, or parks, but rarely, if ever, for a system of highways. Even in contiguous territory, the annexation of which to the city may confidently be expected in the near future, the local authorities, and even private real estate developers, are allowed until the very day of absorption into the larger city or town to proceed with the laying out of streets in an entirely independent manner, as though they were to continue as separate and inde-

[2] See reference to this Plan in Chapter 2, Volume I.

pendent towns, having no relation to each other except that of propinquity.

While the cities of Continental Europe have powers to regulate their growth and development that are unknown in America, they can, as a rule, exercise control over the planning of the territory outside their limits only through the actual ownership of large tracts of land or, in some cases, through an appeal to the au-

act and those which succeeded it will be discussed at some length in the next chapter (see pages 138 to 140 and 145 to 147).

Status of Regional and County Planning in the United States

A nation-wide survey of planning agencies in the United States was made by the National

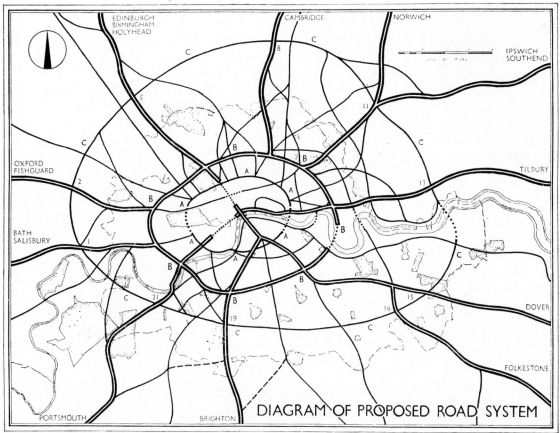

Reproduced by courtesy of the London County Council.

FIGURE 19·2.   ROAD PLAN FOR THE COUNTY OF LONDON

Double lines are arterial roads; single lines are subarterial roads; *A*, *B*, and *C* are "ring-roads."

thority of the state. The British Town Planning Act of 1909 was based upon the idea that in a thickly populated country the plan of every town should be considered in its relation to the country about it and to the street systems of contiguous and neighboring towns, all plans being subject to the approval of a central authority whose jurisdiction extends over the whole of Great Britain. The provisions of this

Resources Committee in 1936.[3] The committee listed 506 metropolitan, county, and district planning agencies as of the end of 1936, compared with only 85 such agencies in 1933. (See Figure 19·3.) The 27 district planning boards included were those studying the common prob-

[3] "Status of City and County Planning in the United States," *Circular* X, National Resources Committee, May 15, 1937.

lems of groups of rural counties, such as schools, water and drainage, highways, and land use, and were a relatively new type of agency.

Of the total, 316 were official, 171 were unofficial, the character of six was not stated, and the sole function of 13 was zoning. Among the comparatively small group of these agencies which were dealing to any extent with urban

Seventeen school and library plans.
Ten public building plans.
Twenty-four drainage and sewerage plans.
Forty-three water-supply plans.
Seven housing plans.
Seven comprehensive zoning ordinances and 31 for use only had been adopted; 25 zoning ordinances were in preparation.
Nineteen agencies had mandatory control of subdivision plats, while 15 were exercising advisory control.

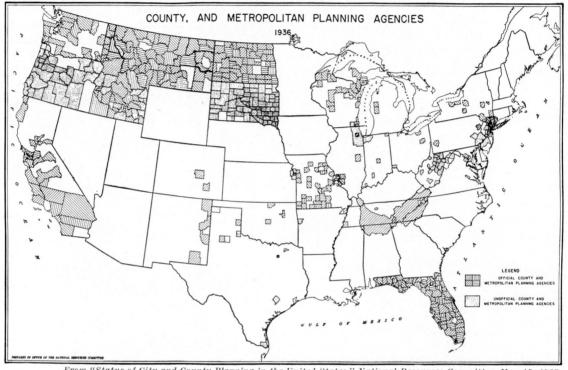

From "Status of City and County Planning in the United States," National Resources Committee, May 15, 1937.

FIGURE 19·3

problems were the metropolitan agencies operating within the urban regions centered on Boston, Buffalo, Cincinnati, Chattanooga, Cleveland, Kansas City, Los Angeles, Milwaukee, Nashville, Rochester, St. Louis, and Washington. The extent of the planning work accomplished by all these metropolitan, county, and district agencies is shown by figures taken from the National Resources Committee survey. Plans had been completed, or were under way, as follows:

Thoroughfare plans by 65 agencies, 16 of which had approved such plans and nine of which had also been adopted officially.
Fifty-one park and parkway plans, nine of which had been approved by the planning boards and five of which had been adopted officially.

A large percentage of the county planning agencies were new ones set up in the northwestern and other rural states in order to participate in planning public works and relief programs. Most of these have since adopted a broader and longer-range conception of their problems, although many are dealing chiefly with rural land use.

Examples of Urban Annexation

Annexation of adjoining territory has been one means by which cities have helped to solve the need for outward extension of their plans.

The consolidation in 1898 of the then city of New York with the city of Brooklyn, many small adjoining communities on Long Island and in the mainland north of the city, and all of Staten Island to form the present city with its 320 square miles of land area, has helped in the planning and execution of its extended rapid transit, highway, parks, sewage treatment, water supply, and other municipal services. Rochester has been pushing out in several directions, providing boulevards, and planning the contiguous territory. Originally seven square miles in area, it had grown to 35.3 square miles in 1940. For a long time the city boundary was some four and one-half miles from Lake Ontario; but after the donation to the city by public-spirited citizens of a park of 450 acres on the lake front and the purchase by the city of an adjoining tract for sewage-disposal purposes, these areas were physically connected with the city by annexing a narrow strip containing a highway between them and the city line. On January 1, 1916, the village of Charlotte on the lake front became a part of the city and was connected with it by means of a boulevard which was annexed at the same time. The river itself has been incorporated within the city limits in order that the former port of Charlotte might become the port of Rochester, while narrow strips along the river banks have also been added in order to protect them and make them available for park purposes. While it would seem that all the remaining territory between the city and the lake front, now in the town of Irondequoit, should eventually be incorporated within the city limits, it may prove that the over-all planning by the Monroe County Division of Regional Planning (Rochester being close to the center of that county) will provide the necessary co-ordination between city and suburban plans.

It is impossible to estimate the time within which contiguous areas will become a part of any city. There have been many instances of sensational growth in area and population, one of the best examples of which is Los Angeles. According to the federal census the population of this city increased 212 per cent during the decade from 1900 to 1910, and a large portion of this increase was undoubtedly due to the absorption of adjoining areas containing quite populous centers. That this process of absorption is still in progress will be seen by reference to Figure 6·24, Volume I, and to Table 30, which shows the successive additions to the city from its original incorporation in 1850 to January 29, 1947, the date and the area added in each case being given in the table. The large San Fernando addition, No. 15, was taken into the city, not with a view to urban development, but primarily in order that the city might use its surplus water supply for irrigating and bringing under cultivation its extensive area, which was at that time greater than all the rest of the city put together.

Outstanding Metropolitan Plans

Space does not permit a detailed description of the techniques and procedures of metropolitan planning, but a brief account will be given of a few of the best known of those already listed.

The most ambitious and comprehensive is the Regional Plan of New York and Its Environs, which covers the portions of the three states of New York, New Jersey, and Connecticut which center on, and are tributary to, the Port of New York. The work was initiated in 1921 by Russell Sage Foundation, established for the express purpose of the "improvement of social and living conditions." Its trustees concluded that one of the most effective ways in which this object could be promoted would be through the preparation of a comprehensive plan for the future development of the district of which New York is the center. A Committee on a Regional Plan of New York and Its Environs was appointed under the chairmanship of the late Charles D. Norton, who had been so successful as first chairman of the Plan of Chicago in starting that great project on its way. The first public announcement of the purpose of this committee was made at a meeting in New York City on May 10, 1922, at which some notable addresses were made and Norton briefly outlined the work which had already been done and what the committee hoped and expected to accomplish.

Very brief extracts from several of the addresses made on the occasion will indicate the

TABLE 30

ADDITIONS TO THE CITY OF LOS ANGELES TO JANUARY 29, 1947, AS COMPILED BY THE CITY ENGINEER
(The locations of the successive additions are indicated by the key numbers in Figure 6·24, Volume I)

Number	Name	Date	Acres	Number	Name	Date	Acres
1	Original city	1781	17,924	52	Lankershim	1923	4,890
2	Southern extension	1859	766	53	Providencia	1924	3,085
3	Highland Park	1895	904	54	Cienega	1924	595
4	Southern and western	1896	6,517	55	Annandale	1924	435
5	Garvanza	1899	440	56	Clinton	1924	34
6	University	1899	1,134	57	Wagner	1924	600
7	Shoestring	1906	11,931	58	Fairfax	1924	1,203
8	Wilmington	1909	6,358	59	Holabird	1925	8
9	San Pedro	1909	2,948	60	Danziger	1925	79
10	Colgrove	1909	5,579	61	Hamilton	1925	282
11	Hollywood	1910	2,848	62	Martel	1925	148
12	East Hollywood	1910	7,112	63	Santa Monica Canyon	1925	109
13	Arroyo Seco	1912	4,416	64	Beverly Glen	1925	521
14	Palms	1915	4,672	65	Venice	1925	2,627
15	San Fernando	1915	108,732	66	Green Meadows	1926	2,285
16	Bairdstown	1915	2,176	67	Buckler	1926	128
17	Westgate	1916	31,149	68	Watts	1926	1,081
18	Occidental	1916	666	69	Sunland	1926	3,848
19	Owensmouth	1917	495	70	Tuna Canyon	1926	4,910
20	West Coast	1917	7,942	71	Mar Vista	1927	3,190
21	West Adams	1918	380	72	Barnes City	1927	1,160
22	Griffith Ranch	1918	149	73	Brayton	1927	48
23	Hansen Heights	1918	5,313	74	Wiseburn	1928	91
24	Ostend	1918	1	75	White Point	1928	7
25	Orange Cove	1918	146	76	Classification Yard	1930	264
26	West Lankershim	1919	746	77	Viewpark	1930	13
27	Dodson	1919	673	78	Sentney	1930	6
28	Fort McArthur	1919	360	79	Tobias	1930	8
29	Peck	1919	286	80	Cole	1931	60
30	Harbor View	1919	112	81	Tujunga	1932	5,568
31	St. Francis	1920	33	82	Lakeside Park	1933	81
32	Hill	1920	71	83	Western Avenue Highlands	1935	74
33	Chatsworth	1920	220	84	Crenshaw Manor	1940	35
34	La Brea	1922	979	85	Fairfax No. 2	1941	168
35	Manchester	1922	212	86	Crenshaw Manor No. 2	1941	60
36	Melrose	1922	430	87	Woodland Heights	1941	9
37	Sawtelle	1922	1,162	88	Palos Verdes	1942	8
38	Angeles Mesa	1922	632	89	Fairfax No. 3	1942	10
39	Angeles Mesa No. 2	1922	216	90	Fairfax No. 4	1942	20
40	Rimpau	1922	90	91	Dominguez	1943	285
41	Hancock	1923	169	92	Florence	1944	48
42	Evans	1923	85	93	Fairfax No. 5	1944	16
43	Ambassador	1923	1,684	94	Florence No. 2	1944	36
44	Laurel Canyon	1923	8,684	95	Florence No. 3	1944	16
45	Hyde Park	1923	770	96	Lomita	1945	11
46	Eagle Rock	1923	2,027	97	Lomita No. 2	1946	5
47	Vermont	1923	16	98	Mesa No. 3	1946	36
48	Laguna	1923	53	99	Mar Vista No. 2	1946	40
49	Carthay	1923	243	100	Angeles Mesa No. 4	1947	262
50	Rosewood	1923	395	101	Mar Vista No. 3	1947	131
51	Agoure	1923	15				

Total area = 289,695 acres, or 452.6 square miles.

reaction of the speakers to the proposed plan. Herbert Hoover said:

The vision of the region around New York as a well-planned location of millions of happy homes and a better working center of millions of men and women grasps the imagination. A definite plan for its accomplishment may be only an ideal. But a people without ideals degenerates—one with practical ideals is already upon the road to attain them.

Lillian D. Wald said:

This seems to me a most important first step towards the most important undertaking that I have heard of for many years. I believe that if it is carried out in logical sequence it will add greatly to the happiness of the people of New York. It links a practical, workable plan with the vision of a city conceived in understanding of the needs of many people, their homes, and those matters most closely related to their daily life.

In indicating the necessity of ignoring arbitrary political boundaries in making such a study, Elihu Root said:

A city is a growth. It is not the result of political decree or control. You may draw all the lines you please between counties and states, a city is a growth responding to forces not at all political, quite disregarding political lines. It is a growth like that of a crystal responding to forces inherent in the atoms that make it up.

After the death of Charles D. Norton in 1923, Frederic A. Delano succeeded to the chairmanship of the Regional Plan Committee.

A series of comprehensive surveys were undertaken to cover physical conditions, economic and industrial trends, social and living conditions, and a survey of laws, existing and needed, to control or effect a plan for the area. An area of 5,528 square miles, embracing 18 counties and parts of four others, was delineated for study. Early in the program planning principles were determined, and studies initiated for a master plan of the region based upon these principles.

The program led to the publication of eight Survey Volumes and two Plan Volumes, supplemented by a map of the Graphic Regional Plan prepared at a scale of 2,000 feet to the inch and printed at a scale of 1 to 62,500 (approximately one mile to the inch). The area studied extended to an average distance of about 50 miles from the New York City Hall, except that it included all of Long Island,

which is about 110 miles in length. The region comprises over 500 separate political subdivisions. The final volume was published in 1931, and the 10-year program had then cost about $1,300,000.

Realizing that a continuing organization was essential and that this should be neither controlled nor financed by a single agency, Russell Sage Foundation wisely created the Regional Plan Association in 1929 as a non-profit membership organization to carry on the work and keep the plan up to date, and withdrew from any active direction of its activities. George McAneny was made chairman of the Board of Directors of the Association and still held that position in 1948.

The Regional Plan Association has maintained an active program involving keeping the plan up to date and actively before public and citizen agencies, carrying on research in planning problems, promoting the establishment of official planning boards and commissions and giving them general advice on their programs, and maintaining a reference library on all planning activities in the region. It has published three progress reports under the title *From Plan to Reality* and special reports on the subjects of blighted areas, traffic and parking, and the economic status of the region. It can rightfully claim the development of an active regional consciousness throughout an area where much bitter rivalry previously existed, the establishment and activation of numerous planning boards and commissions, the co-ordination of official plans for many types of facilities, and the advancement of many of its specific proposals from plans to reality.

Chicago, in many respects, led the way for the New York Regional Plan although it did not attempt as diversified a program nor as elaborate a series of publications. It, too, was undertaken and financed by a private agency, the Commercial Club of Chicago. Initiated in 1906 and prepared under the direction of Daniel H. Burnham, its plan was published in 1909 in a large volume entitled *The Chicago Plan*. While considered primarily a city plan, it ignored political boundaries and extended to a distance of about 30 miles from the center of the city. It related primarily to highways, parks, and the location of public buildings, and some of its outstanding proposals have been referred to in preceding chapters (see Chapters 3, 8, and 10, Volume I). The plan has been

The regional aspects of the Burnham Plan have been continued and enlarged by the Chicago Regional Planning Association, established in 1925 and operating as a co-ordinating agency

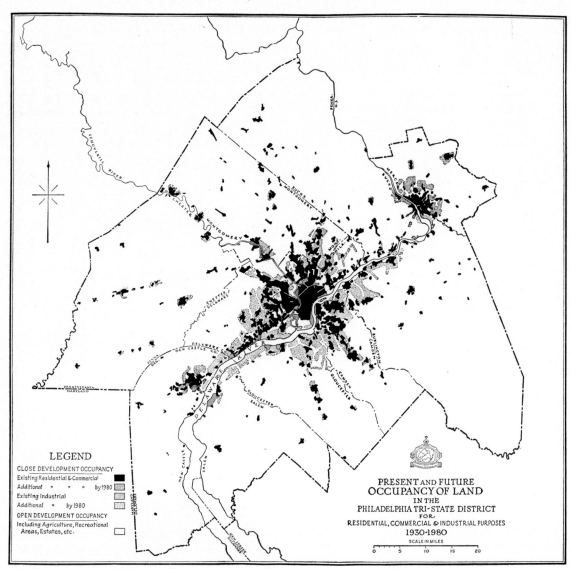

LEGEND

CLOSE DEVELOPMENT OCCUPANCY

Existing Residential & Commercial

Additional   "   "   " by 1980

Existing Industrial

Additional   "   by 1980

OPEN DEVELOPMENT OCCUPANCY

Including Agriculture, Recreational Areas, Estates, etc.

PRESENT AND FUTURE
OCCUPANCY OF LAND
IN THE
PHILADELPHIA TRI-STATE DISTRICT
FOR
RESIDENTIAL, COMMERCIAL & INDUSTRIAL PURPOSES
1930-1980
SCALE IN MILES
0   5   10   15   20

From "Regional Plan of the Philadelphia Tri-state District," 1932.

FIGURE 19·4

actively followed up by an official Chicago Plan Commission, which was reorganized in 1939 and has published numerous reports on various phases of the city's Master Plan. Efforts made to secure citizen participation in Chicago are described in a later section of this chapter (see page 134).

within the 15 counties, forming parts of three states, in the Chicago region. This organization has not developed its own master plan, as did the similar organization in the New York region, but has been very successful in bringing together official and citizen agencies and in promoting and establishing standards for sound zoning, subdivision control, public recreation facilities, airports, public utility systems, and other regional phases of planning. It has limited its activities to problems outside the city of Chicago but has co-operated with the Chi-

oped and published in 1932, with a single volume describing the Federation's findings and proposals. The Federation was discontinued a few years after its report was published, but planning in Philadelphia was actively resumed

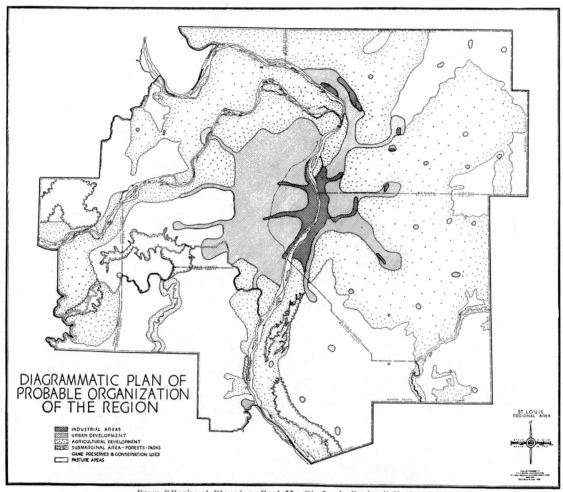

DIAGRAMMATIC PLAN OF PROBABLE ORGANIZATION OF THE REGION

- INDUSTRIAL AREAS
- URBAN DEVELOPMENT
- AGRICULTURAL DEVELOPMENT
- SUBMARGINAL AREA · FORESTS · PARKS
- GAME PRESERVES & CONSERVATION USES
- PASTURE AREAS

ST LOUIS REGIONAL AREA

From "Regional Planning, Part II—St. Louis Region," National Resources Committee, 1936.

FIGURE 19·5. A LAND USE PLAN FOR THE ST. LOUIS REGION

cago Plan Commission in effecting a co-ordination between city and regional plans.

A Philadelphia regional plan was initiated by the formation in 1924 of the Regional Planning Federation of the Philadelphia Tri-state District. It established general and technical staffs and a number of technical advisory committees on which public agencies, public utility companies, and citizens were represented. A master plan, similar in scope to the Graphic Plan of New York and Its Environs, was devel-

in 1943 with the creation of an official city planning commission, which is extending its studies for Philadelphia out into the environs of the city.

In the Buffalo region, a Niagara Frontier Planning Board has been active since 1925 as an official regional board set up under state legislation to plan for Erie and Niagara counties, which include the cities of Buffalo and Niagara Falls. It has studied population trends, economic problems, highways, airports, sewage treatment, and other public works projects and has proved a useful co-ordinating agency. This board has worked closely with an unofficial Niagara Frontier Planning Association organized in 1924.

A St. Louis Regional Planning Commission, with the aid of the National Resources Committee, has prepared extensive studies for the

to be created by interstate compact, or by other legislative action, to prepare unified plans within the St. Louis region.[4]

Contributions of County Planning Agencies

In a few cases regional and county planning have proved synonymous. The outstanding one

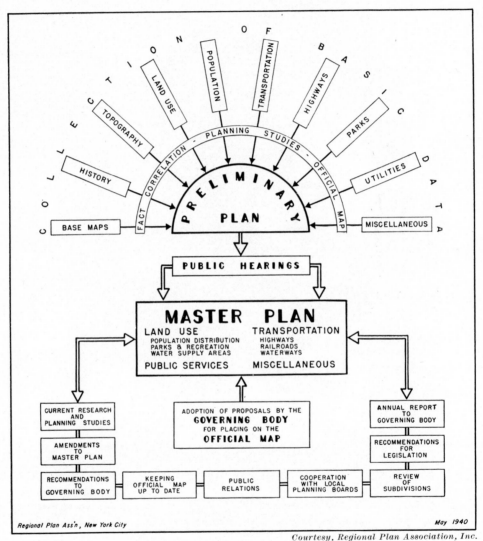

Courtesy, Regional Plan Association, Inc.

FIGURE 19·6. SUGGESTED PROCEDURES AND RELATIONSHIPS IN COUNTY PLANNING

bi-state area centered around St. Louis, Missouri, and East St. Louis, Illinois, and containing all or parts of nine counties. A report analysed the regional problems, presented some recommendations for their solution, and urged the establishment of a governmental agency

is in the County of Los Angeles, where a Regional Planning Commission of the county of Los Angeles was established in 1922. This county has a total area of 4,080 square miles,

[4] *Regional Planning*, Part II—*St. Louis Region*, National Resources Committee, June, 1936.

and, because of its very rapid growth and the peculiar shape of the city of Los Angeles as a result of its urban annexations described earlier co-ordinate the needs of this great metropolitan area. A somewhat similar situation, but on a smaller scale, exists in the Rochester re-

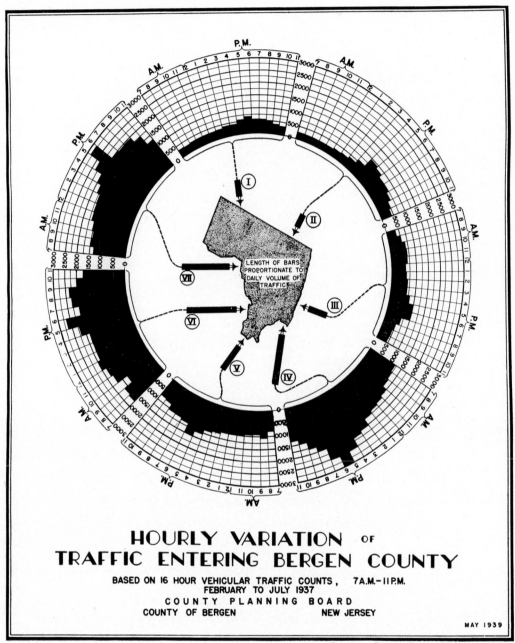

HOURLY VARIATION OF TRAFFIC ENTERING BERGEN COUNTY

BASED ON 16 HOUR VEHICULAR TRAFFIC COUNTS, 7 A.M.–11 P.M. FEBRUARY TO JULY 1937
COUNTY PLANNING BOARD
COUNTY OF BERGEN   NEW JERSEY

MAY 1939

Courtesy, Bergen County Planning Board.

FIGURE 19·7

in this chapter and illustrated in Figure 6·24, Volume I, regional problems have been of great importance and urgency. Both the county and the city have active, well-staffed planning organizations and are doing much to plan for and

gion (also referred to earlier in this chapter), where Monroe County has had a regional planning agency since 1927.

A Milwaukee County Regional Planning Commission has made regional studies for the environs of the city of Milwaukee, and the Board of County Road Commissioners of Wayne County, Michigan, has made comprehensive studies of highways, parks, and related planning problems in the region around Detroit.

In other cases, county planning has done much to solve both urban and rural problems in counties which form a relatively small part of a large metropolitan area. One of the most successful agencies of this kind is the Bergen County Planning Board in the North Jersey section of New York and Its Environs. With the initial aid of the Federal Work Projects Administration and with the Regional Plan Association as technical advisers, comprehensive plans have been prepared on such subjects as zoning, land subdivision, passenger transportation, highways, and land use. A diagram showing recommended scope and procedures is reproduced in Figure 19·6. Close co-operation has been established with the many municipal planning boards in the county. An interesting graphic presentation of the hourly variation of vehicular traffic entering the county via main highways is reproduced in Figure 19·7.

In the same region and likewise utilizing federal work-relief funds, Westchester County made comprehensive county plans under an Emergency Work Bureau, which issued a report in 1936.[5] Planning for the county was later taken over by a County Planning Commission set up under a new County Charter and since then actively engaged in the preparation of county-wide plans.

In both Bergen and Westchester counties, effective use was made of large-scale relief models of the county.

Filling in the Gaps between Municipal Plans

In many cases, county or other large-area planning is the only effective way of filling in the gaps between municipal plans. In the thickly populated countries of Europe and in some of the eastern states of the United States where the towns are close together and fre-

[5] *The Westchester County Planning Survey—a Report of Progress from June 1, 1934 to April 15, 1936,* Advisory Committee on County Planning, Westchester County Emergency Work Bureau, 1936.

quently within sight of each other, the spaces between them need planning as well as the towns themselves. Often there is no metropolitan area involved where a regional agency would offer the logical solution, and if the county has not taken the initiative, a state planning agency offers the best opportunity for effective over-all planning.

The state of New York has come to the aid of the New York region in planning and developing the extensive parks and parkways of the Long Island State Park Commission, and the states of New York and New Jersey have co-operated in establishing the large park reservations under the Palisades Interstate Park Commission.

A striking example of city, county, and state co-operation is provided by the Columbia River Highway running from Portland, Oregon, for some 60 miles up the Columbia River. This road passes through some of the grandest scenery on the continent, winding about mountain spurs 800 feet above the river, again descending to the river bank, passing at the foot of cataracts hundreds of feet in height and through tunnels with arched side openings like those of the famous Axenstrasse along the shore of Lake Lucerne. Snow-capped mountains are frequently in view, and everywhere there is a perfect roadway with parapet walls of good design, ample lighting where the curves are sharp, and attractive bridges spanning the numerous ravines. The unusual features of this road are indicated by the views in Figures 19·8 and 19·9.

The most insistent demand for facilities in these gaps between communities is for better highways, and many states have been developing, with the aid of the United States Public Roads Administration, comprehensive plans for highway networks which will provide the framework for future master plans of many areas now rural in character. Some states are protecting the frontages of these highways from spoliation through strict regulation of billboards and a zoning of marginal strips through unincorporated areas, so as to concentrate business uses at strategic locations. In other cases no thought has been given to the time when the hamlets through which these highways pass will become prosperous villages and the villages will become cities, each growing outward toward its neighbors and all finally becoming a part of some great metropolitan district, where the problems of housing, of adequate light and air, and of recreation, as well as the problems of traffic congestion, of transportation, and of re-

There is need for really constructive planning of the environs of every city and town; not the subdivision into city lots and blocks of the entire territory round about, which would be a distinct misfortune, but the establishment of lines of direct and easy communication between centers, however unimportant they may be at

Oregon State Highway Commission Photos, Salem, Oregon.

FIGURE 19·8. VIEWS SHOWING DIFFICULT CONSTRUCTION ON COLUMBIA RIVER HIGHWAY
Oneonta Rock and Tunnel (*left*) and Bishop's Cap (*right*).

strictions upon the use of property, will become as acute as they now are in the great city to which the small towns are tributary. Some of these problems, in fact, are already present. The slum is not confined to the large city; some of the most insanitary and debasing conditions are to be found in small towns forming the fringe about a great city, but beyond its jurisdiction, and they are not infrequently met with in small villages in the rural districts. It has often been pointed out that congestion of population is not to be measured by the number of people to the acre or to the city block, but by the number of people to the room.

the time. Future growth will be from these centers outward, and is it visionary or extravagant to urge that every one of these small centers should be connected with neighboring communities by roads which may, if necessary, become part of the highway system of a great urban district? The sort of control which is needed to insure intelligent planning of this kind cannot be exercised by the cities; it must be undertaken by some suitable metropolitan or regional agency or by the state itself.

State institutions—educational, charitable, or penal—occupy large groups of buildings covering extensive tracts of land. These have

Oregon State Highway Commission Photos, Salem, Oregon.

FIGURE 19·9. SCENIC SPOTS ON COLUMBIA RIVER HIGHWAY

Vista House, showing view of Columbia River Gorge (*upper view*) and Shepperds Dell (*lower view*).

been set down wherever the officials having jurisdiction at the time thought it advisable to locate them or wherever lands could be most readily secured for the purpose. Little serious study appears to have been given to their location, especially their location with respect to each other. While it may seem a far cry from the location of the public buildings of a city or their grouping to form a civic center to the selection of sites for public institutions scattered over an entire state, the latter problem is not unworthy of careful study.

Organization and Citizen Participation

The private citizen, both individually and through civic associations, has contributed much to the cause of regional and metropolitan planning. Much of the success of the Regional Plan Association in New York was due to the early organization of county and local citizens' councils throughout the region.

Undoubtedly many more official regional planning commissions will be established in the future (legislative progress in that direction will be discussed in the following chapter), but they will need organized citizen support if their work is to be effective. Some interesting proposals as to how this might be brought about were assembled as a result of a nation-wide competition in 1943, financed by an anonymous citizen of St. Louis, for the best proposal for the organization and operation of a Regional Council in a metropolitan area.[6]

The outline for this competition suggested that the regional council be set up so as to consider not only regional area planning but also various human factors, as well as problems of taxation and intergovernmental relationships. It also proposed that the council should be so constituted as to enlist the cooperation of the recognized leaders in the various fields of enterprise and civic interest throughout the area.

[6] The four prize-winning essays were published in full in a pamphlet, *Organization for Metropolitan Planning,* American Society of Planning Officials, 1943, and are summarized in *Planning, 1943,* the Proceedings of the 1943 Annual Meeting of that Society.

The first-prize winner, Harvey F. Pinney, concluded that there would be little change in the present three levels of government—federal, state, local—and that a regional council would therefore cut across the jurisdictions of all three levels. The five main elements of his plan were:

1. The authority of a metropolitan area regional council would be founded on a basic agreement among the federal, state, and central city governments. The focal power should be that of review and approval or disapproval of plans and projects initiated by itself or by other agencies operating in the region.
2. The Council would consist of three representatives of the federal government (a planner, an economist, an engineer), three of the state government (a planner, a local government expert, an engineer), and three of the central city (an economist, a health expert, a housing expert), nominations to be made by official planning agencies of the government represented or by professional associations.
3. The Council would have a secretariat to serve as a staff for research, planning, and technical consultation.
4. Advisory bodies and *ad hoc* committees would be used for developing special data, analyzing community needs and opinions, and appraising technical aspects of plans and projects.
5. A list of specific steps for initiating a movement to set up a regional council in a particular region contained 18 items involving meetings, publicity, consultations with associations and groups, preparation of a brief on the need of a council, tentative plans for organization, and drafts of enabling legislation.

In the discussion of the four proposals, Robert Kingery pointed out:

In the suburban region of Chicago, the making and execution of many plans have been helped by bringing together periodically the persons who have direct responsibility for doing the work in the several adjacent municipalities, counties, and states. Water supply men meet water supply men, park men meet and work with park men, and so on through the several items for which plans are made. . . . The idea of metropolitan planning has been made an actuality. The mystery has been taken out of the word "planning" and it has come to be used as a transitive verb instead of an intransitive verb.

L. Deming Tilton stated that a successful movement toward regional government needed three indispensable ingredients: the will to participate, adequate financial support, and leadership among the officials. He further stated:

Since planning as we understand it is persuasive rather than authoritarian, no fears of any kind should surround this work. Any agency, public or private, official or unofficial, that devotes itself to the development of ideas for regional betterment deserves support. With such an organization, problems can be explored, the planning needs of the area noted, and strategy developed looking toward establishment of an agency having genuine power and influence.[7]

A somewhat similar contest, but aimed particularly at the Boston region, was sponsored by the Boston Society of Architects in 1945. This was set up to "develop citizen interest and citizen participation in a forward-looking and practical master program designed to promote the sound growth and prosperity of the metropolitan area." Ninety programs were submitted; four cash prizes were awarded; and nine honorable mentions were given. The results included three significant items: (1) there was a marked awakening of citizen interest; (2) the prize-winning papers and excerpts from those which received honorable mention have been published under the title *The Boston Contest, 1944;* (3) a Greater Boston Development Committee has been established as a widely representative group to take over and lead citizen participation in future planning for the Boston region.[8]

In discussing a proper metropolitan authority most of the contestants visualized the creation of a new agency with functions similar to or wider than those of the present Metropolitan District Commission, but a body politically responsible to the citizens of the whole metropolitan area and with sources of income that would not place another burden upon real property.

The procedures followed in Chicago provide such an excellent example of the part which an unofficial body of citizens can play in developing an ambitious scheme for the improvement of a great city by recasting its plan that they are worth recounting in some detail. They are applicable to either city or regional planning. Walter D. Moody, former Director of the Chi-

cago Plan Commission, described them as follows:

Rarely in this country is city planning work initiated by the municipal government. Where this is the case the highest degree of success is not attained. The best results have been had where the city planning movement originated with a group of substantial public-spirited citizens, or under the auspices of commercial or civic organizations. The reason is that at the very outset adequate funds must be had for technical advice and for the conduct of preliminary work to the end that public sentiment may be stirred. Appropriations by city administrations for the first need rarely suffice. This is due to the fear of politicians that the censure of the community would be incurred by invading new and untried fields. Under the ordinary power of a city for making appropriations for corporate purposes the second need cannot be covered at all.[9]

Moody outlined the policy adopted by the Chicago Plan Commission, an official body appointed by the mayor of the city to advance the carrying out of the plans prepared by Daniel H. Burnham for the Commercial Club. In naming the members of this commission the mayor pointed out the necessity of taking the public into their confidence "to the end that the whole city and all elements in it may be fully informed as to what is contemplated in this plan for the future." How the commission did this can best be described in Moody's words:

Actuated by this admonition the commission set out on an elaborate and comprehensive educational propaganda. First there was prepared an 80-page illustrated booklet setting forth the technical proposals in the plan. This was shot through with a strong and exhortive appeal to the citizens to get behind the commission in the promotion of the plan. One hundred and sixty-five thousand copies of this booklet were published and distributed gratis to property owners and tenants paying a rental of $25 per month and upwards.

Next there was prepared a textbook on citizenship and city planning for use in the Chicago schools. This study was adopted by the Board of Education, since which 45,000 copies have been issued.

Tens of scores of stories of the plan and the purposes of the commission were written and furnished to newspapers and periodicals.

There was organized an effective stereopticon lecture course. The countries of the world were scoured for illustrations and technical data, for use in embellishing the arguments of the lecturer. Thus the Plan of Chicago has been directly presented in more than 300 lectures, and 100,000 citizens have been reached directly in this way. Invitations for the

[7] *Planning, 1943,* Proceedings of the Annual Meeting of the American Society of Planning Officials, pages 56–58.

[8] From "The Boston Contest," by William Roger Greeley, Contest Chairman, *Journal of the American Institute of Planners,* Vol. XI, No. 1, 1945, page 29.

[9] From "How to Go about City Planning," *The City Plan Quarterly,* March, 1915.

lectures have been received from clubs, societies, business organizations, schools, universities, churches, labor organizations, in fact, from every organized source and from all parts of the city.

The commission even resorted to moving pictures in its work of publicity, two reels occupying forty minutes having been prepared to contrast existing conditions with those which would result from the carrying out of the plan. That this propaganda work was successful is indicated by the extent to which the plan has been carried out, and the fact that an understanding was reached between the city authorities and the Plan Commission that no important work not included in the plan shall be initiated by the city until it has first been referred to the commission.

When a city or regional planning project is undertaken, it is often first necessary to secure funds either through appropriations by some civic organization or by private subscriptions from citizens. In Chicago, as already explained, the work was undertaken and financed by the Commercial Club, and in Brooklyn a similar though less ambitious movement was organized and the funds were raised by a few public-spirited citizens, headed by Frederick B. Pratt and Alfred T. White. The next step is to secure a competent expert adviser to make a thorough study of existing conditions, to suggest what should be done, and to present the recommendations in a clear and convincing fashion. The preparation of a series of attractive pictures will not suffice. They may arouse a good deal of temporary enthusiasm, but the people who are likely to get behind a movement of this kind and support it by their influence and money will want to be shown the reasons for and the probable economic results of the carrying out of the suggestions.

Selected References

"County Planning in Metropolitan Areas as Exemplified by Bergen County, New Jersey, *Information Bulletin* 50, Regional Plan Association, Inc., New York, May 13, 1940.

NICHOLAS, R.: *Manchester and District Regional Planning Proposals* (report of the Manchester District Regional Planning Committee), Jarrold & Sons, Ltd., Norwich and London, 1945.

Organization for Metropolitan Planning, American Society of Planning Officials, Chicago, 1943.

Regional Planning: Part II—*St. Louis Region,* National Resources Committee, Washington, D. C., June, 1936; Part III—*New England,* National Resources Committee, Washington, D. C., July, 1936; Part IV—*Baltimore-Washington-Annapolis Area,* Maryland State Planning Commission, Baltimore, November, 1937.

Regional Plan of New York and Its Environs: Vol. I, *The Graphic Regional Plan* (prepared by the staff of the Regional Plan), 1929; Vol. II, *The Building of the City* (by THOMAS ADAMS, assisted by HAROLD M. LEWIS and LAWRENCE M. ORTON), 1931 (distributed by Regional Plan Association, Inc., New York).

Regional Plan of the Philadelphia Tri-state District, Regional Planning Federation of the Philadelphia Tri-state District, Philadelphia, 1932.

The Mercer County Plan—a Guide for Future Development (RUSSELL VAN NEST BLACK, Consultant), Mercer County Planning Commission, Trenton, N. J., January 1, 1931.

The Westchester County Planning Survey—a Report of Progress from June 1, 1934 to April 15, 1936, Advisory Committee on County Planning, Westchester County Emergency Work Bureau, White Plains, N. Y., 1936.

Questions

1. What conditions have retarded the extension of city planning beyond municipal boundaries?
2. What are some of the physical needs which require regional planning?
3. What types of administrative activities and controls should extend beyond city boundaries? Give examples of such controls.
4. What types of urban facilities have frequently been planned and developed on a regional basis?
5. What was the extent of regional planning activity in the United States as revealed by the National Resources Committee survey of 1936?
6. What cities have used annexation as a means of solving the problem of planning areas beyond their borders? Describe the outstanding example of this policy.
7. Describe the scope of the Regional Plan of New York and Its Environs and the steps taken to assure a continuous program of promoting the plan and keeping it up to date.
8. Describe regional plans made, or under preparation, in four other metropolitan districts.
9. Describe progress made in county planning and its relation to city planning.
10. Why is it especially important and urgent to plan highways on a regional basis, well in advance of the growth of suburban communities?
11. In what ways can the state governments contribute to the better planning of a city and its environs?
12. What types of official regional planning agencies have been suggested?
13. What part can the unofficial citizen organization play in regional planning?

Part Six

Legal, Economic, and Administrative Problems

20

CITY PLANNING LEGISLATION

CITIES OF CONTINENTAL EUROPE, ESPECIALLY those of Germany, have far broader powers than have those of the United States or Great Britain. It may be generally stated that the former can do almost anything not forbidden by law, whereas the latter can do only those things which are permitted or directed by general or special enabling acts. Continental cities are to a large degree independent of the state, although of the ancient free cities under the Hanseatic League only three retained the peculiar privileges which they enjoyed as free cities up to the end of World War II, namely: Hamburg, Bremen, and Lübeck; Frankfort retained these rights until 1866. These free cities were actually city states, such as Genoa, Florence, and Venice once were.

In the English-speaking countries the cities are the creatures of the state, and they are constantly reminded of their dependence. Until recently it was not unusual for cities in the United States to be obliged to go to the state legislature for permission to make any alterations in the city plan, such as a modification in the lines of a street, the closing of an existing or the laying out of a new street, the establishment of a new park, or even in some cases the modification of street details, such as the widening of roadways by reducing the width of sidewalks. A large proportion of the laws enacted at legislative sessions dealt with details of this

kind, which it would be natural to suppose would be determined by the local authorities. In Great Britain special authority of Parliament was required for municipal improvements, especially those involving the expropriation of private property.

During recent decades there has been a disposition to grant American cities a far larger measure of home rule, municipal legislative bodies being authorized to prepare plans for future development and to modify such plans, once adopted, in all their details. Instead of applying to a state legislature for authority to expend money for certain purposes and to issue their obligations for money borrowed, or to recover the cost of improvements by assessment, the cities are now quite generally left to determine these questions for themselves, with the single provision—and that a wise one—that the total city debt may not exceed a certain percentage of the value of real estate within the city as assessed for the purpose of taxation. This percentage varies in different states, and in some cases debt incurred for increasing or improving the water supply is not included in estimating the city's limit of debt-incurring capacity, as municipal water systems are usually self-sustaining and frequently yield a profit. Again, as in New York City, debts incurred for other projects which return enough to care for interest and amortization of the bonds representing their cost, such as the first rapid-transit subway and certain water-front improvements, are also excluded in estimating the limit of bonded indebtedness.

Forms of Home Rule Government

Before discussing legislation that deals specifically with city planning powers, it will be well to review the history of some of the forms of home rule government which give cities basic control over their public works programs.

American cities generally are obliged to conduct their business under charters which define in considerable detail the officers to be elected and appointed and the matters over which such officers shall exercise administrative control. These charters are legislative enactments, and, while many of them are special laws, there is a tendency in some states to prescribe uniform charters for cities of the same class, such class being determined by population. The most notable development of the home rule idea for cities is the "commission" form of government. The first application of this idea was in the city of Galveston. In September, 1900, a violent storm, accompanied by a tidal wave, practically wrecked the city, which is situated on the Gulf of Mexico in an exposed position. The city was already in bad financial condition, and the municipal government was unable to cope with the situation; all the departments and bureaus were paralyzed, and it was soon realized that administration under a city charter, with the limitations imposed by such an instrument, was almost hopeless under such exigent conditions. It is said that in the two years immediately preceding the disaster the city issued some $200,000 in bonds to pay ordinary operating expenses, and that payment for current obligations was made in scrip, cashable only at a discount. The commission plan of government was fully launched in February, 1902, when the bonded debt of the city was about $3,000,000. The new government embarked upon a scheme of permanent improvement which was designed to prevent a recurrence of the disaster which had overtaken Galveston two years before. The most important

of these improvements was the raising of the grade of a considerable portion of the city, at an expense of over $2,000,000, while $225,000 was expended on sea walls and $300,000 on drainage.

In the following decade Galveston successfully financed by bond issues an improvement of its waterworks system and other important municipal projects. In 1898 the assessed valuation of the real estate in the city of Galveston was slightly over $27,000,000, and the tax rate was 1.57 per cent. In 1902, when the commission form of government first became operative, the assessed values had fallen to $20,749,000. In 1913 the assessed values had risen to $36,391,745, and the tax rate, which had risen to 1.68 per cent in 1908, had fallen to 1.10 per cent. The new form of government had proved successful.

Municipal "commission" government is not government by commission, as some of the national or state functions are exercised through commissioners appointed by the executive or created by legislative enactment. The name in general use is said to have been adopted in Galveston for the reason that a majority of the first administrative board were appointed and "commissioned" by the governor of the state to deal with the special conditions existing in that city. Two years later the members of the board were elected, but the name "commission" has persisted. The Galveston commission consisted of five members, one of whom had the title of mayor, although his duties and powers differed little from those of his colleagues. To these men was entrusted the management of the city's affairs, specific functions being assigned to each. The plan worked so satisfactorily in Galveston that it was soon tried in other cities, and at the close of the year 1915 about 400 cities and towns in the United States had adopted it. Des Moines added to the Galveston plan provision for a referendum vote by the people on ordinances, the initiation of municipal legislation by the people, and the recall of elected officials before the expiration of their terms.

Of the 960 United States cities with over 10,000 population in 1936, there were 187, or 19.5 per cent, which had a commission form of

government, although the two preceding decades showed a loss of 11 per cent in the proportion of cities of over 30,000 population
which had this form of government.[1]

The "city manager" plan of government was
inaugurated by Staunton, Virginia, in 1908.
It was established in the city of Dayton, Ohio,
at an election held August 12, 1913. This city,
like Galveston, had been the victim of a great
disaster due to floods in several rivers which
unite within or near the city limits; and while
the idea was already in the air, its adoption
may have been to some extent the result of the
special conditions following this disaster. A
brief abstract of some of the provisions of the
Dayton charter afford a fair idea of its self-
governing features and of the "commission
plan" with the addition of a city manager.

The powers granted to the city included the right
to acquire, construct, lease, operate, and regulate
public utilities; to appropriate the money of the city
for all lawful purposes; to create, provide for, construct, and maintain all things of the nature of public works and improvements; to regulate the construction, height, and material used in all buildings,
and the maintenance and occupancy thereof.

It was stated that the form of government would
be known as the "commission-manager" plan, and
would consist of a commission of five citizens elected
at large. The commission would constitute the governing body and would appoint a chief administrative officer to be known as the city manager.

Any or all of the commissioners or the city manager might be removed from office by the electors,
and the charter stipulated the manner in which such
a recall would be submitted to the voters.

The city manager was the administrative head
of the municipal government and responsible for
the efficient administration of all departments. He
was to be appointed without regard to his political
beliefs, and might or might not be a resident of the
city of Dayton when appointed. He would hold
office at the will of the commission and was subject
to recall.

Departments of law, public service, public welfare, public safety, and finance were provided for,
a director of each to be appointed by the city manager. The commission was authorized to appoint
a city plan board.

Construction and maintenance of all local improvements were placed under control of the commission, which was given the right to levy special
assessments on benefited property, but such assessments were not to exceed the amount of benefits
accruing to any such property. The city should in

no case pay less than one-fiftieth of the total cost
of any local improvement.

Control of subdivision plats, under regulations to
be established by the Director of Public Service,
was provided, and approval of such plats was required before the city could accept as public streets
or alleys any streets or alleys shown thereon, or
expend any public funds for their improvement or
repair.

The manager form of government has gained
rapidly in popularity. It is not confined to
cities or to a municipality with a commission
as its legislative body, being equally adaptable
to a municipality governed by a council or by
a board of trustees. In 1936 about as many
cities of over 10,000 population had city managers as had the ordinary commission form of
government. Laws specifically permitting the
manager system had been adopted in 36 states.[2]

Other "home rule" city charters provide for
varying legislative bodies, such as a City Council, or, as in New York City, a dual body made
up of a Board of Estimate and a City Council.

Early British Town Planning Acts

A pioneer in specific city planning legislation
was the British Town Planning Act of 1909. A
review of its principal provisions and what was
accomplished under it will not be out of place.[3]
While there had long been local and spasmodic
efforts to better such conditions as previously
existed in Lincoln's Inn Fields (described in
Chapter 3, Volume I), the cure of such ills was
expensive, while prevention was cheap. Yet
adequate preventive action continued to be
rare. The British Town Planning Act was designed to stimulate and promote such prevention.

The underlying idea of the act was the prevention of bad development in the future,
rather than the removal of existing evils. For
that reason the act applied primarily to land
in the course of development and likely to be

[1] *Urban Government,* Vol. I, Supplementary Report
of the Urbanism Committee to the National Resources
Committee, 1939, pages 41–44.

[2] *Ibid.*

[3] The following material is taken from the act itself,
official memoranda explaining it, the pages of the
Town Planning Review, and information furnished by
the late Thomas Adams, who was at one time Town
Planning Expert of the Local Government Board and
later Town Planning Adviser to the Canadian Commission of Conservation.

used for building purposes, and only secondarily to land already built upon. The object aimed at was the securing of proper sanitation, amenity, and convenience. It could be availed of by any local authority, and, as soon as application was made to the Local Government Board for authority to prepare a scheme, no compensation was payable in respect of any building erected or contract made which would contravene the proposed scheme. Thus, if it was proposed in the scheme to construct a new arterial road between A and B, the authorities could prevent any building being erected on the line of the proposed road from the moment they applied for permission, that is, before the definite line of the road was agreed upon or made public.

An important consideration evidently in the minds of those who devised this law, which applied not only to every great city but to every town in England, Scotland, and Wales, was that every urban district has a powerful effect upon and is similarly affected by the territory outside its corporate limits. The city plan need not be bounded by the red lines indicating the city or town limits. In the last analysis every part of a thickly settled country either can be included within the limits of a town planning scheme or is so powerfully affected by its proximity thereto that the entire territory will inevitably be influenced by the operation of a town planning law so general in its application. Formerly most projects materially affecting any city, whether that city was great or small, especially one involving the power to acquire land compulsorily, could be carried out only with the express authority of Parliament. Almost the only acts which were quite general in their application were those relating to sanitary housing, such as the Housing of the Working Class Act of 1890 and its several amendments.

The opening section of the 1909 act defined its objective as "securing proper sanitary conditions, amenity, and convenience in connection with the laying out and use of the land and of any neighboring lands." The area which might be included in a scheme was any land in the course of development or likely to be used for building or for open spaces, roads, streets, parks, pleasure grounds, or incidental

works, and could include land already built upon and even land not likely to be used for building purposes if it was so situated that it ought to be included in the scheme.

The Local Government Board was authorized to prescribe provisions for carrying out the general objects of town planning schemes, these objects being given in the widest terms in a schedule incorporated in the act. This schedule included the laying out and improvement of streets and roads and the closing or diversion of existing highways; the erection of buildings and other structures; the provision of open spaces, both private and public; the preservation of objects of historical interest or natural beauty; the construction of sewerage, drainage, and sewage-disposal facilities; the provision of lighting; the development of water supply; the extinction of private rights of way or other easements; the disposal of land acquired by the local authorities; the removal, alteration, or demolition of any work which would obstruct the carrying out of the scheme; the making of agreements by the local authorities with owners and by owners with each other; the right of the local authorities to accept any money or property for the furtherance of the object of any town planning scheme, and the regulation of the administration of such money or property; the limitation of time for the operation of the scheme; the co-operation of the local authorities with the owners of land included in the scheme; and the imposition upon land that would be increased in value by the operation of a town planning scheme of the sum to be paid on account of that increase in value.

A town planning scheme under the act could originate in any one of three different ways:

1. Land-owners might formulate a scheme which the Local Government Board could authorize, or after public inquiry could compel the local authority to adopt.
2. Any representation might be made to the Local Government Board that a scheme ought to be prepared by a local authority, and the board could, after public inquiry, order a scheme to be so prepared.
3. A local authority might prepare a scheme if a *prima facie* case was made out and the sanction of the Local Government Board obtained.

A scheme proposed and adopted by any local authority could not become effective unless it was first approved by the Local Government Board, which could refuse its approval except with such modifications and subject to such conditions as it saw fit to impose.

The expenses which could be incurred by a local authority included: (1) the cost of preparing and promoting a scheme to be charged in the general tax of the district; (2) the cost of acquiring land for the purpose of carrying out a scheme; and (3) compensation allowed the land owners for injury, but not including any allowance for the limitation the adopted scheme might impose as to the number, height, or character of buildings which might be erected.

The 1909 act was amended in 1919 and again in 1925. In 1932 the scope of the planning law was widened, and the old act was superseded by the more comprehensive Town and Country Planning Act described later in this chapter (see page 146).

Both the 1909 act and a Liverpool act of 1908 went considerably further than any current American practice. The Liverpool act provided that the Liverpool Corporation might require any land owner who proposed to develop his property to submit a general scheme for such development, and it might require streets to be of a prescribed width, with the provision that compensation had to be paid if a main thoroughfare was required to be more than 80 feet wide, or any other street more than 36 feet wide, which was known as the by-law width. That is, the city might require for main thoroughfares the giving, without compensation, of sufficient land to provide a street not more than 80 feet in width, and compensation was paid only for the area taken in excess of this width, while for subsidiary streets no compensation was paid except for a width of over 36 feet. The corporation was further authorized to require buildings to be set back any distance from the street, with the proviso that if that distance was more than one-tenth the width of the street, compensation had to be made. It will be seen that under this law the city of Liverpool might without cost to the taxpayers require buildings in a new main thoroughfare to be placed 96 feet apart, and in other new streets 43.2 feet apart.

The corporation was also given the power to prescribe new building lines in old streets, and might require the owners to pull down existing buildings in order to widen a street, in which event compensation was, of course, paid to the owner; but such compensation was reduced by the amount of betterment which accrued to the land owner in each case. The corporation was also authorized to negotiate with land owners for a give-and-take line for straightening streets and for the setting apart of land for a public park or open space in exchange for the execution of new street improvements by the corporation without expense to the property owners. The granting of these liberal powers to the city of Liverpool was unprecedented, and the act was adopted only after protracted debate and in the face of considerable opposition.

The extent to which the 1909 Town Planning Act was put to work and the accomplishments under it are revealed by figures in a monthly statement of the Ministry of Health, made as of June 1, 1922. Up to that date 170 separate local authorities had worked on 282 schemes involving a combined area of 745,936 acres. Of these, 143 had been authorized by the Local Government Board in accordance with the original act. In accordance with the 1919 amendment, 12 had received final approval and four preliminary approval from the Ministry of Health. The schemes involved areas varying from a few acres to several thousand acres.

As an example of the kind of restrictions imposed by these schemes upon the owners of property there is given in Appendix A the provisions in the scheme advanced by the Ruislip-Northwood Urban District Council, made available through the kindness of Thomas Adams. The territory covered by this scheme is northwest of London proper in Middlesex County, on the edge of what is known as Greater London, and covers an area of 5,906 acres. The Local Government Board decided that the restrictions as to height and character of buildings and space about buildings were so reasonable that no compensation would be allowed the owners of the property by reason of such restrictions.

American Planning Legislation of 1913 and 1914

General planning legislation on the American continent dates from 1913 in both Canada and the United States.

In that year the Province of Alberta, Canada, enacted enabling legislation under which town planning schemes could be prepared for the whole area of any city in the province. Provisions were made for carrying out the plan, for financing, for requirement of five per cent of the area of new subdivisions for public parks, and for controlling the space about buildings, their character, and their height. The Minister of Municipalities could force any backward city to make or execute a town planning scheme. A more complete summary of its provisions will be found in Appendix B.[4]

In the following year, 1914, the Dominion of Canada adopted a general town planning act prepared by a committee appointed by the Commissioner of Conservation. It established a board under the Department of Municipal Affairs to administer the act. This board was given power to advise, approve or alter, and confirm plans submitted by local boards or other bodies. Only the chairman of the central board, who also acted as the executive head of its staff, was salaried.

Every municipal authority was authorized to create a local housing and town planning board consisting of the mayor, the municipal engineer, and the health officer, and not less than two rate-payers, to be appointed for two years, one of them preferably an architect and the other a financier. This board was given power to acquire, receive, hold, sell, lease, and dispose of lands and any interest therein. The municipal authority creating this board also had the power to appoint a housing and town planning commissioner, who would be the executive officer of the local board. It was the duty of such local board to prepare and constantly keep up a comprehensive plan of the whole territory, showing tentative schemes in both its developed

[4] See also "The New Alberta, Canada, Town Planning Act," by James W. Davidson, *Proceedings of the Fifth National Conference on City Planning,* Chicago, 1913, on which Appendix B is based.

and its undeveloped portions for facilitating the advancement of permanent improvements in sanitation, transportation, conservation, and beautification of the municipality. The general act further provided that expenses incurred in preparing a scheme be paid out of current revenue or from the proceeds of a special tax not to exceed one-fiftieth of one per cent of the assessed values of municipalities having a population of under 200,000, and one one-hundredth of one per cent of the assessed value in the case of municipalities having over 200,000 population.

In general, this 1914 Canadian act appears to have been based on the 1909 British Town Planning Act, with some simplification of procedures, but in other respects it closely followed the Alberta act.

The states of New York and New Jersey were the first of the United States to adopt general legislation authorizing cities to appoint planning commissions. Both acts were adopted in 1913.

The New Jersey act provided that the mayor of any city of the first class could appoint a city plan commission to consist of not more than nine citizens, while any commissions already existing were continued, but with the powers and duties conferred by the act upon commissions created under it. It became the duty of such commissions to prepare from time to time plans for the systematic and further development of the city. They could consider and investigate any project tending to the development and betterment of the city and make such recommendations as they deemed advisable concerning the adoption thereof to any department of the municipal government. All questions concerning the location and architectural design of any work of art, statue, or memorial within the city had to be referred to the commission for its consideration and report before final action was taken. All plats or replats of land within the city limits had to be submitted to the commission before they were approved, although approval by the commission was not required.

The New York act authorized any city or incorporated village to create a city or village planning commission, such commissions in cities of the first class to consist of not more than eleven, in cities of the second class of not more than nine, and in cities of the third class and incorporated villages of not more than seven members; not more than one-third of the members in any commission could hold any other public office. The legislative body of the municipality creating a planning commission could at any time provide that, before the municipal board or officer having final authority took action, any one or more or the following matters should be referred to the planning commission for its report: the adoption of any map or plan, including plans for drainage, sewers, water systems, or water-front development or public structures thereon; the location of public buildings, bridges, statues, or monuments, highways, parks, playgrounds, or any other public open spaces.

This New York act also had two important new features. The first authorized the planning commission to map and study areas beyond the municipal boundaries but closely related thereto. The other, in connection with control of subdivisions involving new streets, authorized ordinances to forbid the filing of such maps in any office of public record until a copy of the plan, plat, or description had been submitted to and approved by the planning commission.

Modern State Enabling Acts for Municipal Planning

Modern state enabling legislation authorizing municipalities in a state to engage in comprehensive planning had its genesis in the provisions added to the Village Law and the General City Law of New York State on April 30, 1926, and added to the Town Law of New York State one year later. The bills on which this action was based were sponsored by a citizens' committee which had the active support of the Regional Plan of New York and Its Environs and the aid of Edward M. Bassett, the head of the Legal Division of the Regional Plan.

These new laws were designed to find solutions to certain fundamental planning problems, described by the Regional Plan as follows: [5]

1. Confusion resulting from a failure to understand the difference between public and private streets, and the fact that the latter are a form of "private easement."
2. The need of better understanding of the means of establishing public streets, which include: offer by the owner and acceptance by the city of a deed to the street, acquisition by the city through condemnation under the rights of eminent domain, and dedication through performance by the city of construction of utilities or other acts of public control which would indicate its acceptance of the street.
3. Inadequate street widths and street layouts not conforming with adjoining subdivisions, because of the absence of any official maps showing municipal plans for future streets and parks.
4. The instability of mapped streets and the practice of erecting buildings in the beds of such streets.
5. The need of a master plan, prepared by an advisory agency, to show the future requirements and to provide the basis of advice to the legislative body.
6. The need of an adequate system of well-placed small parks.
7. The importance of combining platting of land with zoning.

The New York laws provide practically identical powers for cities, villages, and towns, and together make the planning process available to all parts of the state. A brief summary of their provisions follows: [6]

Official map. The legislative body is authorized to adopt an "official map" which it can amend or add to at any time. This official map shall show the streets, highways, and parks theretofore laid out, adopted, and established by law. In towns this official map applies only to unincorporated areas within the town, leaving to any village therein the right to prepare and adopt its own official map.

Creation and appointment of planning board. In each case the legislative body may create by resolution or ordinance a planning board of five members with overlapping terms. The city and village laws provide for the continuing of any commission existing under previous laws. The chairman is to be

[5] See *Neighborhood and Community Planning,* Regional Survey of New York and Its Environs, Vol. VII, 1929, pages 292–296.

[6] See *Local Planning and Zoning Powers and Procedures in the State of New York,* Division of State Planning, Albany, N. Y., 1939, prepared by Harold M. Lewis, Consultant. The following summary of New York legislation draws on this report. Later editions, entitled *Local Planning and Zoning,* were prepared and published by Bureau of Planning, Department of Commerce, 1942, and July, 1945.

appointed by the mayor of a city, the board of trustees of a village, and the town board of a town.

Employees and expenses. The board has the power to employ experts and the required staff and to incur other necessary expenditures provided they all come within the appropriation made for the board each year by the legislative body.

Official map changes. The legislative body may not make any change in the official map before referring it to the planning board for report, but such report must be made within thirty days to be considered.

Special and general reports. The legislative body may also refer any matter other than an official map change to the planning board for a special report. The planning board may also, on its own initiative, make such investigations, maps, reports, and recommendations in connection therewith as it deems desirable.

Approval of plats.[7] The legislative body may by ordinance or resolution authorize the planning board to approve plats showing new streets or highways. A public hearing must be held by the board on each such proposal, and the board may either approve, modify and approve, or disapprove the plat. The showing on the plat of a park or parks suitably located for playground or other recreation purposes may be made a requisite for approval. The board shall require that the streets be such as to afford adequate light, air, and access of fire-fighting equipment and shall take into consideration the prospective character of the development, whether dense residence, open residence, business, or industrial.

Record of plats. Where a planning board has been given control over subdivisions by the legislative body creating it, no plat of a subdivision shall be filed in the office of the county clerk or register until it has been approved by such board and such approval endorsed thereon. Every street on such a plat then automatically becomes part of the official map of the municipality, but remains a private street until it is formally accepted as a public street by the local legislative body.

Permits for building in bed of mapped streets. To preserve the integrity of the official map, no permit may be granted for the erection of a building in the bed of any street or highway shown on such map, except that, where this will result in undue hardship to the owner, the board of appeals or other similar board having power to make variances in zoning regulations may, after hearing, permit a building which will increase as little as possible the cost of opening such a street or highway, upon conditions inuring to the benefit of the municipality.

Municipal improvements in streets. No municipal street utility or improvement may thereafter be constructed until the street has been placed on the official map, nor may a permit be issued for the erection of a building unless a highway giving access to it has been placed on the official map. Provision is made for exceptions to the latter requirement

[7] The subject of subdivision control is so important that it is discussed in considerable detail in the following chapter, "Control of Land Subdivisions," pages 150 to 158.

where it would entail practical difficulty or unnecessary hardship.

Changes in zoning regulations by planning board. When approving a subdivision plat the planning board is authorized to either confirm the zoning regulations relating to the land or make a reasonable change therein after a public hearing. The owner may submit with the plat a building plan as the basis for such a zoning change, but such plan shall not involve a greater average density of population than that previously required for the district in which the land is located.

Court review. Adequate provision is made for court review of the acts of the planning board.

These New York laws have since been strengthened and improved by several amendments, mostly involving additional powers which are given to the planning board. The 1938 amendments included provision for a "master plan," which is prepared and adopted by the planning board itself and shall show desirable streets, bridges and tunnels and the approaches thereto, viaducts, parks, public reservations, roadways in parks, sites for public buildings and structures, zoning districts, pierhead and bulkhead lines, waterways, routes of public utilities, and "such other features, existing and proposed, as will provide for the improvement" of the city, village, or town "and its future growth, protection, and development, and will afford adequate facilities for the public housing, transportation, distribution, comfort, convenience, public health, safety, and general welfare of its population." The planning board may hold public hearings before adopting any part of the master plan, but is not required to do so. Such master plan provisions are essential parts of all modern planning legislation.

Another important part of the 1938 amendments is the right to require the installation of improvements before final approval of a subdivision plat. Under these provisions the planning board may insist "that all streets or other public places shown on such plats shall be suitably graded and paved, and that sidewalks, street-lighting standards, curbs, gutters, street trees, water mains, sanitary sewers, and storm drains or combined sewers shall be installed, all in accordance with standards, specifications, and procedure" acceptable to the appropriate municipal departments, or, alternatively, that a performance bond sufficient to cover the full cost of these, as estimated by the planning board or other appropriate municipal departments designated by the planning board, shall be furnished to the city, village, or town by the owner. If, during the term of such an improvement bond, the planning board shall decide that the extent of building development in the subdivision has either not been sufficient to warrant all the improvements contemplated or requires additional improvements, the planning board may, after public hearing, modify its requirements accordingly.

In a city or village these modifications may require either an increase or decrease in the improvements required, and the face value of the performance bond shall thereupon be increased or reduced by an appropriate amount. In a town only such modifications may be made as will reduce the requirements, and the performance bond shall thereupon be reduced by an appropriate amount.

Municipalities in other states have, in some cases, required installation of utilities under the general provision in their state laws authorizing them to adopt and enforce regulations for the control of subdivisions. New York was the first state to specify in detail the form of such prerequisites.

The country-wide adoption of adequate state legislation for municipal planning was speeded and guided by the preparation of a standard act by the United States Department of Commerce.[8] This act provides for both a "municipal plan" (corresponding to the "official map" in the New York legislation) and a "master plan," gives the planning commission extraterritorial control over subdivisions within five miles of the corporate limits of the municipality, and authorizes the commission to include in its regulations for control of subdivisions the required installation of streets and other utilities before final approval.

Zoning Legislation

The subject of zoning has been dealt with in Chapter 12, Volume I, where it was pointed out

that zoning is an essential part of city planning. This chapter also discussed some of the recent trends in zoning standards and legislation.

Like planning, the zoning powers of a municipality are based on enabling legislation adopted by the state. After the establishment of zoning in New York City in 1916, several states adopted enabling acts allowing municipalities therein to adopt comprehensive zoning regulations. The United States Department of Commerce took a leading part in promoting sound zoning legislation, as it did in the field of planning. Its Advisory Committee on Zoning published both a *Zoning Primer*, referred to in Chapter 12, Volume I, and a standard state enabling act,[9] which was used extensively throughout the country.

It is possible to provide in a single act for the zoning of all types of governmental areas within the state, either incorporated or unincorporated, and this has been done in many cases. New York and Pennsylvania, on the other hand, have provided separate enabling acts for different kinds of municipalities. In each case, as in planning legislation, the acts are permissive only, but any municipality adopting a zoning ordinance must make it conform closely to the provisions of the enabling act for its state if it is to be sustained by the courts.

Considerable variety will be found in the content and sequence of zoning ordinances. They will vary with the character of the community, the complexity of its land use pattern, and the legal status of zoning in the state. An arrangement found suitable by the author in a moderate-sized community is as follows:

TITLE AND STATEMENT OF ENACTMENT
   I. Short title.
  II. Definitions.
 III. Designation of districts.
 IV. Use regulations for residence districts (separate subhead for each type of district).
  V. Height and area regulations for residence districts.
     Height.
     Area of lot.

[8] *A Standard City Planning Enabling Act*, by the Advisory Committee on City Planning and Zoning, United States Department of Commerce, 1928.

[9] *A Standard State Zoning Enabling Act under Which Municipalities May Adopt Zoning Regulations*, Advisory Committee on Zoning, United States Department of Commerce, Revised Edition, 1926.

Building setback lines.
Side yards.
Rear yards.

VI. Use regulations for business districts (separate subhead for each type of district).

VII. Height and area regulations for business districts.
Height.
Building setback lines.
Side yards.
Rear yards.
Offstreet loading, unloading, and parking space.

VIII. Use regulations for industrial districts (separate subhead for each type of district).

IX. Height and area regulations for industrial districts.
Height.
Building setback lines.
Rear yards.
Offstreet parking space.

X. Special regulations for garages and public automobile filling stations.

XI. General provisions (applying to all or several districts).
Non-conforming uses and buildings.
Restoration of existing buildings.
Courts.
Site plans for large residential developments.
Miscellaneous.

XII. Board of appeals.

XIII. Interpretation and administration.
Interpretation of regulations.
Enforcement and penalties.
Filing of plans; building permits.
Certificate of occupancy.
Fees.

XIV. Amendments.

XV. Validity.

XVI. Repeal of inconsistent ordinances.

XVII. Date when effective.

The building zone map, showing the boundaries of the areas within the different types of districts, is legally a part of the zoning ordinance and should be referred to as such in the ordinance. In some small suburban communities there may be only a single type of residence district; in a large city there may be as many as a dozen different types, varying from a highly restricted one-family district requiring minimum lots of an acre or more to districts where large multi-family structures and relatively high densities are permitted.

County and Regional Planning

Legislation for county and regional planning has been adopted either as special acts relating to specific counties or groups of local governments, or as state-wide enabling acts. Most of the official county and regional planning commissions fall in the latter classification.

The enabling acts for county and regional planning are quite similar to those for municipal planning, but with the emphasis on county-financed projects and general use of land studies; little if any control over the subdivision of land is provided. The County Planning Enabling Act adopted by New Jersey in 1935 has a provision requiring any local authority which has the power to approve plats to transmit the proposed plat to the county planning board, which shall be given 20 days to make a report thereon. The local authority, however, retains the right of final decision as to approval or disapproval.

This New Jersey act also provides that any group of municipalities, either independently or in co-operation with one or more county boards of freeholders, may establish a regional planning board to plan any region defined by such a group.

County planning agencies have also been established under county charters, the procedure followed in Westchester and Nassau counties in New York State. The Nassau County charter had some novel planning features, but while it became effective in 1937, it was not until several years later that the County Planning Commission authorized thereunder was appointed. While the chief function of the planning commission is the preparation of a master plan for the county, it is also given the power to pass upon improvements within those parts of cities or villages within 300 feet of any boundary thereof which adjoins a portion of the county for which the county commission has adopted a master plan. Likewise, the approval of the County Planning Commission is required for any future zoning ordinances in so far as they affect territory within 300 feet of a town boundary.

Recent British Planning Legislation

British planning legislation superseding the pioneer British Town Planning Act of 1909, described earlier in this chapter (pages 138 to

140), includes a series of acts starting with the Town and Country Planning Act of 1932. This broadened the 1909 act to cover planning of urban as well as rural areas and facilitated the acquisition of land for garden cities. It also extended zoning to built-up areas, and it aimed at control of premature subdivision of vacant lands by authorizing a use zone in which land could be restricted against general development. Powers for regional or joint bodies were enlarged.

There then followed a series of reports by special agencies which provided the basis for further legislation. They were the Royal Commission on the Distribution of the Industrial Population (later known as the Barlow Commission), dealing with urban problems; the Scott Committee, dealing with problems of the countryside; and the Uthwatt Committee, which reported on the financial problems of planned development and reconstruction. Each of these recommended a separate Ministry for planning. World War II, starting about the time the Barlow Commission reported, seems to have accentuated planning progress in England and to have emphasized the need for greater national participation in that field.

As a result of these reports the policy was adopted of redistributing industry through Great Britain, of limiting the population in certain areas, and of moving the people out of present congested centers, part of this exodus to be used in establishing new towns. The first major step to reach these objectives was the new Town and Country Planning Act of 1944 (preceded by an Interim Act of 1943). There was created a Ministry of Town and Country Planning in the British Government. The 1944 act had the following four primary purposes: [10]

a. To give local authorities a simpler and more expeditious procedure for the compulsory purchase of land.
b. To enable local planning authorities to dispose of land acquired under the act for development

[10] See "The British Town and Country Planning Act," by W. S. Morrison, Minister of Town and Country Planning, *The American City,* April, 1945, pages 65–67; also "The Work and Establishment of the Ministry of Town and Country Planning," by the same author, *Journal of the American Institute of Planners,* Vol. XI, No. 1, 1945, pages 5–9.

by private individuals or to enable them to develop such land themselves in order to secure its best use.
c. To make provision for financial assistance from the central government towards the redevelopment of war-damaged areas and associated "overspill" areas.
d. To restrict the price paid to owners whose land is compulsorily acquired under the act by reference to 1939 prices.

The new Ministry was organized with divisions dealing with establishment, public relations, legislation, plans, and research. It aimed at joint activity and mutual support by local and central planning authorities.

The New Towns Act of 1946 authorizes the creation of public corporations (comparable to the Tennessee Valley Authority in the United States), appointed and entirely financed by the government, to plan and develop a series of new satellite towns. It is proposed to start about twenty such projects over a 10-year program and to use about 10 per cent of all building labor in their construction. Some of the specifications set up for these towns and the progress made up to 1947 on the program have been described in Chapter 18, "Decentralization of Industry and Residence" (page 114). The site of any new town could include as its nucleus the area of an existing town.

A new Town and Country Planning Act of 1947 provides a consolidation of all former planning powers of the government. It also sets up a new planning system which, according to the White Paper which accompanied the bill, "for the first time makes practical such projects as the reconstruction and redevelopment of old towns, the preservation of green belts, provision of open space in overcrowded areas, the allocation of land for factories, etc." Every part of England is to have a plan in three years; the planning areas are larger than before. The Ministry of Town and Country Planning is to establish ten regional offices in addition to its London headquarters. Each of these must prepare "planning summaries." Seven interdepartmental regional committees are established.

A second part of the 1947 act deals with compensation and betterment, the latter term meaning increases in value due to public actions. All development rights of undeveloped land are to be acquired in the name of the government, and a sum of £300,000,000 was set aside to pay for such rights over all of Great Britain. The present value is, in effect, made the new use value, and the proportion of any increased values (betterment) to be collected by the government will be determined by the Minister. Haphazard building is forbidden, and local planning made compulsory. The act has many controversial features, and American city planners will be interested in seeing how it works out.

Urban Redevelopment Legislation

The general problems of urban redevelopment were discussed in Chapter 15, "Redevelopment of Blighted Areas," including reference to some of the legislation aimed at promoting such programs.

The first state enabling act of this type was the Redevelopment Corporation Law of New York, adopted in 1941. The basic philosophy of this law, as described by Thomas S. Holden, chairman of the committee of the Commerce and Industry Association of New York which drafted it, was "the principle of reorganization of the managerial and financial structure of insolvent properties." It provided for the exercise of condemnation in assembling a site, either by a redevelopment corporation or by a city for a corporation, but before instituting condemnation proceedings the corporation must have acquired a majority control (51 per cent by area and by assessed valuation) of the property within the area to be developed. An exemption from taxation on any increased values resulting from the improvement could be granted by the municipality for a period not to exceed 10 years. The act was aimed at encouraging private initiative and private capital to enter the redevelopment field.

The following year, 1942, the New York State Legislature adopted a second act, called the Redevelopment Companies Law, which was liberalized by amendments in 1943. This was framed specifically to encourage life insurance companies to invest in large-scale housing projects. It permitted tax exemption for increased values up to 25 years and the right of condemnation, up to 100 per cent of the needed property, to be exercised by a city as agent for the company.

The status of such legislation, as reported by the Urban Land Institute in August, 1946, has been summarized in Chapter 15 (see page 40). Holden has grouped such acts as based on one of the following concepts: [11]

1. The principles of business reorganization (the 1941 New York law, the Michigan law, the Wisconsin law).
2. The principles of granting powers of eminent domain for public purposes, without financial inducements (Illinois and Kentucky).
3. The principles of limited-dividend housing corporations (the 1942 New York law with 1943 amendments, the Missouri law, the Massachusetts law).
4. The principle of bailing out with subsidies (the Maryland law and, as an incidental but not primary feature, the Wisconsin and Missouri laws).

One of the latest enabling acts is the District of Columbia Redevelopment Law (Senate 1426), sponsored by the National Capital Park and Planning Commission and prepared with the advice of the late Alfred Bettman.

It is agreed among city planners that comprehensive master planning should be a part of the procedure of urban redevelopment, and that this should include at least the general location of public utilities for transportation and terminals and the general distribution of land uses; that enabling legislation should require and direct the planning agency to make a comprehensive land use plan; that redevelopment should be for the best economic use of the land and may well include business and industrial structures as well as housing; that public housing, where required, may form part of a redevelopment project; and that proceeds from any redevelopment areas within a municipality or urban area should be pooled in determining the justification of the program.

[11] *Postwar Urban Redevelopment,* by Thomas S. Holden, statement at Conference on Urban Problems, United States Chamber of Commerce, Washington, D. C., September 29, 1943.

Local Procedures

The final determination of local plans should, under American procedures, be retained by the municipality. In many cases the translation from plan to reality seems disappointingly slow. The need for patience and co-operation has been pointed out as follows by the late Robert H. Whitten:

> The formal confirmation of a tentative comprehensive plan will come slowly. It will probably be inexpedient to ask for an official confirmation of any but the most essential parts of a comprehensive plan developed by the city plan office. The city plan office in formulating its picture of the future city will consider many facts and factors that will necessarily have an important bearing upon its comprehensive plan and which may be tentatively included in the plan, and which it would be unnecessary and inexpedient to submit for official confirmation. . . .
>
> The city plan office should realize at the start that its one big job is the development of a comprehensive plan; that it will not usually be in a position to make a unique contribution to the solution of particular problems until it has this comprehensive picture of the future city. It should, therefore, guard against frittering its time away on numberless apparently urgent and immediate problems and thus lose the opportunity of ever becoming the real controlling force in shaping the future city. This does not mean that the city plan office may not with propriety advise in regard to questions where its preliminary studies show that failure to act would imperil the probable future plan.[12]

Many of the larger cities have established art commissions or juries, the function of which is to examine and report upon the location of and plans for important buildings, bridges, and other monumental structures and all works of art, such as fountains, monuments, and statues. The question is frequently raised as to whether or not such functions should be combined with or merged in those of the officer, board, or commission having control of the city plan. The two problems, however, are quite distinct. An art commission or jury should be composed of art experts, but the kind of ability and experience required to pass judgment upon the city plan is very different, and more satisfactory results have been secured where these functions have been kept entirely separate.

[12] "Constitution and Powers of a City Planning Authority," by Robert H. Whitten, *Proceedings of the Seventh National Conference on City Planning,* Detroit, June 7–9, 1915, pages 140–141.

Among other types of legislative control related to planning and zoning, but done by local ordinance under police powers, are regulation of automobile trailers, licensing and control of offstreet parking facilities, and special regulations for business signs. In Southern California the growth of trailer parks has been so rapid that some city and county planning commissions have dealt with them as subdivisions of land and set up special standards to which they must conform.

Selected References

A Standard City Planning Enabling Act (prepared by Advisory Committee on City Planning and Zoning), United States Department of Commerce, Government Printing Office, Washington, D. C., 1928.

BASSETT, EDWARD M., FRANK B. WILLIAMS, ALFRED BETTMAN, and ROBERT WHITTEN: *Model Laws for Planning Cities, Counties, and States,* Vol. VII, Harvard City Planning Studies, Harvard University Press, Cambridge, Mass., 1935.

BETTMAN, ALFRED (edited by ARTHUR C. COMEY): *City and Regional Planning Papers,* Vol. XIII, Harvard City Planning Studies, Harvard University Press, Cambridge, Mass., 1946. (Chapters 18–20 inclusive deal with urban redevelopment legislation.)

BLACK, RUSSELL VAN NEST (assisted by MARY HEDGES BLACK): *Building Lines and Reservations for Future Streets,* Vol. VIII, Harvard City Planning Studies, Harvard University Press, Cambridge, Mass., 1935.

Local Planning and Zoning—a Manual of Powers and Procedures for Citizens and Government Officials, Bureau of Planning, New York State Department of Commerce, Albany, N. Y., July, 1945.

Municipal and County Planning Legislation and Procedures in New Jersey, New Jersey State Planning Board, Trenton, N. J., Revised September, 1939.

Questions

1. What is the fundamental difference between the powers of cities on the continent of Europe and in the United States?
2. Describe trends in the twentieth century which have given municipalities in the United States increased control over the various elements of a city plan.
3. Describe a typical "commission" form of city government.
4. What were some of the principal provisions of the British Town Planning Act of 1909? How could a town planning scheme be initiated under this act?
5. What were some of the fundamental planning problems which the modern state enabling acts,

as initiated in New York in 1926, were designed to solve?

6. How can the integrity of the master plan and the official map be preserved?

7. What are the principal elements of a master plan as described under modern state enabling legislation?

8. What types of enabling legislation have provided for municipal zoning?

9. What is the relationship between a zoning ordinance and a building zone map?

10. What provisions have state legislatures made for county and regional planning?

11. What new types of planning powers are provided for in British legislation, as consolidated in the Town and Country Planning Act of 1947?

12. What types of state legislation have been adopted to promote urban redevelopment?

13. What other types of legislative control, closely related to planning and zoning, may be adopted by municipalities under their general police powers?

21

CONTROL OF LAND SUBDIVISIONS

BEFORE THE TURN OF THE TWENTIETH CENTURY, the right to make such use of private property as seemed most advantageous to the owner, until the property were taken from him by due process of law, was taken for granted. Nearly all cities have suffered from the exercise of this alleged right, as outlined in Chapter 12, Volume I, but owners were, until recently, disposed to insist on complete freedom of action in the subdivision of property as well as the use to which it should be put. The first general recognition that control of character of development aids stability and improves the sale value of subdivided property was apparent in the use of private deed restrictions. However, the deed restriction principally controls the character of development which may take place on the individual parcel after its sale, without regard for the quantitative or qualitative aspects of subdivision of land as such. It is therefore more closely related to zoning than to subdivision control.

Results of Lack of Control

Unrestricted subdivision of land has had very serious and far-reaching effects on communities in most metropolitan areas of the United States. These results may be classified into two types: effect on the physical plan, and effect on the finances and general development of the municipality. The effect on the physical plan is the more obvious of the two. Unintelligent subdivision has resulted in some very bad street systems, with inadequate thoroughfares, lack of separation of through and local traffic, un-matched streets, leaving dead-ends and small jogs, lack of conformity to topography, resulting in excessive grades and dead-ends, excessive street area, and undesirable block sizes. In addition, lot shapes and dimensions have been wasteful and undesirable, with inadequate widths, excessive depths, and frequent acute-angle corners. Again, disregard of topography has had unfortunate results in lots of excessive slopes, impossible of access, or at elevations lower than would permit connection with economical sewer lines in streets. Large areas have been subdivided without allowance for public recreation facilities, schools, community centers, and other essential areas of public use. Figure 21·1 shows a section of Syracuse, New York, in which most of the bad results of uncontrolled subdivision may be found.

Speculation in land, an established American practice, resulted in many fly-by-night operators buying acreage at a low figure, subdividing on paper, regardless of the suitability of the property for such development, and selling these "building lots" by any high-pressure methods they could devise, counting on clearing a profit with the sale of a small proportion of the total number of lots in the subdivision. When sales showed signs of slacking off on a given "development," the operator left that subdivision to start a new one elsewhere. Since such promotions usually were financed by arrangement with the owner, the promoter had no investment in the land, and therefore no interest in any phase of the development of the area beyond selling enough lots to make a quick profit. The owner was left with a piece of property spotted by small holdings of other individuals which frequently made the remainder useless, because of its shape, for any purpose could make no use of his land. Frequently the original owner lost his holdings in the subdivision at tax sale. When this happened, the white

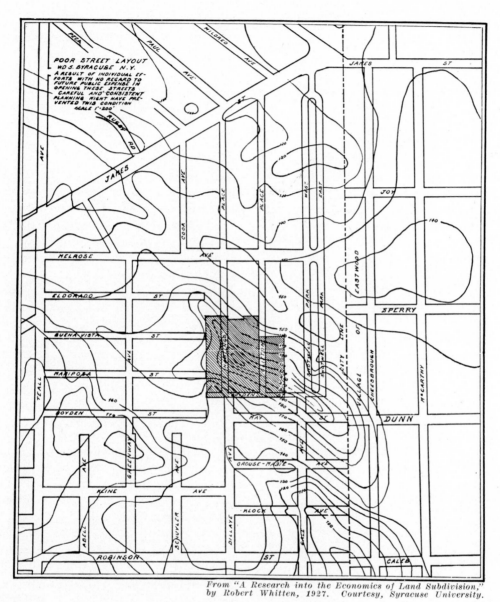

From "A Research into the Economics of Land Subdivision,"
by Robert Whitten, 1927. Courtesy, Syracuse University.

FIGURE 21·1. RESULTS OF IMPROPER SUBDIVISION IN A SECTION OF SYRACUSE, NEW YORK
Hatched area in center shows property acquired by the city through tax-payment defaults.

except building lots, which often never would be needed as such. Furthermore, most of the desirable lots already had been sold by the developer. The land was now assessed as building lots instead of acreage, which increased the taxes on the owner, yet in many instances he

elephant became the burden of the city, county, or state, and the taxpayers were the losers.

The taxpayers also lost in other ways. A few of the purchasers of lots in the above-described subdivisions actually built homes on their land. They wanted public services—water, sewers, street paving, sidewalks, lighting, etc.—and so petitioned the municipality, which thereupon constructed some or all of these improvements. The cost of such construction frequently was assessed on the benefited properties, many of which were vacant. Many holders of indi-

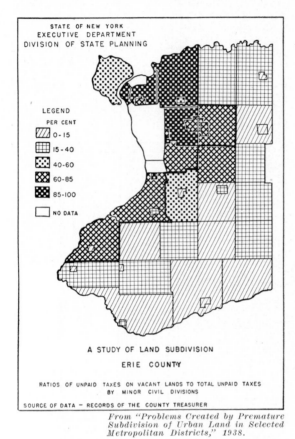

STATE OF NEW YORK
EXECUTIVE DEPARTMENT
DIVISION OF STATE PLANNING

LEGEND

PER CENT

0 - 15

15 - 40

40 - 60

60 - 85

85 - 100

NO DATA

A STUDY OF LAND SUBDIVISION

ERIE COUNTY

RATIOS OF UNPAID TAXES ON VACANT LANDS TO TOTAL UNPAID TAXES
BY MINOR CIVIL DIVISIONS

SOURCE OF DATA — RECORDS OF THE COUNTY TREASURER

From "Problems Created by Premature Subdivision of Urban Land in Selected Metropolitan Districts," 1938.

FIGURE 21·2. TAX DELINQUENCY IN ERIE COUNTY, NEW YORK, IN 1936

In the eight towns suburban to the city of Buffalo, tax arrears on vacant property amounted to almost 90 per cent of total accumulated tax arrears.

vidual vacant properties found the taxes more than they wished to pay; those parcels became tax delinquent, and eventually the burden of that delinquency fell upon the taxpayers of the city, county, or state, depending on the working of the tax law in the particular locality. In effect, the taxpayers in already developed areas were forced to pay for public improvements of no use to them and of very little use to anyone else, since vast numbers of building lots in "sour" subdivisions never have been improved.

The extent of this problem in some urban and suburban areas is staggering. In the unincorporated portion of the town of Tonawanda in Erie County, New York, adjacent to the city of Buffalo, the following conditions were found in 1936 for lots in recorded subdivisions only: [1]

Of 27,422 lots, 25,258, or over 92 per cent, were vacant.

Of total assessed values of $15,882,245, $7,216,000, or over 45 per cent, was on vacant lots.

Of the vacant lots, 20,828, or almost 83 per cent, were tax delinquent.

Of total accumulated arrears of taxes and special assessments for 1934 and prior years amounting to $2,987,546, $2,897,552, or over 97 per cent, was on vacant lots.

These accumulated arrears on vacant lots amounted to over 40 per cent of the total assessed value of all vacant lots.

A similar situation was found in the Detroit metropolitan area in 1938, although exactly comparable figures cannot be given because of special provisions in that state which allowed tax moritoria and deferred payments as a result of the economic depression of 1929–1936. In the unincorporated portions of the towns of Dearborn, Nankin, Redford, and Taylor, Michigan, at the tax sale of 1938 (which did not include properties in arrears on which deferred payments were being made) 66.5 per cent of all lots in subdivisions were advertised. Of those advertised for sale, 98.3 per cent were vacant.[2] Of 68,511 tax deeds held by the state of California in 1937, 64,200, or 93 per cent, were subdivided lots.[3] In the state of New Jersey, the borough of Fort Lee installed extensive public improvements in a considerable subdivided area, which subsequently became tax delinquent (see Figure 21·3). As a result, the borough was unable to pay the interest on its bonds. A bondholders' suit in federal court resulted in the appointment of receivers in about 1940, known as the Board of Liquidation of the Borough of Fort Lee, which

[1] *Problems Created by Premature Subdivision of Urban Lands in Selected Metropolitan Districts,* by Philip H. Cornick, Division of State Planning, Albany, New York, 1938, pages 144–145.

[2] *A Study of Subdivision Development in the Detroit Metropolitan Area,* Michigan Planning Commission, 1938, page 31.

[3] *The Subdivision of Land,* by Robert E. Merriam, American Society of Planning Officials, 1942, page 1.

was given certain strict controls over the finances of the borough. This case is unusual, but such a result has been avoided in other localities only by differences in degree and in the various tax laws.

There are other losses to the community in bad subdivision. The owners of many lots,

estimated that in the United States as many as 15,000,000 vacant lots existed in subdivisions in 1938.[4] At one family per lot, this would be enough for over 55,000,000 persons, as compared with the 1940 population of the United States of about 131,700,000, or half again as many additional families as are expected in

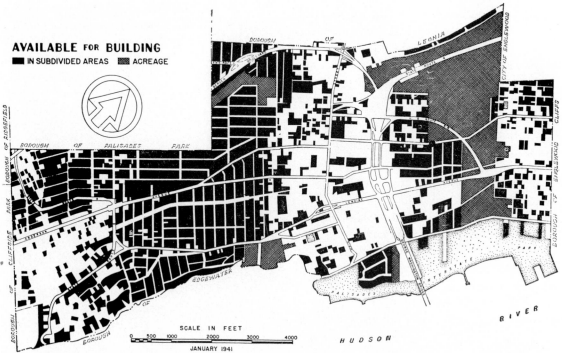

AVAILABLE FOR BUILDING
■ IN SUBDIVIDED AREAS ▨ ACREAGE

SCALE IN FEET
0 500 1000 2000 3000 4000

JANUARY 1941

Courtesy, Regional Plan Association, Inc.

FIGURE 21·3.   UNUSED SUBDIVISIONS IN THE BOROUGH OF FORT LEE, NEW JERSEY, IN 1940

In the vacant subdivided area in the southeast portion of the borough between Anderson and Lemoine avenues all street improvements had been installed.

long since tax delinquent, cannot be found, and as a result clear title is difficult to obtain on such properties. This factor, plus the spotty development which all too often takes place, makes reassembly of subdivided land always difficult and sometimes impossible, thus further discouraging productive use of these uneconomic waste lands. The sparsely distributed houses in "sour" subdivisions still require police and fire protection, mail deliveries, and schools.

Phases of Subdivision Needing Control

Subdivision needs control in a quantitative, as well as a qualitative, sense. It has been

this country in 1960. The vast bulk of these vacant lots is in undeveloped subdivisions, and many never will be used for homes or anything else unless they can be reassembled into large parcels. In some areas there is a legitimate demand for new subdivision, but the supply must be kept in reasonable relationship to the demand if many of the economic wastes discussed in the foregoing section are to be avoided.

With the advancement of neighborhood planning concepts (see Chapter 13, page 3) the demand will be increasingly for larger properties capable of unified development, rather than

[4] *Land Subdivision Manual,* American Society of Civil Engineers, 1939, page 47.

individual lots. Also, as our metropolitan populations approach stability, the necessity for assembling large tracts from many small lots becomes more apparent (see Chapter 15, "Redevelopment of Blighted Areas," page 40), and whereas hitherto the land usually has been subdivided and further subdivided, that process will have to be reversed in many of the older parts of our cities. Our legal and economic machinery, being geared to the established process, does not run smoothly in reverse. Techniques are needed which will facilitate consolidation of properties in order to make useful land in "sour" subdivisions and to permit rehabilitation of blighted areas in accordance with modern neighborhood planning principles.

Adequate and intelligent qualitative control of subdivision is almost impossible without comprehensive land planning. A master plan shows the general requirements of any particular area with reference to the community as a whole, and so sets up general requirements for any property to be subdivided. To assure suitable physical development of a site, the subdivision should be required to conform to adequate standards in the following respects:

1. Conformity with the master plan and official map.
2. Street locations, widths, grades, curves, cross-sections, and improvements.
3. Block and lot shapes, dimensions, and building lines.
4. Open spaces and areas of public use.
5. Public utilities.

Other requirements which will benefit the community are offers of dedication by the subdivider of proposed streets, open spaces, etc., in the subdivision, and performance bonds or other guarantees covering the installation of utilities.

Methods of Subdivision Control

For reasons stated in the previous section, the agency which should have the power to control subdivision is logically the planning board. This is the usual practice, where there is such an agency. The board, when so empowered, adopts regulations and standards for subdivision plats within its jurisdiction, and approval of each plat by the planning board is required before lots can be sold in that subdivision.[5] It is customary to require submission of a preliminary plat to the board for discussion and suggestions, following which a final plat is submitted to, and acted on by, the planning board. To serve as a guide to the prospective subdivider by indicating the type of layout deemed suitable for various acreage areas within their jurisdiction, some planning boards prepare in advance subdivision plans of such areas. Figure 21·4 shows an example of such an advance plan.

Control of the amount of subdivision generally has not been achieved directly as yet. As of the end of 1942, Washington was the only state which prohibited the platting of new subdivisions unless the subdivider could show a need for the proposed development. However, there are regulations and influences which approach this result indirectly. Many subdivision regulations now require the subdivider to pay. for the installation of streets, sidewalks, curbs, sewers, water mains, lighting, etc., within the area subdivided. This eliminates the speculative subdivider to a large extent because too great an investment of capital is required. Furthermore, it encourages relatively complete development of any given area, since the cost of street improvements adds materially to the cost of each lot, reducing the profit margin for the developer, and requiring a higher percentage of sales before expenses are cleared.

The Federal Housing Administration also has had a strong influence on subdivision in an indirect way. Since FHA insurance on a loan results in materially decreased financing costs, most potential home builders want an FHA-insured mortgage. But the FHA will insure loans only in areas which meet their standards, and their standards are high in order to assure stable values. The subdivider, in effect, is required to follow good practice in order to sell his lots.

[5] A set of model land subdivision regulations are given in Appendix C, pages 208 to 211.

Present Extent of Control

The above-mentioned influences, plus a growing public awareness of past real estate bubbles, have resulted in a tendency toward the at least mitigate some of the bad effects on the municipality by keeping the supply of newly subdivided lots more nearly proportional to the demand.

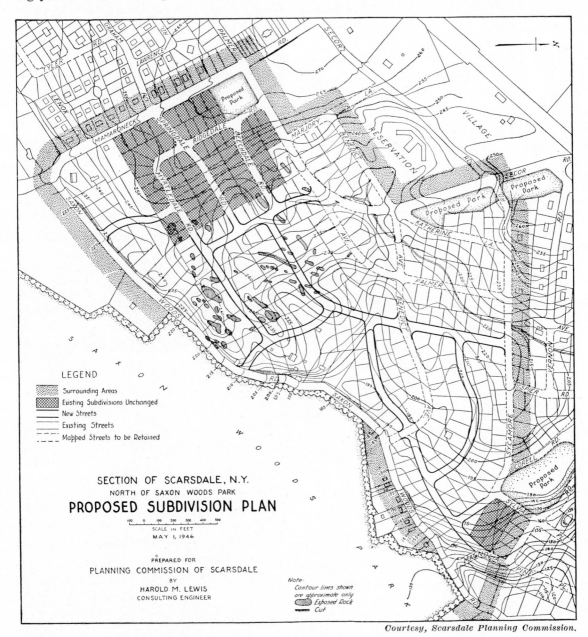

LEGEND

Surrounding Areas
Existing Subdivisions Unchanged
New Streets
Existing Streets
Mapped Streets to be Retained

SECTION OF SCARSDALE, N.Y.
NORTH OF SAXON WOODS PARK
PROPOSED SUBDIVISION PLAN

SCALE IN FEET
MAY 1, 1946

PREPARED FOR
PLANNING COMMISSION OF SCARSDALE
BY
HAROLD M. LEWIS
CONSULTING ENGINEER

Note·
Contour lines shown
are approximate only
Exposed Rock
Cut

Courtesy, Scarsdale Planning Commission.

FIGURE 21·4. SUBDIVISION PLAN FOR AN AREA STILL IN ACREAGE HOLDINGS, MADE BY THE PLANNING BOARD FOR THE GUIDANCE OF POTENTIAL SUBDIVIDERS

bles, have resulted in a tendency toward the sale of completed homes rather than building lots. This practice by no means assures the buyer of fair value for his money, but it does

The National Resources Committee stated that in 1936, of 933 official city planning boards reporting, 275 had mandatory control of subdivision plats; and, of 316 official county, metropolitan, and district planning boards reporting, 20 had mandatory control. Half of the county planning boards exercising mandatory subdivision control were in California.[6] Unquestionably a considerable additional number of planning boards have since acquired such powers. As of September, 1944, some form of subdivision control enabling legislation for municipalities had been enacted by all but six states.[7] The same source showed enabling legislation for county subdivision control in 21 states, and for some form of regional subdivision control in four states. Various regulations differ widely in scope and detail, but the subject is too complex to permit analysis here.[8]

In order to reclaim for some useful purpose abandoned subdivided areas which are tax delinquent, the state of New York has permissive legislation, passed in 1939, aimed at simplifying tax-foreclosure procedure and making it cheap enough to be worth while for relatively low-value property.[9] Under this law, a holder of tax liens on properties on which taxes have been unpaid for four or more years can join in one court action all liens held by him, although they may be on variously owned parcels of property, and receive clear title to such properties in a single judgment. Formerly, separate proceedings were required against each nominal owner of tax-delinquent property, making reassembly of most tax-delinquent subdivided property too expensive to be practical. Under the new law, either an individual or a tax district can be plaintiff in such action.

Legal Aspects

As in all other phases of law, the interpretations of the courts today show a tendency to recognize increasingly the rights of the community over the rights of individual property owners in planning and subdivision control. Nevertheless, certain phases of subdivision control, such as the size of individual lots, have been held not to be a proper part of subdivision regulations, but a part of zoning. The question of definition of a subdivision is important, as it may furnish a legal loophole for the subdivider if the law is not carefully drawn. Authority to regulate platting derives from the police power of the state. Thus individual regulations must promote the community health, safety, morals, or general welfare, and court decisions have held that this power also may be used for the public convenience, general comfort, and prosperity.

The Municipal Planning Act of New Jersey is reasonably typical of state enabling acts. It empowers the governing body of a municipality to appoint a planning board, and provides that:

> The governing body may by ordinance authorize and empower the planning board to adopt regulations governing the subdivision of land within its jurisdiction. . . . Before action is taken [by the planning board], a hearing after notice shall be given. . . . The planning board may thereupon approve, modify and approve, or disapprove such plat, taking due regard to its conformity with the official map. The planning board shall take the action . . . within 30 days from and after the date of the submission of the plat to it for approval . . . otherwise such plat shall be deemed to have been approved.

The law then goes on to provide that the submitted plat may show parks and that the board shall require suitable standards for streets and drainage and shall consider "the prospective character of the development, whether residence, business, or industrial."

The enabling laws of New York State are basically similar, except that they are much more detailed in their standards for subdivision plats, and such standards are mandatory. Furthermore, the New York law requires that installation of all street improvements be made or financially guaranteed by the developer before the plat can be approved by the planning board.[10] Both the New York and New Jersey

[6] "Status of City and County Planning in the United States," *Circular* X, National Resources Committee, May 15, 1937.

[7] According to testimony given before the Senate Subcommittee on Housing and Urban Redevelopment. The exceptions were Florida, Mississippi, Rhode Island, Utah, Vermont, and Wyoming.

[8] A thorough analysis of the subject may be found in *Subdivision Regulations,* by Harold W. Lautner, Public Administration Service, Chicago, 1941.

[9] Article VII-A, Title 3, of the Tax Law of the State of New York.

[10] These provisions were described in considerable detail in Chapter 20 (page 143).

laws prohibit the county clerk from filing any subdivision plat in an area within the jurisdiction of a planning board having authority to approve subdivisions unless the plat has been approved by the board.

The fact that the municipal boundaries often do not include all the area subject to subdivision, the development of which may affect the municipal nucleus, raises the question of jurisdiction outside such municipalities. When the metropolitan area lies entirely within a county or counties which exercise subdivision control, the problem is simply solved, but county subdivision control is not yet common. In some states a more direct approach has been used by granting municipalities extraterritorial control.[11]

Extraterritorial control of subdivision by municipalities is not fully satisfactory. Since the power is granted to minor civil divisions, the problem of overlapping jurisdictions arises where two or more which have adopted subdivision regulation are adjacent. And how shall the distance outside the municipal boundary, in which extraterritorial control is granted, be determined? Furthermore, there is the situation of the metropolitan area which overlaps state lines, such as the New York, Philadelphia, and St. Louis areas. Although subdivision control is a regional problem, region-wide authority in such interstate areas seems to be a very remote possibility (see Chapter 19, "Planning for the Urban Region," pages 133 to 135).

The planning board, in exercising its power of subdivision control, probably exerts its greatest single influence on the welfare of the community. For this reason it is vitally important that the planning board act with a high degree of wisdom and vision. Subdivision regulations should be so drafted as to let the board use discretion, because rigid requirements are too likely to result in rigid plans, without variety and having only negative virtues. Creative ingenuity in design should not be stifled by the regulations nor by the planning

[11] Some degree of control beyond their limits was available in 1944 to municipalities in 31 states, according to testimony given before the Senate Subcommittee on Housing and Urban Redevelopment.

board, provided the unorthodox design can be shown to have advantages over the conventional approach.

Selected References

A Check List for the Review of Local Subdivision Controls, National Housing Agency, Washington, D. C., January, 1947.

A Study of Subdivision Development in the Detroit Metropolitan Area, Michigan Planning Commission, Lansing, Mich., June, 1939.

CORNICK, PHILIP H.: *Premature Subdivision of Urban Areas in Selected Metropolitan Districts,* Division of State Planning, Albany, N. Y., 1938; *Premature Subdivision and Its Consequences,* Institute of Public Administration, Columbia University, New York, 1938.

"Defects of Existing Subdivisions Suggest Need for More Effective Control," *Information Bulletin* 46, Regional Plan Association, Inc., New York, September 18, 1939.

"Land Subdivision," *Manual of Engineering Practice* 16, American Society of Civil Engineers, 1939.

Land Subdivision in New Jersey, New Jersey State Planning Board, Trenton, 1938.

LAUTNER, HAROLD W.: *Subdivision Regulations—an Analysis of Land Subdivision Control Practices,* Public Administration Service, Chicago, 1941.

MERRIAM, ROBERT E.: *The Subdivision of Land—A Guide for Municipal Officials in the Regulation of Land Subdivision,* American Society of Planning Officials, Chicago, October, 1942.

Model Subdivision Regulations (prepared by Advisory Committee on City Planning and Zoning), National Bureau of Standards, Department of Commerce, Washington, D. C., December, 1936.

Neighborhood Design and Control—an Analysis of the Problems of Planned Subdivisions, National Committee on Housing, Inc., New York, August, 1944.

Questions

1. What are some of the physical defects that have resulted, particularly in metropolitan areas, from the unrestricted subdivision of land?
2. Describe how uncontrolled subdivision has created serious financial problems for the purchasers of lots. For the municipality. For other taxpayers in the community.
3. To what extent are vacant subdivisions found in typical suburban areas on the edge of a metropolitan district? In the United States as a whole?
4. Why will it prove necessary to consolidate many of these distressed properties to bring them back to a useful status?

5. What are the principal forms of control necessary to assure good subdivision planning?

6. What is the best agency to use in the control of subdivisions? Why?

7. How has the Federal Housing Administration assisted in subdivision control?

8. To what extent was subdivision control being practiced in the United States as revealed by the National Resources Committee survey of 1936?

9. What has been done to simplify public acquisition through tax foreclosure of lots in abandoned subdivisions?

10. What legal steps are necessary to give a municipal planning board control over subdivision plans?

11. Why is some discretion by the planning board essential in any subdivision regulations it may adopt for the guidance of land developers?

22

THE ECONOMIC VALUE OF A CITY PLAN

WHILE IT IS GENERALLY CONCEDED THAT A SOUND city plan must be based upon a sound economic order for the community, it is difficult to appraise, in dollars and cents, the value of planning. This can be done more readily for the area immediately contiguous to a public improvement than for the community at large, as it is hard to capitalize the advantages of any improvement or betterment which is for the free use and benefit of the general public. The problem is sometimes approached from the opposite direction, that is, by estimating the pecuniary loss suffered by individuals, by groups of individuals, or by corporations through delays and increased expenses which are due to a bad plan, but estimates of this kind should be subjected to careful scrutiny before conclusions are drawn from them.

It has been said that figures do not lie, and yet we know that they can and often do lie outrageously. Statistics, if skillfully handled, can be made to prove almost anything. Estimates could be presented which have doubtless been made with care and published in entirely good faith, but they have been collected for the express purpose of proving something, and those who have made them have been so intent upon formulating a case that other contributing causes may have been lost sight of.

It is quite obvious, for instance, that if goods are to be moved from one point to another, and if it is necessary in doing so to follow two sides of a triangle instead of traveling along the hypothenuse, there is a loss of time and an increase in cost; but to take a traffic census and apply that estimated loss to every load or ton

which is hauled over the longer route, under the assumption that each would have taken a more direct route were it available, might lead to a false conclusion. To compute the delays which occur to traffic and apply them to the hourly expense of a motor vehicle and operator and to argue that all these costs can be saved by eliminating the cause of the delay may be misleading. If the vehicle is a passenger car on a pleasure drive, is the driver's time worth anything? If it is a truck, can one neglect the personal equation of the driver and the improbability of his disposition or capacity for a sustained maximum effort during the entire working day?

When an attempt is made to estimate the value to the city or the state of the more robust and vigorous manhood and womanhood which would result from better living and working conditions, and the consequent saving in the annual budget for charities and the maintenance of order, we are again dealing with something which we know to be of enormous advantage, but which can scarcely be expressed in dollars and cents. Some estimates of this kind are worthy of serious consideration, but an effort should be made to avoid conclusions which are unwarranted or other than conservative.

It may not be possible to express the advantages of a good city or town plan in money. John Burns, who may be called the father of city planning legislation, has said that investment in a good plan, whether for new parts of a city or for the correction of older parts, if regarded for a period of a year, may appear expensive; if considered for a period of five years, it will be profitable; if considered for a period of 50 years, it will be an investment which in subsequent days will make the community regret that it did not adopt it sooner. Burns further notes that the neglected hamlets of a hundred years ago are the squalid industrial towns and cities of today, and he pleads that we should so arrange the physical life of a hamlet, village, town, or city that it can grow naturally and at each stage avoid the cost, nuisance, ugliness, and squalor which one sees wherever a town encroaches on the country.

Can a City Afford Not to Plan?

Senator Dwight W. Morrow, a few days before his death, made an oft-quoted statement on the evils of not planning. He said, "We hear a good deal about the cost of a city plan. Somebody ought really to write a book upon the cost of not planning." The occasion was the presentation of a county plan to the people of Mercer County, New Jersey, in 1931, but the following remarks of Senator Morrow are equally applicable to a city plan:

> Of course, nobody believes that anybody is wise enough to make a plan that will be carried out. It would be a very unfortunate thing if any generation were completely tied to the plans of their fathers. I haven't any doubt that the people that are sitting here 50 years from now, with perhaps a copy of this book containing the plan, will look upon it and make fun of parts of it and say, "What strange people they were that wrote this." But nevertheless if the people of a community keep interested in the subject, this particular plan and the fact that it is there for somebody to wrestle with and struggle for and change, will affect this community for much more than 50 years; and as I tried to say at the beginning with some apologies—that it is not going to cost anything—it is going to cost a great deal. It is going to cost a great deal in money, and it is going to cost a great deal in thought and in sacrifice of time of the loyal men and women that come after you in this community. I feel completely confident, however, that it is not going to cost as much to do it in accordance with a plan as it would cost to do it without a plan.

That a city also cannot afford to be niggardly in its plans is eloquently expressed in the words of Daniel H. Burnham, inspired by his plan of Chicago:

> Make no little plans; they have no magic to stir men's blood, and probably themselves will not be realized. Make big plans; aim high in hope and work, remembering that a noble, logical diagram once recorded will never die, but long after we are gone will be a living thing, asserting itself with ever-growing insistency. Remember that our sons and grandsons are going to do things that would stagger us. Let your watchword be order, and your beacon beauty.

General Assessments for Public Projects

There are certain public facilities which are essentially local improvements and the cost of which should be borne by the local area, either through requiring the developer to provide them, or, if built by the municipality, through some form of benefit assessment, a subject discussed in more detail in the following chapter (pages 178 to 183). Where projects are of larger scale, the problem is more complicated.

It is often urged that improvements designed to correct the obvious defects in a city plan be carried out at the general expense, a favorite argument being that the increased taxable values will more than provide for the interest and sinking-fund charges on the debt which may be incurred for this purpose. This argument may be a sound one in specific cases, but it is used so often and in connection with so many projects where the benefited districts would overlap that it should not be taken too seriously. If there is to be an increase in taxable values resulting from an expenditure of public funds, the entire public should reap the benefit due to such increased revenue from taxation, and the owners of the property thus enhanced in value can justly be assessed for any improvement which will result in peculiar benefit to them.

This principle was the basis for the "betterment" provisions in the British Town and Country Planning Act of 1947 (see Chapter 20, "City Planning Legislation," page 146), but has been long applied to special cases in the United States, notably in park projects. A few specific cases are described below.

Central Park in New York City was acquired and its improvement commenced in 1858. Up to the end of 1873 the city had invested in this project nearly $14,000,000, of which about $5,000,000 was for land, and nearly $9,000,000 for improvements. Salem H. Wales, President of the Park Board in 1873, noted that during the period between the beginning of this undertaking and the year last named the average increase in values in other parts of the city had been about 100 per cent and, had this rate of increase been applied to the property within the three wards contiguous to Central Park,

even if Central Park had not been bought and improved, but it is unreasonable to suppose that it would have been so great. If we cut the figures in two and conclude that values within these three wards were increased 400 per cent, or multiplied five times, as a result of this improvement, it is likely that we would not be far wrong.

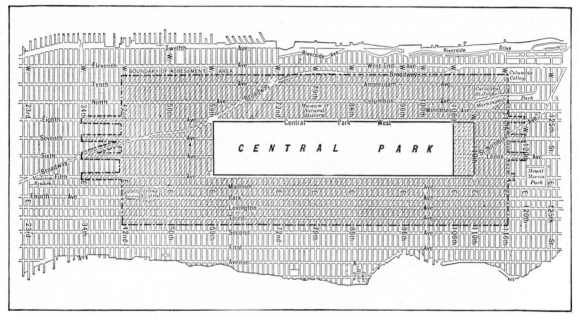

FIGURE 22·1. THE AREA (*shaded*) UPON WHICH WAS ASSESSED 32 PER CENT OF THE COST OF ACQUIRING CENTRAL PARK, NEW YORK CITY

its value in 1873 would have been about $53,000,000, whereas it actually was $236,000,000, so that the increase for the period, instead of 100 per cent, as in other parts of the city, was nearly 800 per cent.

The assumption that this increase was entirely due to the acquisition and development of this park would be unwarranted. As property changes from acreage to city lots the percentage of increase in value is greater than during any other period of development. Much of this advance in value may be speculative, but that there is a real increase due to the land having become marketable cannot be questioned. During the period covered by the increase in taxable values about Central Park, the great northward movement in population and improvement began; and there would undoubtedly have been a marked advance in value

The practice of assessing on a local area at least part of the cost of acquiring new streets and widening existing streets is quite general in the United States, and the methods employed are outlined in the following chapter (see pages 183 to 185). The persistence of this policy when once begun and its adoption by cities which formerly paid the cost from general funds are conclusive evidence of its wisdom. The same practice could with propriety be applied to the acquisition of parks.

In the case of Central Park about 32 per cent of its acquisition cost was assessed upon the large area of benefit shown in Figure 22·1. In the case of Prospect Park, a similar project acquired by the city of Brooklyn (now borough of Brooklyn, city of New York) under various acts of the state legislature from 1860 to 1868, 38.5 per cent was similarly assessed

(Figure 22·2). The reason for not extending the area of benefit beyond one side of Prospect Park was that the land on that side lay beyond the city limits, and assessments could not legally be imposed upon it. Leading from Pros-

along these parkways, however, was undoubtedly due to lack of transit facilities. The parkways were of very great general, but of relatively small local, benefit. Had the abutting property been put in touch with the rest of the

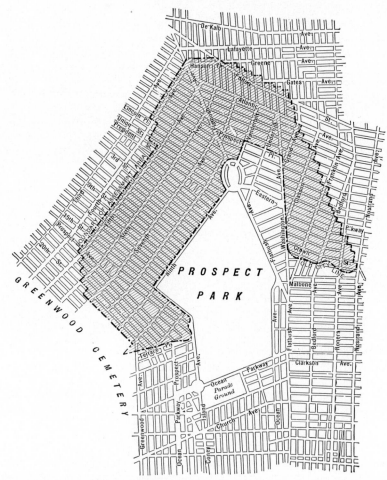

FIGURE 22·2. THE AREA (*shaded*) UPON WHICH WAS ASSESSED 38.5 PER CENT OF THE COST OF ACQUIRING PROSPECT PARK, BOROUGH OF BROOKLYN, NEW YORK CITY

pect Park southwardly to the ocean through towns not then a part of the city and eastwardly to what was then the city line, parkways 210 feet in width were laid out and improved, and the failure, for more than a generation, of the contiguous property to respond either in value or development to these improvements might be cited as instances to disprove the contention that city planning improvements have an actual and measurably money value. The absence of a marked increase in realty values

city by adequate transit lines a marked enhancement of values would promptly have followed. The conclusion, therefore, must be that the planning was not complete; that attractive parkways were provided without adequate means of getting to or from them.

Kansas City, Missouri, has created a very complete system of parks and parkways (see Figure 10·2, Volume I), and, instead of incurring a debt and leaving the bill to be paid by posterity, the people of the city have felt so sure of their immediate value to the community that the acquisition costs have always been assessed on a local area of benefit. The boundaries of the benefit district are determined in each case by the Kansas City Board of Park Commissioners, and there are no legal restrictions on what these boundaries may be. The city is divided into two park districts for levying a special maintenance tax on real estate. Substantial park and parkway areas have been donated to the Park Department. Some funds from city bonds voted in 1930 were allocated to the Park Department for construction purposes.

Denver early established a somewhat similar policy, the city being divided into four park districts, upon the property within which was assessed the cost of acquiring additional parks and parkways. The assessments were graded according to the distance from the park or parkway acquired. From information kindly furnished by H. F. Meryweather, then City Engineer, it appears that in one district the assessments varied from $2.98 for each lot 25 by 125 feet in size near the parks to $1.16 for the more remote lots. In another district they ran from $5.09 to $2.26 a lot, in a third from $33 to $0.50 a lot, and in the fourth district, covering the central part of the city and containing the civic center where the expenditure for this purpose was nearly $3,000,000, the assessments ran from $1,000 to $3 a lot. The initial expenditure was provided for by the issue of 15-year bonds, the interest and amortization of which were met by fifteen annual assessments upon the property in each district. The cost of grading, curbing, and paving the parkways was also met by local assessments imposed in decreasing amount upon the property lying within 750 feet of each of the parkways.

Reconstruction to Eliminate Economic Losses

Instances may be cited where towns have grown very rapidly and have developed into great commercial or industrial cities, although their plans violate almost every principle laid down by city planning authorities. Their growth, however, has been due to certain natural advantages and to the general development and prosperity of the districts tributary to them, and they have grown in spite of the handicap of a poor plan. When its defects and the embarrassment to business due to them become apparent, vast sums are often spent to cure the faults which might have been discovered and avoided had sufficient study been given to the plan when it was first under consideration. Thus the increased cost of doing business for a period of years and the large sums spent in the correction of the plan might have been saved.

The cost of reconstruction has run far into the millions in nearly every large city except Washington, which was so planned as to provide for future growth. One of the largest items involves the replanning and reconstruction of the street system in downtown districts of large cities. Cost figures collected by Harland Bartholomew in 1929 showed that in cities of over 1,000,000 population street-opening and widening projects had cost from $2,000,000 to $19,000,000 per mile; in cities in the 250,000 to 1,000,000 population class they had generally cost about $1,000,000 per mile but in some cases had been considerably higher.[1] Bartholomew stated:

> The large number of projects and their great cost indicate that consciously or unconsciously cities are striving to bring about more or less definite functional design of the street system of the business district and consequently bring about a logical traffic movement.
> Where such large sums of money are involved, it is evident that thorough planning should precede initiation of projects in order that initial mistakes of improper width or location may be avoided.

Other types of changes involve demolition of structures to create needed open spaces, and relocation of public buildings and services. It is obvious that the total of such costs would reach staggering figures. The beneficial results of such changes as have been made will be evident upon comparison of the taxable values in the vicinity before and after the improvements have been carried out.

[1] "Street Replanning in Downtown Districts of Large Cities," by Harland Bartholomew, *Planning Problems of Town, City, and Region*, 1929, pages 197–220.

Delays caused by traffic congestion, unnecessarily long hauls, and double or triple handling of goods where one such operation might have sufficed cause economic losses to a community. But, as already stated, attempts to reduce these losses to dollars and cents are likely to be misleading, although such figures have frequently been presented as arguments in favor of the improvement of existing conditions. Some figures for losses due to vehicular congestion alone have been presented in an earlier chapter.[2] An example of an over-all estimate is given below.

Assume a city where a million passengers are carried by transit vehicles operating in the public streets—and this number is greatly exceeded in several large cities—and that the loss in time due to traffic congestion averages 10 minutes a day; the total daily loss of time would be equivalent to 20,833 working days of eight hours each. If the average pay of those who were subjected to this delay is assumed to be $7, and if but one-half of this time is a loss to their employers, the total loss in productive work during a year of 300 working days would be about $21,875,000, to say nothing of the loss in efficiency by reason of worry and wear and tear in reaching the places of employment. This would represent four per cent on about $550,000,000. If in the same city there are 60,000 motor and horse trucks that are subject to an average delay of half an hour a day, and if they represent a cost of $10 for a day of eight hours, their loss in time, all of which would fall upon the employer or owner, would represent a value of $11,250,000 during a year of 300 working days, which is equivalent to four per cent on another sum of about $281,000,000. It may be argued, from these figures, that the expenditure of $831,000,000 would be justified if all these losses could be eliminated.

But it is possible to show the value of a good plan—one that will permit orderly development and economical methods of doing business—without resorting to such assumptions as the above. At least it is possible to show the heavy toll exacted from the people of a city by the lack of a plan permitting reasonable economy in supplying their daily needs. A conspicuous example is to be found in the Port of New York and the manner in which its operations are conducted.[3]

Example of Operations in the Port of New York

The communities about New York Harbor are supplied and fed by 12 railroads, the rails of but three of which enter New York City (those of only one of the three reaching Manhattan Island). The other nine have their terminals on the New Jersey side of the Hudson River and deliver their freight to New York by carfloats, lighters, and motor trucks (Figure 6·4, Volume I). All the railroads have tried to secure such locations for their terminals as would give them some strategic advantage over their competitors. They have taken for such use a very large part of the New Jersey water front and many piers on the New York side, which should properly be devoted to shipping. The operations have been conducted at excessive cost and, although it was conclusively shown during the two World Wars that unified operation would greatly increase the capacity of the port and reduce costs, when each war emergency passed, the same system of extravagant competition was revived.

A Port District has been established by joint action of the states of New York and New Jersey. The Port of New York Authority was created in 1921 by treaty between the two states, approved by the United States Congress and the President. Within the Port District, which contains sheltered waters with a shore line of about 650 miles, there are nearly 2,000 piers, wharves, and quays. The area includes all or parts of 17 counties and in 1940 housed a population of about 10,671,000. In 1939 the trunk-line railroads carried into, out of, or through the Port District 74,232,000 tons of freight each year, while 6,011 foreign and domestic ships entered and 6,083 cleared the port.

---

[2] See discussion of economic aspects of congestion in Chapter 9, "Street Traffic and Design," Volume I.

[3] Some of the transportation and terminal problems in the Port of New York have already been discussed in Chapter 6, "Transportation and Port Development," Volume I.

Together these ships brought or took from the port nearly 65,000,000 tons of freight by water. The food requirements alone of the people in the Port District amount to about 9,000,000 tons per year.

An exhaustive investigation of the port operations was made by the New York–New Jersey Port and Harbor Development Commission in 1920, from which it appears that the cost of handling goods at Manhattan carfloat pier stations, or inland rail stations, based upon pre-World War I conditions in 1914, was $1.60 a ton; for goods handled at Brooklyn, Harlem, or Bronx stations $1.48 per ton; and for goods delivered by lighter, $2.14 per ton, these figures covering only the cost to the carriers. In addition there was the expense of trucking and handling all freight within the Port District. The cost of these operations within the Port of New York District was found to be greater than the line-haul cost of transporting the same ton of freight from Philadelphia, and even from Buffalo, to Jersey City. As the railroads make shipside or pier deliveries or collections of carload freight within the lighterage limits of the port at the regular rates, terminal expense is absorbed in the freight rates and must be paid by the shipper and then passed on to the consignee and the consumer.

The Port of New York Authority, the creation of which followed the report of the Bistate Commission referred to above, submitted a report and comprehensive plan to the governors of the states of New York and New Jersey, under date of December 21, 1921. This report states substantially as follows the fundamental conditions that are necessary to a proper solution of the port problem:

1. Unification of terminal operations within the Port District.
2. Consolidation of shipments at classification points, eliminating duplication of effort and inadequate loading of equipment.
3. Direct routing so as to avoid centers of congestion and long truck hauls.
4. Terminal stations to be, as far as practicable, union stations.
5. The use of existing facilities as parts of the new system, avoiding sacrifice of existing capital investment, and the consent to such co-ordination by state and local authorities.
6. Delivery of freight to all parts of the port without break in bulk wherever this is practicable.
7. Improvement of waterways to provide access to such portions of the port as are best adapted to each kind of commerce.
8. Provision of motor-truck routes between terminals and industrial establishments not equipped with railroad sidings and for distribution of building and other materials which must be handled by truck.
9. Definite measures for prompt relief of existing conditions while the larger and more comprehensive plans are being carried out.

Much progress has been made in the application of these principles, particularly in regard to terminal facilities and their unified operation. The inland and water-front terminals constructed by the Port of New York Authority, or under construction by them in 1947, have been described in Chapter 6, Volume I.

The Comprehensive Plan (see Figure 6·6, Volume I) of 1921 called for belt lines, the most important of which was the Middle Belt Line passing through the heart of the Port District and connecting, by means of a tunnel under the Upper Bay, all existing railroad facilities on both sides of the harbor. Around this backbone were planned numerous marginal and connecting belt lines to permit the handling of railroad freight to all sections of the district without employing lighters or carfloats.

Some progress has been made in improving physical connections on parts of these belt lines, but over the years many of them have become obsolete through changes in land usage and the requirement that railroad tracks shall not cross public streets at grade.

The Port Authority was able to improve the joint usage of Belt Line 13 along the New Jersey shore, simplify interchange schedules, and eliminate circuitous routes and excessive charges. An attempt on the New York side to open a connecting route between the New York Central Railroad tracks in The Bronx and the Long Island Railroad tracks on Long Island, by way of the Hell Gate Bridge in lieu of the carfloat route, achieved only limited success. The Interstate Commerce Commission ruled that such a route could be used in an emergency, when fog and ice interfered with the carfloat route, but that the owners of the Hell Gate Bridge could not be compelled to receive the New York Central freight by this all-rail route.

The most important section of the Middle Belt Line, still to be completed, is the tunnel under the Upper Bay in place of the carfloat routes across the harbor between the New Jersey termini and the Long Island Railroad and the New Haven Railroad. The engineering and economic problems have been thoroughly surveyed, but up to 1947 the unit savings from abandonment of water facilities and the volume of traffic had not been sufficient to support the costs of this large capital improvement.

The Port of New York Authority has greatly facilitated vehicular movement between the New York and New Jersey sides of the port by construction of four interstate bridges and one interstate tunnel (Lincoln Tunnel) to supplement the Holland Tunnel, which it also operates. It is proposed to serve the central business districts by a series of inland terminals as already described (Chapter 6, Volume I).

In 1947 the activities of this bi-state agency were expanded by its taking over, under a 50-year lease agreement with New York City, the completion of Idlewild Airport and the revamping of LaGuardia Airport. The Port of New York Authority also negotiated, in 1947, a similar agreement with the city of Newark which will make possible an enlarged development and operation of Newark Airport and permit the joint operation of all three airports for the best advantage of the region as a whole.

A great port is one of the features that cannot be planned far in advance; the development of its commerce cannot be foreseen, but enormous expenditures are justified in order to correct defects when they become apparent.

Other Evidence That Planning Pays

Hindsight is more convincing than foresight in trying to establish the economic soundness of city planning and city rebuilding. There are many demonstrations that cities which have had the courage to correct defects and to plan with vision have benefited through increased growth and prosperity, and that their

citizens have readily paid the bills. What induced these cities to undertake great and costly improvements? It was not merely the desire to spend public funds, which inevitably increased the burdens of taxation. It was experience, which proved that other improvements had paid.

Did Paris make a good investment when it spent hundreds of millions of francs in beautifying the city and making it a more attractive place in which to live and do business? Did it pay Vienna to create its great Ringstrasse and, by placing along it important public buildings, make it one of the show streets of the world? Did it pay Dresden to build along the river front the beautiful Bruhle Terrace, called the "balcony of Europe"? Have Houston and Los Angeles regretted their expenditures to convert inland cities into profitable seaports? Does Chicago feel that it has acted wisely in the reclamation and park development of its lake front? Have Boston and Kansas City realized their investments in comprehensive park systems? Have Buenos Aires and Rio de Janeiro been repaid for expending large sums in the improvement and beautification of their water fronts? Do New York City and adjoining Westchester County feel that their great systems of parkways have been worth the cost? Ask the citizens of any of these communities, and see what they will say.

Yes, a good city plan pays, even though the benefits cannot always be computed in money; but the price paid has often been a heavy one. Constructive city planning in the early stages of urban growth can avoid much of the enormous cost of later rearrangement.

There is one other result of improvements which will facilitate buiness; they will almost always bring about better and more wholesome living conditions for employees. They will let in the light and air. They will permit the workers to spend more of their time at home; or, with the same expenditure of time, they will be able to have their homes farther away from the noise and confusion of the town and to rear their families amid better surroundings. A town which is capable of great undertakings to improve business conditions should be equally solicitous of the living conditions of its people, and should see that the streets on which their homes are located will be well cared for, that open spaces will be provided for their recreation, and that good drainage, pure water, and sanitary housing will be assured them. These benefits should be theirs by right, just as facilities for conducting business are the rights of the merchant and the manufacturer.

Selected References

BARTHOLOMEW, HARLAND: "Street Replanning in Downtown Districts of Large Cities," *Planning Problems of Town, City, and Region,* Proceedings of the Twenty-first National Conference on City Planning (Niagara Falls, N. Y.), 1929, pages 197–220.

BERRY, CHARLES W.: *The Financing of Local Improvements by Local, Borough, or City-wide Assessments,* Report to the Board of Estimate and Apportionment, New York City, May, 1930.

KESSLER, GEORGE E.: "Actual Distribution of the Cost of Kansas City Parks and Boulevards" (with discussion), *Proceedings of the Fifth National Conference on City Planning* (Chicago), 1913, pages 138–162.

MORROW, DWIGHT W.: *The Value of Community Planning* (address on occasion of presentation of the County Plan to the people of Mercer County, New Jersey), The Mercer County Planning Commission, Trenton, N. J., 1931.

ROTERUS, VICTOR: "The Economic Background for Local Planning," *Planning 1946,* Proceedings of the Annual Meeting held in New York City, May 6–8, American Society of Planning Officials, Chicago, 1946, pages 83–91.

Questions

1. What are some of the difficulties and the pitfalls to be avoided in attempting to compute the dollars and cents savings of good planning?
2. On what basis should it be determined whether a project be financed at general expense, by some form of benefit assessment, or by a combination of the two?
3. What types of public works are particularly suitable for local assessments upon benefited property? Give examples of such procedures in specific cities.
4. What types of economic losses have resulted from city plans that failed to provide for the growth which has occurred? What types of reconstruction projects have proved necessary to remedy such conditions?
5. Taking the Port of New York as an example, what were some of the economic losses that led to the establishment of the Port of New York Authority?
6. What measures were deemed necessary for a proper solution of the port problem in the Port of New York?
7. Describe the progress made in carrying out a comprehensive plan for the Port of New York.
8. Give examples where bold planning has resulted in outstanding improvements that have proved economically sound.

23

FINANCING A CITY PLAN

THE TITLE OF THIS CHAPTER MIGHT ALMOST BE expanded into the comprehensive one of "financing a city," to such a large degree does the financing of a city plan include the great number of things that are generally known as city improvements. It would not, of course, include the maintenance of the city schools, which is usually the largest single item in the annual municipal budget, although it would include the location and acquisition of sites for school buildings and provision for proper playgrounds in connection with them. It would not include the cost of administering the departments of public safety, of corrections, and of charities and the other social activities of the modern city, except, as in the case of the schools, to provide for the proper location and the effective grouping of their buildings where possible. It would include the development of a street and park system and the acquisition of the land needed for them, the location and purchase of sites for and the erection of public buildings of all kinds, bridges, monuments, fountains, or other structures which may dignify and adorn a city or may make it ridiculous, depending upon their location and design. It would include a proper and effective scheme of lighting, an adequate system of water supply and all its appurtenances, provision for drainage and sewage disposal, and a general scheme of street pavement, which should not be left to the caprice of the property owners in each street, and provision for the maintenance and renewal of pavements and the planting and care of trees, which should not be confined to parks and boulevards.

All these things, and more, have a vital influence on the appearance of a city and should therefore be included in its general plan. To secure them as needed and in proper sequence will require not only wise forethought and the highest technical skill, but sane and prudent methods in financing them.

Some who have written and spoken somewhat oracularly on the subject of city planning appear to believe that the cost of securing a proper city plan consists, first in the expense of propaganda to arouse sentiment in favor of the preparation of the plan, and then in paying some experts for a study of the local situation, in more or less surveying, and finally in the making of a lot of maps, studies, and pictures. These are exhibited and admired, if the pictures are attractive; a handsomely printed and bound report is issued and talked about for a time; the citizens congratulate themselves upon the fact that their town is soon to become another Paris; and finally someone asks what it is all to cost. The answer, if a frank one, is quite sure to dampen the enthusiasm which has been aroused; the plans are soon forgotten and the pictures put in storage, to be brought out and shown, perhaps, at a few city planning exhibitions.

The slow growth of a proper city plan and the years of painstaking work required to produce it have been outlined in other chapters. What concerns us here is the manner in which a rational and comprehensive plan is to be progressively carried out and sanely financed.

Sources of Municipal Income

There are several ways in which the cost of improvements included in the plan can be met: by direct assessment upon the property which would be benefited by each particular improvement, by making the expense a general city charge, or by a combination of the two methods. When the city pays all or a part of the cost, the funds for the purpose must be raised in the annual tax levy or they must be borrowed; that is, the city must use either its cash or its credit.

picion, and the only recourse of these cities is to the method of direct assessment, general taxes, or the use of their credit, which is really the same thing as general taxation extended over a term of years.

The subjects of taxation and municipal land policies are closely allied to that of financing public works. These subjects have been

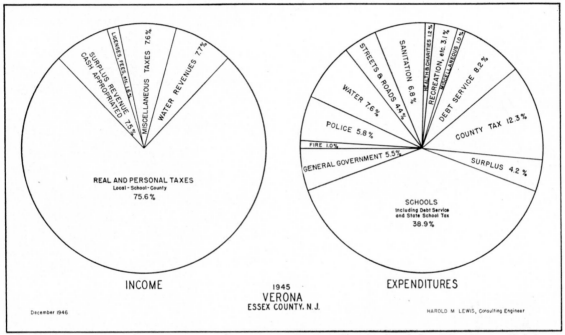

Courtesy, Planning Board, Borough of Verona, New Jersey.

FIGURE 23·1

As a basis for any financial study the city planner needs a simple over-all picture of all sources of municipal income. These are generally available in the published budget, but can advantageously be reduced to a diagrammatic form showing the proportions of the total from each source. Such a diagram appears in Figure 23·1, which shows both income and expenditures for a community of about 10,000 population. The dependence upon real and personal taxes is a characteristic that has been common to American cities. In contrast, many European cities have large revenues derived from profitable enterprises in which they have engaged and in some cases from land speculation. Such municipal ventures are very rare in American cities and are still regarded with sus-

touched upon in preceding chapters [1] and will be discussed further in the following chapter, "Municipal Land Policies."

While federal aid for highways outside urban areas has long been an American policy, its extension to urban highways is relatively recent. State aid for education is another typical American procedure. During the depression of the 1930's federal grants for municipal public works were instituted under the United States Public Works Administration program, involving both loans and grants. Federal and state aid for public housing was also instituted. Such governmental financial aid was carried

[1] See reference to increment tax on page 37 and to the betterment tax established in Great Britain in 1947 (page 146).

over, on a much more limited basis, into the postwar period after World War II. In 1947 there was in many parts of the country a demand for the return to local financing for ordinary municipal improvements and utilities, although there were many proponents of federal aid in public housing and in education and other social fields.

The use of self-liquidating public authorities, authorized by state legislation to acquire prop-

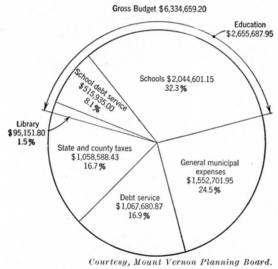

Courtesy, Mount Vernon Planning Board.

FIGURE 23·2. THE 1938 BUDGET DOLLAR OF THE CITY OF MOUNT VERNON, NEW YORK

erty and to sell their bonds in the private market, has offered a relatively new means of financing projects that were formerly considered municipal public works. In this category come port authorities, bridge and tunnel authorities, public housing authorities, parking authorities, and market authorities. Examples of some of these agencies have been referred to in other chapters. Usually they enjoy indirect aid in the form of tax exemption and, in the case of the public housing authorities, some direct grants; many of the earlier ones had the advantage of federal Public Works Administration grants in the initial financing of their projects.

Municipal Expenditures

Some study of the distribution and trends in municipal expenditures for various purposes

is necessary to determine the extent of public works that can be financed in the future. The expenditures diagram for Verona, New Jersey, in Figure 23·1 and the diagram for the Mount Vernon, New York, budget dollar of 1938 (Figure 23·2) are quite similar, although the latter community had about seven times as much population as the former. In each case, school costs were the major factor, totaling about 40 per cent.

A study of trends of departmental expenditures over a period of 10 to 15 years, with some projections into the future, will often prove useful. Such a study for Sacramento is shown in Figure 23·3.

Borrowing to Pay

The feeling is common and not unnatural that, if one plans more for the future than the present, coming generations, which will reap the benefit, should bear the greater part of the burden. This is a comfortable sort of theory, but it has led to the adoption of plans of financing improvements by state and city authorities which were not only short sighted, but in many cases reckless and indefensible.

Several states, during the early days of automobile growth, authorized by public referendum large bond issues involving 50-year and 60-year bonds for the improvement of state highways. While a portion of the work done was of a permanent character, such as the widening and straightening of the roads, the improvement of grades, and provision for drainage by substantial structures of masonry or steel, a very large proportion of the expenditure was for road surfaces, many of which did not last for more than 10 years. Borrowing money for 50 or 60 years to pay for 10-year roads is obviously unwise.

The state of Maine adopted a different and quite novel scheme for financing its road improvements. Under a law enacted in 1913, serial bonds, the last of any series being payable within 41 years, were authorized to be issued in amounts not exceeding $500,000 in any one year, with the provision that not more than $2,000,000 of these bonds shall be outstanding at any one time, the bonds bearing interest not exceeding four per cent. The peculiar provision of this law was that these bonds are to be cared for from the receipts for automobile licenses. With $2,000,000 in bonds outstanding and one-fortieth of this sum to be retired in any one year, $130,000 would have to

reckless financing was that adopted by several towns near New York which have since been incorporated within the city limits. In 1865 the state legislature authorized three of these towns to raise by loan the sums of $3,500, $6,500, and $2,500 respectively, which sums were to be appropriated to the improvement

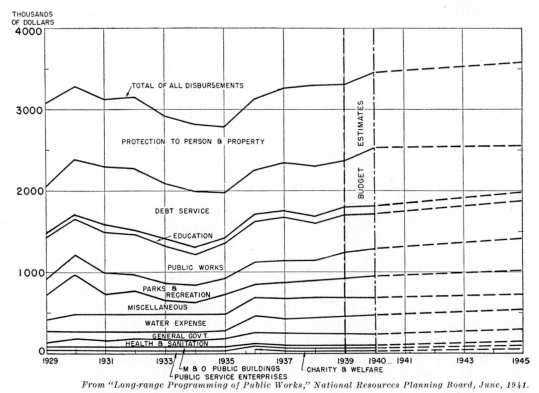

From "Long-range Programming of Public Works," National Resources Planning Board, June, 1941.

FIGURE 23·3. ACCUMULATED GRAPHS OF MUNICIPAL DISBURSEMENTS BY CLASSIFICATION, CITY OF SACRAMENTO

be provided annually for interest on the outstanding bonds and for the retirement of those falling due. A capitalization of estimated receipts from such a source, which prudence would dictate should be devoted to upkeep, appears to be a dangerous method of financing road improvements, especially in view of the probability that before the last of any series of bonds is retired it will be necessary to replace the road surfaces several times, and to meet this expense the entire receipts from automobile licenses, over and above the amount required to care for the bonds, would probably be needed and even might be found inadequate.

Perhaps the most extraordinary instance of

of a certain highway beginning at the Harlem River and passing through the three towns named. The act provided that each town should issue bonds for the amount required to meet the cost of that part of the improvement within its limits, and that these should bear seven per cent interest and should be so drawn as to become due in sums not exceeding $1,000 in any one year. In 1868 the law was amended by substituting for the sums named for each town the words, "such sums as may be necessary." This was the result: the town which was first authorized to spend $6,500 actually expended the sum of $112,500, some of the bonds being in amounts of $1,000, but most of them

$500. There were altogether 178 different bonds, the last one of which will become due in 1980. The town which was originally authorized to issue $3,500 in bonds actually issued its obligations to the amount of $278,000, and the last of these bonds will fall due in the year 2147. These two towns have since become a part of the city of New York, and that city has been obliged to assume all their obligations, so that in the annual tax budget there appears each year provision for paying off one of the bonds for each of these towns, together with interest at seven per cent on those which remain outstanding. While the first legislative act provided that two towns, now a part of the city of New York, might incur debts aggregating $10,000, which should be entirely paid off in not more than 13 years, an actual debt of $390,500 was incurred and saddled upon the city in such a fashion that it could not be entirely paid for 278 years after the first bonds were issued.

Such excesses have led to the establishment in most states by the legislatures of debt limits beyond which their municipalities may not go. For example, in New York State no city may have outstanding bonds (except those for self-liquidating projects, such as water supply, or other special exceptions granted by the legislature) in excess of 10 per cent of its assessed valuation of real property; in a New Jersey borough the board of education may borrow up to eight per cent of the assessed valuation in the borough, and the borough government may issue additional bonds up to seven per cent of the assessed valuation.

It seems easy to pay with borrowed money, particularly when the money can be borrowed for 50 years, or the span of two generations. The habit of paying in this way is easily acquired and is broken with difficulty. When anything is paid for with money borrowed for a period longer than the possible or even probable life of the article purchased, the city's credit is improperly used. A corporation which pays for its betterments from earnings is on a sound basis. When large earnings are used to pay excessive dividends, and betterments and renewals are paid from borrowed money representing additional obligations, there is danger. When interest on existing debt is paid from funds raised by incurring more debt, disaster is imminent.

Almost the only source of revenue of most cities is their power to tax. Their credit is due to this power plus the value of their own property. The larger the debt which has been incurred for projects which are not self-sustaining, the greater will be the demands upon a city's taxing power to meet interest and sinking fund charges due to such debt, and the less will be its ability to undertake new improvements and at the same time meet the enormous running expense of the modern city. It might not be a forced comparison to say that the ordinary services which a city renders to the public through its administrative departments, the expenses of which are met by the regular tax levy, are the dividends which it pays to its stockholders, while for its betterments and renewals it must issue bonds or levy special assessments.

Every bond issue requires an increase in the tax levy for a term of years in order to meet interest and amortization charges, curtailing by just so much the amount which can be expended upon municipal housekeeping expenses. In order to keep the tax rate within reasonable limits, expenses which should properly be met from the tax levy are often paid with borrowed money. Is not the city which adopts this policy actually doing the same thing as the business corporation which incurs additional debt in order to pay dividends?

The rate of interest and amortization will have a considerable effect on the total cost of financing any improvement. This has often been discussed in reports on financing low-rental housing and is illustrated in Figure 14·5 (page 23). As one city planning commission has pointed out:

When public improvements are financed by long-term bond issues, the total charge on the taxpayers is frequently doubled by the accumulation of interest charges added to principal payments. Thus over a period of years they pay out $20,000 for an improvement that cost only $10,000 to build.[2]

[2] *Progress Report, 1934,* City Planning Commission of the City of Yonkers, page 195.

Pay as You Go

To avoid the annual payment of tremendous interest charges on borrowed funds, many cities are turning to what is called a pay-as-you-go policy for financing needed capital improvements. This involves the use of current funds,

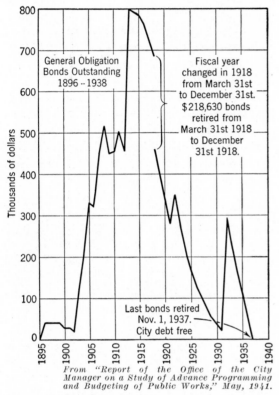

General Obligation Bonds Outstanding 1896-1938

Fiscal year changed in 1918 from March 31st to December 31st. $218,630 bonds retired from March 31st 1918 to December 31st 1918.

Last bonds retired Nov. 1, 1937. City debt free

From "Report of the Office of the City Manager on a Study of Advance Programming and Budgeting of Public Works," May, 1941.

FIGURE 23·4. GENERAL OBLIGATION BONDS OUTSTANDING, 1896 TO 1938, CITY OF KALAMAZOO, MICHIGAN

raised by each year's taxes, for progressively completing needed projects. Milwaukee, Wisconsin, and Kalamazoo, Michigan, were pioneers in adopting such a policy; the rate at which Kalamazoo's debt was retired is shown in Figure 23·4.

To provide for varying rates of income and need, a pay-as-you-go policy should include the setting up of a reserve fund in good times, or times of low expenditure, upon which the municipality may draw when extra funds are needed for capital improvements. A small community suddenly needing a major improvement, such as a new borough hall or high

school, will probably have to continue to use bonds for such an occasion, but even small municipalities can, with a little advance planning, finance from current taxes such projects as street paving, playgrounds, and extensions to sewer and drainage systems.

The charter of the city of New York, effective January 1, 1938, provided for a gradual shifting to a pay-as-you-go basis by requiring that the proportion of the cost of capital improvements to be financed currently be increased two per cent per year; that is, it shall be two per cent the first year, four per cent the second year, and so on, taking 50 years for the complete transition.

An inquiry conducted by the village of Scarsdale, New York, in 1945 revealed 203 municipalities in all parts of the country which financed capital projects entirely or in large measure on a pay-as-you-go basis. Of these, 51 were in the New York metropolitan area.[3]

Trends in Assessed Values and Tax Rates

As long as taxes on real estate continue to be a main source of municipal income, the city planner is interested in the trends in such figures as an index of future means of financing the master plan. Such figures might well be compiled for the preceding 20 years and projected into the future. Such a study is illustrated in Figure 23·5. This includes two estimates for future assessed values, the lower one being based on the probable population growth and the upper one on a maximum growth which might be encouraged by sound planning.

Old cities, particularly crowded ones suffering from large blighted areas, do not offer such opportunities of increased income from real estate taxes. In large areas they may be faced with declining values. During the period after World War II, many such cities, appreciating this situation, were giving serious study to the development of new sources of income for financing their public works programs.

[3] *Financing Postwar Construction Program of the Village of Scarsdale, N. Y.,* Village of Scarsdale, March 31, 1947.

Use of Excess Condemnation

A portion, at least, of the expense of acquiring new streets and parks, or of widening existing streets, or of any other improvement involving the expropriation of land, can sometimes be met by the exercise of the right of

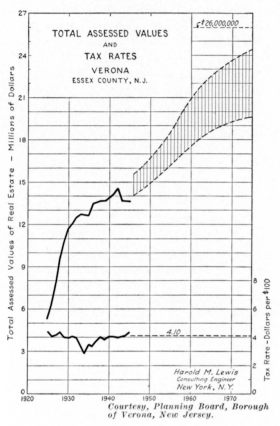

TOTAL ASSESSED VALUES
AND
TAX RATES
VERONA
ESSEX COUNTY, N.J.

Harold M. Lewis
Consulting Engineer
New York, N.Y.

Courtesy, Planning Board, Borough of Verona, New Jersey.

FIGURE 23·5

excess condemnation. This involves the taking of more land than is needed and the sale of the surplusage after the improvement has been carried out and the increase in values due to it has been realized. While this power has long been exercised by European cities, it has infrequently and reluctantly been granted to those of the United States.

Most of the state constitutions limit the compulsory taking of private property to the precise land needed for a specific public improvement, and constitutional amendments are necessary before this power of excess condemnation can be exercised. Such amendments, when made, commonly go no further than to

permit the state legislatures to authorize by general or special acts any or all of the cities in the state to acquire more land than is needed for a specific purpose.

Among the causes that have retarded the use of excess condemnation in the United States are the following: (1) the term is an unfortunate one, both the words "excess" and "condemnation" being such as to arouse public antagonism; (2) it requires an increased first cost of improvements; (3) city attorneys are often reluctant to use a new and untried procedure; and (4) local property owners and real estate operators are reluctant to relinquish the opportunity of large speculative profits from the sale of adjoining properties.

The first general state enabling legislation was adopted in Massachusetts in 1911 and read as follows:

> The Legislature may by special acts for the purpose of laying out, widening, or relocating highways or streets, authorize the taking in fee by the Commonwealth, or by a county, city, or town, of more land and property than are needed for the actual construction of such highway or street: *provided, however,* that the land and property authorized to be taken are specified in the act and are no more in extent than would be sufficient for suitable building lots on both sides of such highway or street, and after so much of the land or property has been appropriated for such highway or street as is needed therefor, may authorize the sale of the remainder for value with or without suitable restrictions.[4]

A New York State act adopted at the general election of 1913 provided:

> The legislature may authorize cities to take more land and property than is needed for actual construction, in the laying out, widening, extending, or relocating parks, public places, highways, or streets, provided, however, that the additional land or property so authorized to be taken shall be no more than sufficient to form suitable building sites abutting on such park, public place, highway, or street. After so much of the land or property has been appropriated as is needed therefor, the remainder may be sold or leased.

An amendment previously submitted to the people, which did not contain the restriction as to the amount of land or property which might be taken in excess of that actually needed for

[4] Later Article XXXIX of the Constitution of Massachusetts.

construction, was rejected at the general election of 1911.

The idea of excess condemnation is based, in part, upon a very practical consideration and, in part, upon a theory which is regarded as thoroughly sound in European countries, but which has not yet been generally accepted in America. The practical consideration is that it will avoid the serious mutilation of property by leaving unusable remnants. If these remnants can be taken by the city, they can be combined into marketable lots, and the development along the line of the new or widened street will be more rapid and its appearance will be more sightly. It is not uncommon to see narrow strips of property too small to accommodate buildings left along a new street which is an important traffic thoroughfare, and which would be lined with valuable business houses if these strips could be combined and added to adjacent property to furnish proper sites for such buildings. The separately owned remnants are commonly rented for advertising signs or for bootblack, lunch, or news stands, cigar shops, or some business that can be carried on in a few square feet of space.

The theory referred to is that of the right of the city to take for itself a part of the unearned increment or the increase in value of property which has been brought about through no act of the owner, but through the growth and development of the city or some public improvement carried out by the city. This idea is gradually making headway in the United States, and it is quite probable that it will soon be generally accepted as equitable and businesslike.

The extent to which shrewd investors are able to profit by city undertakings may be illustrated by a concrete example. In a large city in the United States it became necessary to increase the width of a certain street from 50 to 80 feet, and to accomplish this a strip 30 feet in width was taken from the property on one side of the street for the entire distance, reducing the depth of the lots on this side from 100 to 70 feet. One particular lot, 20 feet in width, with an old three-story brick house on it, was bought just before the widening by a man who habitually kept himself well informed concerning con-

templated improvements, the price paid being $11,000. He was awarded $10,000 as compensation for the destruction of the house and for damage to the lot owing to the decrease in its depth; but so greatly did the widening of the street increase the value of the abutting property that within a few months he sold the remnant, a lot but 70 feet in depth, with no building on it, for $12,000, or $1,000 more than the cost to him a few months earlier of the full-depth lot and house, besides having been paid damages to the amount of $10,000.

The city, to finance this improvement, was obliged to borrow the sum of $2,022,700 for a term of 30 years. The municipal authorities had determined to assess upon the neighboring property one-third of the cost of the improvement, but there were vigorous protests against the injustice of such a procedure, and by a mandatory legislative act the entire cost was thrown back upon the municipal treasury. Had the city possessed the power to acquire the entire row of lots on the side of the street which was to be taken for the widening it might have been able to sell the surplus land, not at the 100 per cent profit realized by the individual referred to, but for such a sum as would nearly, if not quite, have covered the cost of the undertaking, and would thus have secured the improvement without incurring a large debt for a long term of years.

The possibility of a broader use of excess condemnation than was contemplated by the original state enabling acts has been pointed out as follows by Frank B. Williams: [5]

The thoroughfare is not the only improvement with which excess condemnation may be used; indeed it may be used as a part of most public works. Thus, a new city hall properly located and constructed will cause neighboring land values to increase; and the public by proper business management could secure the profit which its enterprise has created, condemning and reselling the land for that purpose. A beautifully designed city hall is not the structure of beauty it should be unless it has an appropriate setting. Often the cheapest and indeed the only feasible way of obtaining some measure of setting is by control of the architecture of near-by buildings. In similar ways the construc-

[5] "The Present Status of Excess Condemnation in the United States," by Frank B. Williams, *Transactions of the American Society of Civil Engineers*, Vol. 89, 1926, page 793.

tion of parks may be made a source of income to offset in part their cost, their beauty and utility being increased by the control of the neighborhood which only excess condemnation will give.

The amount of additional land to be taken will depend upon the relation of the site of the public improvement to the lots bordering upon and contiguous to it. For an important new street, it may be desirable to acquire at least one additional lot in the rear in order to provide building lots with a depth suitable for the increased importance of the street. If the lots front upon an intersecting street and it seems desirable to rearrange them so that they will have their frontage on the widened street, it will be necessary to acquire two, three, or even four additional lots in order to permit advantageous replotting.

The right of excess condemnation, when granted, should be used with caution and should not be exercised with a speculative purpose. It will, as already pointed out, increase the first cost of improvements; but if sound business principles govern the procedure, the additional expenditure will be recouped within a reasonable time, and the final net cost is likely to be very materially reduced.

The London County Council has been following this plan since 1855, with the result that the cost of opening the following streets was reduced by the resale of excess property to the extent noted below: [6]

	PERCENTAGE
Garrick Street, from Longacre to King Street, completed in 1861	72
Southwark Street, from Blackfriars Bridge to High Street, 1864	37
Queen Victoria Street, from Blackfriars Bridge to Mansion House, 1871	53
Widening Tooley Street and other connecting streets, including provision for "rehousing 1,100 persons of the laboring class"	17
Shaftesbury Avenue, from Piccadilly Circus to Broad Street	33

The Shaftesbury Avenue improvement is cited as an instance where a desire to acquire as little property as possible was unfortunate,

[6] From *History of London Street Improvements, 1855–1887*, by Percy J. Edwards, Clerk of the Improvement Committee, published 1898.

and the opinion is expressed that it would have been better if the council had not been "imbued with such a strict spirit of economy as that which led it to avoid the acquisition of expensive buildings by adopting an irregular line for the new street, and to sacrifice almost every consideration on the score of cheapness."

One of the London improvements which has frequently been referred to as illustrating how a great public enterprise, involving the expropriation of real estate, might be financed is the so-called Strand-to-Holborn improvement, including the widening of the Strand and Southampton Row and the construction of Aldwich and Kingsway.[7] It appears that the total cost of this improvement to March 31, 1910, rounded off in American dollars, was as follows: [8]

Acquisition of property	$27,237,000	
Sundry charges, including rehousing and architectural designs	944,000	
Construction, including pipe subway and tracks for tramcars	1,906,000	
Total		$30,087,000

The credits to the account were:		
Receipts from sale of land	$ 1,741,000	
Estimated value of surplus land	17,588,000	
Total credits		19,329,000
Net cost		$10,758,000

This statement appears to cover simply the disbursements and receipts on account of capital. It is not improbable that the London County Council made ground leases for long terms from which it derives substantial annual rentals. If the receipts from that source were capitalized and credited to the capital cost, the amount might be considerably further reduced. When we take the above figures as they stand, however, it will be noted that of the total credits, nine per cent consists of cash receipts and 91 per cent of the value of surplus land,

[7] This project was described in some detail in Chapter 3, Volume I.

[8] From paper by George W. Humphreys, Chief Engineer of the London County Council, presented before the Institution of Civil Engineers in 1910.

while of the gross capital cost, 5.8 per cent had already been recouped and 58.5 per cent was represented by the estimated value of surplus land, the remaining 35.7 per cent representing what the people of London were paying for this improvement. That it was greatly needed is beyond question, and that it is worth the price cannot be doubted; but references to it as an enterprise which produced a direct financial return have been very misleading.

In but a single instance does the London County Council appear to have made an actual financial profit from an enterprise involving the taking of land, and that was in the case of Northumberland Avenue, which was cut through from Trafalgar Square to the Thames Embankment. Northumberland House and its extensive grounds were taken in this improvement, but there were no valuable trade interests to be acquired and paid for, while the surplus property abutting on the new street was so advantageously located that it was sold at such generous prices that the receipts from the sales exceeded by nearly 120,000 pounds sterling the entire cost of the acquisition and improvement of the street, including the building of pipe subways. Thus there was an actual profit of 17 per cent from the undertaking. This affords an illustration of an unearned increment which the city took for itself. The great increase in value certainly was not due to any act of the former owners of the property, but to an important improvement, initiated and carried out by the municipal authorities, the benefit from which was very promptly reflected in a great increase in the land values.

That in many of the improvements carried out by the London County Council in which the right of excess condemnation was exercised the recoupment from the sale of the surplus property was a relatively small percentage of the cost was due in large degree to the fact that the land required was formerly devoted, not to ducal palaces, but to tenements, and that the Housing of the Working Classes Act required the authorities to provide homes for the working people who might be dispossessed, the expense of doing so being a part of the cost of the improvement.

Many of the German cities have bought large quantities of land, in many cases, no doubt, in connection with the carrying out of specific street improvements, but their purchases have been so extensive and their main purpose has been so different that they will be considered in the following chapter, "Municipal Land Policies."

An example of excess condemnation in the city of Rochester, New York, in a project to connect four dead-end streets by extending an-

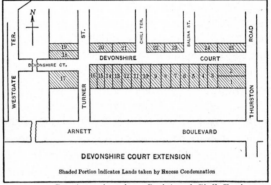

Courtesy, American Society of Civil Engineers.

FIGURE 23·6. EXCESS CONDEMNATION AS EMPLOYED IN ROCHESTER, NEW YORK, IN THE OPENING OF A NEW STREET

other street over a tract of vacant farm land in a moderately priced residential section, is illustrated in Figure 23·6. This was the first use of such powers in Rochester and netted the city a profit of about $1,500 over the cost of opening the streets as planned.[9]

Lex Adickes

A somewhat related procedure, under which irregular parcels of land can be taken over, replotted, and reassigned, is that devised by Dr. Adickes of Frankfort; the law under which it operates is known as the "Lex Adickes." While it provides a means of recasting the physical plan of a street and lot system, its objective is primarily a financial one, and it is therefore logical to discuss it in this chapter.

[9] Paper by A. L. Vedder, "Excess Condemnation in City Planning—A Symposium," *Transactions of the American Society of Civil Engineers,* Vol. 89, 1926, page **797**.

Under this law, where existing property lines are so inconsistent with those of a rational street plan that the parcels left after laying out a street system cannot be profitably used, the city may, if one-half of the owners, who also own not less than half of the land in such a tract, give their consent, take over the entire tract, lay out a proper street system with such open spaces as may be thought necessary, taking out for streets and open spaces as much as 40 per cent of the entire area, and redistributing the remaining land among the owners in such a manner as to give usable plots of an area corresponding with their original holdings less their proportion of the space taken for public use, for which no payment is made. The success of such a policy will, of course, be dependent upon the equity of the redistribution. While this must be done somewhat arbitrarily, it is probably done fairly. In most cases the owner of each parcel taken will naturally hope to obtain an advantageous location in the reallotment. Some owners must be disappointed; but that the plan has been successfully followed in German cities is evidence that substantial justice is done, while the great advantage to the city at large in securing a better street plan and increasing the value of the remaining property is quite obvious.

An instance of an attempt to make reallotments somewhat in this manner is noted by C. M. Burton in his pamphlet, "The Building of Detroit." After a fire which nearly destroyed this town in 1805, an act of Congress authorized the laying out of a new town to include the site of the old one and 10,000 acres adjacent. Burton wrote:

As all the lot owners in the former village claimed an ownership in certain parts of the town, and as it was impossible to give them their original holdings unless the old town with its narrow streets and small lots was retained, the citizens concluded to lay out a new town and give lands free to the old lot owners in exchange for their former possessions. The judges were to adjust claims for these lots. Every person over 17 years of age who was in Detroit at the time of the fire was to have a lot in the new town containing 5,000 sq. ft. The lands which remained were to be sold and the proceeds used for building a courthouse and jail.

In response to an inquiry as to whether this plan was ever carried out, Burton advised that, while proceedings for the distribution were commenced soon after the act was passed, and attempts had frequently been made since to have the Common Council perform the duties imposed upon the "governor and judges" acting as a land board under the act of 1806, nothing had been accomplished.

An interesting example of a similar procedure, but involving acquisition and resale, is provided by Marshfield, a resort community in Massachusetts, where about 500 cottages were destroyed by a disastrous fire in 1941. With the aid of the State Planning Board, county officials, and the Massachusetts Institute of Technology a complete scheme of rehabilitation, involving an improved layout of streets and lots, has been effected. It was reported in 1947 that, while World War II had delayed rebuilding, practically all the lots had been sold, and construction was expected to proceed rapidly. The before and after plans are shown in Figure 23·7.

In this case the Massachusetts excess condemnation act, quoted on page 174, provided the basic authority, but this was supplemented by a special act described as follows by Elisabeth M. Herlihy, Chairman of the Massachusetts State Planning Board:

A legislative bill was prepared authorizing the town to proceed under the provisions of the constitutional amendment of 1911 to take property in the most congested parts of the burned area, to rearrange the lots in accordance with the aforementioned plan, and to sell the new lots back to private owners. The bill indicated the streets to be widened, laid out, or relocated, and described in detail with ownership and area 344 separate parcels of land together with additional lots belonging to the same owner. The bill also authorized the Selectmen to use as much of this property as might be needed for the construction, widening, and improvement of streets and ways and thereafter to convey the remainder thereof for value with or without suitable restrictions. The Selectmen were also authorized to borrow such sums as might be necessary, not exceeding in the aggregate $160,000, to carry out the provisions of the act.[10]

The Use of Special Assessments

Many city planning projects are not self-sustaining, particularly those involving the cor-

[10] "It Can Happen Here—The Story of Marshfield," by Elisabeth M. Herlihy, *The Planners' Journal*, October-December, 1941, pages 12–17. The bill was adopted as Chapter 628, Massachusetts Acts of 1941.

rection of defects due to lack of proper planning. In such cases it may be assumed that the property affected by them already has been

In the more fundamental work of city planning, where unoccupied territory is being developed, the property will not have been as-

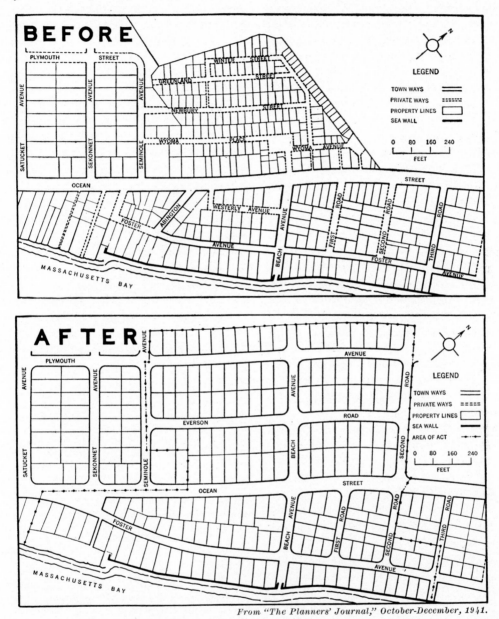

From "The Planners' Journal," October-December, 1941.

FIGURE 23·7. A SECTION OF MARSHFIELD, MASSACHUSETTS, BEFORE AND AFTER REPLANNING WITH AN IMPROVED SYSTEM OF STREETS AND LOTS

assessed for the acquisition and improvement of streets which were at the time considered adequate for local needs. The widening and rearrangement of streets in built-up sections will, however, improve conditions and increase values, and a part of the expense should, therefore, be placed upon the property benefited.

sessed for improvements, and consequently the acquisition and construction of new streets can properly be assessed upon the adjoining or neighboring property according to benefit, such benefit representing the entire cost in the case of local streets and a portion of the cost in the case of thoroughfares of more than local, or even of metropolitan, importance. One principle should invariably be recognized: namely, where there is local benefit, there should be local assessment. There can be no improvement which has been intelligently planned and executed which will not result in some local benefit. Also, no improvement, however small or large, will be of equal benefit to the entire city, and to distribute the burden of paying for it over the whole city according to taxable values is unfair in that the assessment is not placed according to benefit. The owners of property in the immediate vicinity are frequently enriched at the expense of those whose holdings are entirely outside the district directly affected.

Some may think that this statement should be so modified as to exclude certain great improvements, such as public buildings, bridges, docks, and rapid-transit lines, and yet there is doubtless a local benefit resulting from these. The City Club of New York several years ago showed that as a result of the building of the first rapid-transit subway in New York, the actual land values in those portions of upper Manhattan and The Bronx which were most directly affected were within seven years increased $80,500,000 above the normal increase for that period. The cost of that part of the subway passing through the districts where this rise in values took place was about $13,000,000, while the cost of the entire subway from the Battery north was $43,000,000. It is quite evident that if the $13,000,000 which was spent on that part of the subway traversing the district so notably benefited had been assessed directly upon the property, its owners would still have netted a neat profit of some $67,500,000, while, had the cost of the entire subway been assessed upon the same limited district, the net profit to the land owners would have been $37,500,000. Was it fair that property in distant parts of the city, entirely unaffected by this great project, should bear the same proportion of the burden as that which was so conspicuously advantaged?

The local benefit was so clearly established that the Rapid Transit Law was amended to permit the assessment of any part of the cost of future subways, but up to 1947 all attempts

at such a procedure had been vehemently and successfully opposed. It was argued that as property owners along the first route had secured their benefit without direct tax, those along new lines should have the same privilege; also that property owners paid the city for benefits received through their taxes on increased real estate assessments. Neither of these arguments, nor New York City's continued reluctance, until 1948, to increase the five-cent fare, appear sound to the writer, who agrees with Colonel William J. Wilgus that, "An equitable division of cost of service between the passenger through the fare, the neighboring property owner through assessment, and the business man and citizen through general taxation, should make feasible the timely expansion of rapid-transit facilities without weighing too heavily upon any of the interests affected." [11]

Assume that an important new building is to be erected in a part of the city where real estate values are relatively low, or at least stationary, and that this building—a new city hall, courthouse, library, or municipal office building—is to be of a monumental character and is to be provided with a site which will be suitable to its design, or that provision is to be made for a group of such buildings which will ultimately be erected. It is quite certain that the neighborhood in which such a building or such a civic center is to be located will assume a new character, and that the property all about it will be increased greatly in value. It may be doubled, or even trebled, by the time the first of these buildings is completed. Is it fair or just that the owners of the property in its vicinity should be enriched through no action of their own, and that they should bear only the same proportion of the expense, according to the taxable value of their holdings, as will those owning property in distant parts of the city, the value of which will be slightly if at all affected? A considerable portion of the benefit will undoubtedly be general and extend to the entire city, but that there will be also a local benefit cannot be doubted. There may be

[11] *Transit and Transportation*, Vol. IV, Regional Survey of New York and Its Environs, 1928, page 168.

doubt as to the equity or wisdom of assessing any part of the cost of the building or buildings themselves, although that is a debatable question; but with respect to the effect of location of the site and the erection of the buildings upon the particular neighborhood there can be little question.

It needs no extended argument to prove the equity and wisdom of local assessment wherever there is local benefit. That this policy has not been carried out in the past is no reason why it should not be done in the future. That certain property owners have heretofore been treated with prodigal liberality is no good reason why others should benefit through a continuation of an irrational and essentially unfair policy. To the degree that the assessment plan is adopted, to the same degree will the city place itself upon a cash rather than upon a credit basis. It may be urged that the adoption of such a policy would discourage the agitation for and execution of many desirable city planning projects; that American cities have been slow to appreciate the advantages of intelligent city planning, and now that there has been a marked awakening it would be unwise to suggest the adoption of a policy which might dampen this new-born enthusiasm. A desire for something which involves no direct cost is not a sign of intelligent interest. We are learning that the improvement of our cities pays. That is a hopeful sign. If we have simply reached the stage where we want better conditions only if someone else is to pay the bills, the hope has not a very substantial basis. If we want them badly enough to pay for them ourselves in proportion to the benefit we feel sure will follow, we are making real progress.

Assuming that a case has been made in favor of assessing the cost of all improvements in accordance with prospective benefit, we are still confronted with a very difficult problem. The direct and indirect benefit must be estimated in advance. We cannot first carry out our city planning schemes and afterwards determine how the cost is to be met. Furthermore, we must determine to what extent the benefit will be strictly local, to what degree it will extend to a larger tributary area, and, again, how much

it will mean to the entire city or metropolitan district.

In the small town—and no town is so small that these problems will not arise—the creation of a public square about which or in which the chief buildings, including, perhaps, the churches, are to be grouped, is of general interest and benefit to the entire community. All public activities, and even recreation and amusements, will center there, and it will be conceded that the town itself should properly pay the expense. The most valuable property will be that fronting upon this square, so that if its creation will result in special benefit to the surrounding property, that property will bear a correspondingly large burden. If the main street of the town needs widening, straightening, or extending, the benefit again will apply to the entire community. But the town grows and becomes a city. Other main streets must be provided; other centers of activity or recreation are needed. These new projects will still result in some general benefit, but in a large measure of special benefit. The effect upon the property in their neighborhood will be proportionately greater and more exclusive than in the case of the first village green or town square. The entire community will doubtless feel the benefit of the new improvement, but in less degree, as it tends to create a new center and diffuse, rather than concentrate, business and other activities. The town can still afford to contribute toward the expense, but the fair proportion to be assumed by it will be less in proportion to the amount of special benefit resulting to the particular locality.

The ability of the town or city to contribute toward the expense of such undertakings will vary in different cases, depending upon the other burdens which it may have assumed or to which it may have pledged its credit; depending upon whether the city is deriving substantial revenue from privileges granted to public service or other corporations or individuals; depending upon whether it is conducting certain activities at a profit or whether they are being conducted at a loss for the benefit of the public using them; and depending especially upon whether the city has already borrowed to such an extent that an issue of further obligations would impair its credit. Again it remains for the town or city to determine, if it is to pay all or a portion of the cost of any particular improvement, and even if its credit is such that it can borrow the funds necessary, whether it will issue its bonds for a long term of years, or whether it will carry out the improvement on a cash basis by providing for it in one or more tax levies or by short-term bonds which will be retired soon after the completion of the work.

The entire cost of strictly residential streets, the purpose of which is to give light, air, and access to the dwellings located upon them, can properly be imposed upon the abutting property, as the benefit will be entirely local. When a highway is given a more generous width, in the expectation that it will be called upon to accommodate a certain amount of through traffic, the benefit is more general, and the assessment area may be extended to a line midway between it and the next street of more than residential width. The major part of the expense should, however, be confined to the abutting property, so that the cost to it is somewhat more than that of a narrower street. In the case of arterial thoroughfares, or of the first street to be opened through an undeveloped territory, the effect of which will be to give access to and stimulate the development of a large district, the area of benefit may be correspondingly enlarged.

When it is proposed to develop a thoroughfare of exceptional width in the form of a boulevard or parkway, the entire city or metropolitan district will be substantially benefited and should bear a portion of the expense; in fact, the state or federal government may derive an advantage which would justify its assumption of a portion of the cost.

This same principle of assessment for benefit might be applied to parks. Some small parks are of strictly local benefit, and their cost can properly be placed upon the district in which they are located. Every park, whether small or large, is of some local benefit, even if such benefit is deemed to consist solely in unobstructed light and air to the property on the surrounding streets.

In the case of street widenings or the cutting of new streets through built-up sections, the local advantage is less marked, though it will always follow. The mere fact that a widening or extension is required to accommodate traffic is conclusive evidence that the street has assumed more than local importance. The width of the road as widened is not an index of its local or general importance. There may be cases where the opening up of a new street of a width commonly given to local streets, and extending for a very short distance, would, on account of its strategic position, be of great general and of little local benefit.

A summary of the field of special assessments is provided by Philip H. Cornick's division of them into four types: "(1) special charges for outlays made by a governing body for the abatement of a nuisance; (2) special charges for outlays resulting from the improvement of publicly owned appurtenances to private property; (3) special levies imposed on properties within a district created for the purpose, for all or part of the cost of specified public improvements constructed or services rendered within the district; and (4) special assessments imposed on properties benefited by public improvements or services in proportion to, and not in excess of, the amount of such benefit." [12]

The practice of assessing the cost of street or local improvements started early in the United States and is probably more general than in other countries. One of the earliest statutes which specifically recognized this procedure was enacted in 1787 by the state legislature of New York; it read in part as follows:

And for the better affecting thereof it shall and may be lawful to and for the mayor, aldermen, and commonalty of the said city in common council convened, to cause to be made an estimate or estimates, of the expense of conforming to such regulations aforesaid and adjust an equitable assessment thereof among the owners or occupants of all the houses and lots intended to be benefited thereby in proportion as nearly as may be, to the advantage which each may be deemed to acquire respectively. And in order that the same may be safely and impartially performed, said common council shall,

12 "Equitable Zoning and Assessments for City Planning Projects," Progress Report of Committee of City Planning Division, *Proceedings of the American Society of Civil Engineers*, February, 1936, page 207.

from time to time, appoint five sufficient and disinterested freeholders for every such purpose, who, before they enter into the execution of their trust, shall be duly sworn before the said mayor or recorder, to make the said estimate and assessment fairly and impartially according to the best of their skill and judgment; and a certificate in writing of such estimate and assessment being returned to said common council and ratified by them shall be binding and conclusive upon the owners or occupants of such lots so to be assessed respectively; and such owners or occupants respectively shall thereupon become and be liable and be chargeable, and are hereby required to pay such person as shall be au-

dimensions nor its cost. An improvement involving an expenditure of $1,000,000 in one part of the city may be more distinctly local in its beneficial effect than one costing $50,000 in another section. No fixed rule can be established to govern the distribution of expense. Both the distribution and the area of local assessment must be determined after a painstaking investigation. Such investigation should not be intrusted to a different individual, board, or commission in each case. There should be

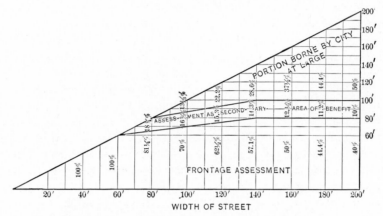

FIGURE 23·8. DIAGRAM SHOWING PROPOSED METHOD OF DISTRIBUTING THE COST OF ACQUIRING STREETS OF DIFFERENT WIDTHS BETWEEN THE ABUTTING PROPERTY AND LARGER AREAS OF BENEFIT

thorized by said common council to receive the same, the sum at which such house or lot shall be assessed to be employed and applied for and toward the making, altering, amending, pitching, paving, and scouring such streets, and making, constructing, and repairing such vaults, drains, and sewers aforesaid; and in default of payment thereof or any part thereof it shall be and may be lawful for the mayor, recorder, and aldermen of the said city or any five of them of whom the mayor or recorder be one by warrant under their hands and seals, to levy the said sum or sums of money so assessed, by distress and sale of the goods and chattels of the owner or occupant of such house or lot, so assessed, and refusing or neglecting to pay the same; rendering the over-plus, if any there be, after deducting the sum assessed and the charges of distress and sale to such owner or occupant respectively, or their legal representative.

Examples of Assessment Procedures

It is quite apparent that the relative local, district, or general benefit of any street or other improvement can be determined neither by its

a permanent body to carry on all such investigations. This body should not be large, and it should be so constituted that its entire personnel cannot be changed at once, thus insuring continuity and consistency of policy. The members should be versatile men whose training has fitted them for their difficult and delicate duties. The misleading evidence commonly called expert testimony on existing and prospective values will be of little assistance to them. They should be qualified by experience and intelligence to form their own conclusions.

While no definite rule can be adopted to govern the distribution of assessments representing the district and general benefit, it should be possible to prescribe a method of determining the extent of local benefit, particularly in the case of new streets, boulevards, and parks. In New York City rules were adopted by the Board of Estimate in 1939 to determine the future basis of apportioning the costs of these and other projects.[13] A summary of the principal provisions of these rules appears as Appendix D (see pages 212 to 213).

A plan for distributing the acquisition costs of streets between the frontage area, a secondary area of benefit, and the city at large is shown in Figure 23·8. Under this plan the proportion assessed on the immediate frontage would vary from 100 per cent for a street 60

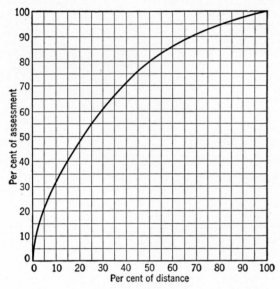

FIGURE 23·9. DIAGRAM SHOWING A METHOD OF GRADING ASSESSMENTS FOR BENEFIT ACCORDING TO THE DISTANCE FROM THE STREET OR PARK TO BE ACQUIRED

feet wide to 40 per cent for a street 200 feet wide. This diagram shows the regulations in effect in New York City pending the adoption of the 1939 rules and may still be appropriate for use in other cities. If the destruction of buildings is involved, it would be reasonable to assess such building costs on the secondary area of benefit, or to include them in the general city assessment if the improvement is of sufficient importance to involve general benefit.

A diagram showing a method used in New York City for grading assessments for park acquisition before the city started to acquire

parks with general city funds is reproduced as Figure 23·9. In accordance with this, 32.5 per cent of the assessment would be placed on the first 10 per cent of the distance to the outer limit of the area of benefit, 55 per cent upon the first 25 per cent, and 80 per cent upon the district extending half way to the boundary of the assessment area. This diagram could also be used to determine the extent and boundaries of the area of benefit for graduated assessments for either a street or park when the amount of the frontage assessment has been decided upon. In the case of parks, the size and shape of the park and the facility of access to it from other parts of the city should be taken into consideration.[14]

The charter of the city of New York provides for two special funds to facilitate financing its program of assessable improvements: one of these is called the street and park openings fund and the other the street improvement fund. Into each is paid all proceeds from assessment bonds or collection of assessments for the types of projects indicated by their names, and from each the respective types of projects are financed outside the city's capital budget. If such a project does not involve the expenditure of more than $10,000, a Local Improvement Board may authorize it without action by the Board of Estimate if the Chief Engineer of the Board finds that technical requirements have been complied with and that the improvement conforms to the master plan of the city so far as adopted.

The presumption is that both these funds will be self-sustaining, inasmuch as when assessments are not paid promptly, interest at the rate of seven per cent annually is charged as a penalty. The funds, however, occasionally have to be replenished to make good the assessments which fall upon city property, the por-

---

[13] Rules for Apportioning the Cost of Assessable Physical Improvements, Street Opening Proceedings and Parks, Playgrounds, Public Beaches, and Sites for Sewage Treatment and Sewage-disposal Plants, adopted by Board of Estimate, November 16, 1939.

[14] A formula was developed for use in New York City for determining the extent of an area required to bear equitably the whole or part of the cost of a street or park opening where the benefit extends a considerable distance from the improvement. This formula and its method of application are described in an article by Berthold Scheiman, Assistant Engineer, Board of Estimate and Apportionment (now Board of Estimate), New York City, published in Roads and Streets, October 3, 1923, pages 722-725.

tion of the cost which is occasionally assumed by the city, and such small portions of individual assessments as cannot be collected owing to a provision in the city charter that no assessment can be levied which, for a single improvement, exceeds one-half the fair value of the property.

In other cities the right to assess has been availed of in carrying out extensive city planning or replanning projects, as well as for purely local improvements. For example, one of the earliest improvements in the carrying out of the Chicago Plan was the widening of Roosevelt Road (Twelfth Street) from 66 feet to 108 feet for a distance of two miles and from 50 feet to 118 feet for about one-eighth of a mile. The acquisition cost of the land needed was $3,259,708, of which $1,490,490, or nearly half, was assessed upon a benefited area of a little over five square miles involving 29,500 pieces of property. The remainder and the cost of construction were expended from public money, of which $1,750,000 was a city-wide bond issue approved by the voters in 1913 specifically for this improvement. The widening of Michigan Avenue, Chicago, from 66 feet, partly to 127½ feet and partly to 141 feet, including the development of a considerable portion with two levels, involved a total cost of $13,762,302, of which $5,534,703 was for acquisition of property and cost of litigation. The length of the improvement was about five-sixths of a mile. There was a special assessment of $5,926,702 upon a benefited area of 2½ square miles involving 18,400 pieces of property. The balance was financed out of an $8,800,000 city-wide bond issue approved by the voters. The street was opened to traffic in May, 1920.

There has been, however, an increasing tendency to finance such large-scale improvements at general city expense, particularly where they are carried out as part of a comprehensive plan from which all sections of the city will benefit. An example is provided by St. Louis, which floated a bond issue in 1923 which included funds for carrying out extensive street improvements. In accordance with its powers under the state constitution of Missouri, the city adopted the policy of obtaining a portion of the cost of such improvements by levying assessments against benefited property, both abutting and in an area determined by the court. Since 1941 the city administrations have adopted the policy of avoiding benefit assessments for street-widening projects and have included all the cost of acquisition as a city-wide charge to be financed from bond funds. While the paving costs of such projects have, up to 1947, been locally assessed to the extent that they represented an ordinary street improvement and any excess has been paid from bond funds, it seemed likely that the city may also assume all the paving costs in future projects.[15]

In a great capital city the costs of municipal administration of certain improvements may be so great that they cannot in justice be imposed entirely, or even in part, upon the community. Former President Taft, writing of the special difficulty of financing the improvement of Washington, said:

While they have to pay but half of the expense of the city government, that half is greater than most cities of Washington's class impose upon their people. There are two reasons for this. The first of these is that no other city of its class has so many unusual expenses to meet. For instance, no other city has so many square feet of street surface to maintain. . . . In every department of its activities its expenses are somewhat unusual, this being due to the fact that the city is the home of the federal government and must meet all the requirements of a National Capital. The second reason why the burden of even one-half of the expenses of the city government is heavier than the expenses of most cities is that Washington has but one industry, which is government, and that industry but one product, which is politics. With no important wealth-producing industries to swell the incomes of the people of the capital, with every activity discouraged that would detract from the beauty of the city, per capita ability to pay taxes is smaller in Washington than in most cities. Hence, it is that even the half-and-half plan still leaves Washington a rather heavily taxed municipality.

Taft quoted from a report of a committee recommending the adoption of the half-and-half plan the following statement:

There is something revolting to a proper sense of justice in the idea that the United States should hold free from taxation more than half of the area of the Capital City, and should be required to maintain a city upon an unusually expensive scale, from

[15] From information supplied by H. Shifrin, Consulting Engineer, St. Louis, Missouri, December 15, 1947.

which the ordinary revenues derived from commerce and manufactures are excluded; that in such a case the burden of maintaining the expenses of the Capital City should fall entirely upon the resident population.

Combination of Assessment and Excess Condemnation

In some cases it may be argued that if the city is to acquire more land than is needed for a particular improvement, it would obviously be unfair to assess upon an area of benefit any part of the expense of acquiring such additional land, or even acquiring the land actually needed for the improvement, if entire parcels which include surplus land are to be taken. There is no reason, however, why the principle of assessment should not be combined with that of excess condemnation, and there is no good reason to believe that assessments for improvements of this kind would be increased, while it is quite likely that the burdens would be lightened.

If a portion of a lot containing a building falls within the lines of the improvement, and if only the portion required for such improvement were to be taken and paid for, it is probable that the owner would be paid for the complete destruction of the building and for the mutilation of the lot by decreasing its depth or spoiling its shape. If the entire lot were taken, it would seem fair and proper to credit the expense of acquiring that portion of the lot needed for the improvement with the salvage, if any, on the building, owing to the fact that some of it will be left; in many cases this will represent a very small proportion of the value of the building, but it will sometimes be considerable.

It might also be fair, if the entire lot were taken, to charge up to the improvement only such proportion of the land value as is represented by the part of the lot area falling within the lines of the proposed improvement, thus lightening the burden of assessment by eliminating the element of consequential damage. This might be unfair to the city at large, in view of the fact that the remnant of the lot falling outside the improvement which the city has to buy is worth less than the proportion of the original lot value determined by the relative area, and an equitable treatment would be somewhere between the two methods of estimating which have been described.

It does not seem necessary to depart from the prevailing method of levying assessments in such cases. The city, having acquired the frontage on the new or widened street, could properly assume the same share of the assessment as would have been imposed upon the remnant of the plot had it remained in private ownership, so that the assessment imposed upon other land within the area of benefit which was left in private ownership would not only be no greater than if no excess of land had been taken, but would actually be decreased by the elimination of, or at any rate the material decrease in, the item of consequential damage.

Capital Improvement Program

One of the principal objectives of a city planner's study of municipal finance is the preparation of a reasonable and practical program for the carrying out of capital improvements. This involves priority listings for the principal proposals included in the master plan for the municipality. A plan that cannot be carried out in a reasonable length of time by financial means within reach of the municipality is an extravagant plan which may do more harm than good.

Some city planning reports have included detailed schedules, year by year, for the order and cost of carrying out capital projects. The actual determination, however, of just when a project shall be executed and how it shall be financed is a legislative function and the responsibility of the elected officials rather than an appointed planning commission. The latter's main function at this stage of a municipal program is to see that the project conforms with an over-all plan for the community.

The extent to which capital, non-assessable improvements can be paid for out of current funds will be shown by the differences between estimated income and outgo (Figure 23·10); beyond that they must be financed by other means. The inventories of public works sponsored by the Public Works Administration and National Resources Committee in 1935 and the latter organization in 1936 did much to make municipalities think seriously about programming public works. But these inventories were largely wishful thinking of what the municipalities would like to do and in most cases did not indicate any serious thought as to how the projects might be financed.

The program, in so far as it may be prepared by the city planner, has been described as follows:

A suitable way of approaching the problem would be to prepare three lists of projects: one which might be carried out within the next six-year period; a second group for consideration within the ensuing six-year period, and a third group which would include projects for later consideration. It would be desirable to have approximate cost estimates for projects in the first two groups, and the total cost for each group should not exceed that which could reasonably be financed within the period.

Even such a program will be subject to changes caused by unforeseen conditions. Certain projects may involve legal obstacles which will require their postponement. In other cases conditions may arise which will make it possible to go ahead at once with projects listed for later consideration. Still other projects may become impracticable due to new improvements in their path which will greatly increase their cost.

In any event, the city planner can make a valuable contribution to putting public works programming on a sound basis. He should grasp this opportunity and not shirk the responsibilities that go with it.[16]

A procedure in practice in many cities is to have a one-year capital budget, adopted each year by the legislative body and establishing its program of public works for the current year, supplemented by a long-range program for the succeeding five or six years.

Such a procedure was established by the New York City charter of 1938 and gave the city planning commission considerable control over the city's capital budget. Both a one-year capital budget and a capital program for the five calendar years next succeeding are required, and the planning commission makes the first draft of each. No project not in the commission's first draft may be added by the Board

[16] "Long-range Capital Improvement Programming and Budgeting," by Harold M. Lewis, *The Planners' Journal,* January-February, 1938, page 4.

of Estimate without first being referred to the city planning commission. If the commission recommends the project, the Board of Estimate may then add it forthwith; if the planning

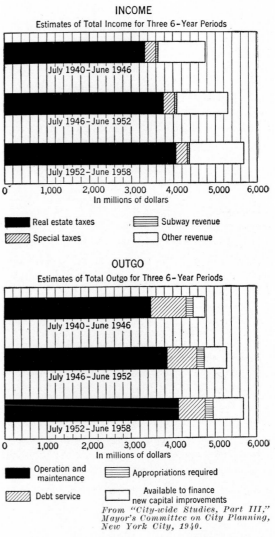

From *"City-wide Studies, Part III,"* Mayor's Committee on City Planning, New York City, 1940.

FIGURE 23·10. A STUDY FOR THE FINANCING OF PUBLIC IMPROVEMENTS IN NEW YORK CITY

commission does not recommend it, the Board may include the project only by a three-fourths vote. The section of the charter relating to the capital budget is given in full as Appendix E (see pages 214 to 216).

In each case the improvement program becomes a variable, to be adjusted each year in the light of modifications in the master plan, private developments, and the financial condition of the municipality. Its success involves close co-operation between the executive, the legislative body, the financial officer, and the planning agency.

Selected References

ADAMS, THOMAS, HAROLD M. LEWIS, and THEODORE T. McCROSKEY: *Population, Land Values, and Government*, Vol. II, Regional Survey of New York and Its Environs, 1929. (Distributed by Regional Plan Association, Inc., New York. See, particularly, Part II, "Land Values," pages 132–192.)

"Equitable Zoning and Assessments for City Planning Projects" (Progress Report of Committee of City Planning Division), *Proceedings of the American Society of Civil Engineers*, February, 1936, pages 207–212. Also discussion and bibliography, by GEORGE H. HERROLD, *Proceedings*, August, 1936, pages 973–980.

"Excess Condemnation in City Planning—A Symposium," by FRANK B. WILLIAMS, A. L. VEDDER, CHARLES WELLFORD LEAVITT, and FREDERICK H. FAY (with discussion), *Transactions of the American Society of Civil Engineers*, Vol. 89, 1926, pages 791–840.

Financing Postwar Construction Program of the Village of Scarsdale, N. Y., Village of Scarsdale, March 31, 1947.

HALL, ALBERT H.: "The Preparation and Administration of a Municipal Capital Budget (A Manual of Procedure and Practice)," *Publication* 16, New York State Conference of Mayors and Other Municipal Officials, Bureau of Training and Research, Albany, N. Y., 1932.

LEWIS, HAROLD M., HAROLD MERRILL, and CHARLES WILTSE: "Long-range Capital Improvement Programming and Budgeting," *The Planner's Journal*, January-February, 1938, pages 1–7, American Institute of Planners, 77 Massachusetts Ave., Cambridge, Mass.

Long-range Programming of Public Works, National Resources Planning Board, Washington, D. C., June, 1941.

Programming Public Improvements in the City of New York (City-wide Studies, Part III), Mayor's Committee on City Planning, City of New York, 1934–1938. (Published, 1940, and distributed by Regional Plan Association, Inc., New York.)

Public Works Planning, National Resources Committee, Washington, D. C., December, 1936. (See, particularly, Part III, "Division of Costs and Responsibility.")

Questions

1. What sources of municipal income are generally available for financing public works?
2. To what extent have state and federal funds been available for financing local projects?
3. How may municipal expenditures be analyzed to determine the amount of funds available for future public works?
4. Give examples of the unwise use of borrowing power to finance public works.
5. What controls have states established to prevent excessive borrowing by municipalities?
6. What is meant by a pay-as-you-go policy of financing public works? Give examples of its successful use.
7. What is excess condemnation? What factors have retarded its use in the United States?
8. What are the practical considerations and the basic theory back of excess condemnation?
9. What is meant by "Lex Adickes"? How may this be applied to reduce the cost of city planning projects?
10. What principles should govern the determination of whether an improvement should be financed by local assessment?
11. What types of large public projects justify an assessment of at least part of their cost upon a local area of benefit? Give examples of such procedures.
12. Describe four types of special assessments.
13. How should the division of expense between city-wide and local areas and the distribution and area of a local assessment be determined?
14. What special factors affect the means of financing public works in large capital cities?
15. How may local assessment and excess condemnation be combined?
16. How may a city planning commission participate in the establishment of a capital improvement budget and program?

24

MUNICIPAL LAND POLICIES

THE DETERMINATION OF A MUNICIPAL LAND policy involves many administrative problems and is a direct responsibility of the elected officials making up the legislative body of a city or other municipality. The subject has been discussed in detail in other books and reports; in this volume it can be touched upon only briefly and from the point of view of its effect upon the carrying out of a comprehensive master plan.

Some cities may have adopted certain policies with respect to the control and ownership of land within the city limits and outside its boundaries for the express purpose of providing funds for carrying out city planning projects or for other municipal activities. The land policies considered herein, however, are those which have for their chief purpose the control of the price of land, the prevention of land speculation, and, as a result of such control, the reduction of rents. In other words, the purpose is chiefly social, or it relates to the social aspects of city planning. This relationship has been brought out in the chapters dealing with housing and the redevelopment of blighted areas (see pages 16 and 34).

The cities of Continental Europe, especially those of Germany, have gone so much further in the control of land prices through restrictive regulation and investment in land by the cities themselves that instances of results accomplished through the adoption of such policies must be drawn chiefly from the cities of those countries, although note will be made of the active propaganda for the adoption of these policies and of the arguments advanced in their favor in the English-speaking countries. In Great Britain, and to an even greater extent in the United States, there has been a strong feeling that the city should not be an owner of real estate other than that needed for public purposes and that investment in land with a view to a profit from its resale or to controlling land prices is not a public purpose. In Germany, on the other hand, such investments are believed to be a perfectly legitimate municipal function; at least they are held to be legitimate and wise by the municipal authorities.

Nevertheless, even in prewar Germany, with its disposition to submit to regulations and policies imposed upon the people by municipal officers who had firmly established their reputations for honest and efficient administration in all other governmental details, there were protests against the severity of some of the regulations affecting the use of land, and against attempts of the state and municipal authorities to control or keep down real estate values. There was a "Protective League of Land and Home Owners" with headquarters in Berlin and branches or affiliated organizations in other cities which opposed some of these policies, or what were considered extreme, arbitrary, and unwarranted applications of others believed to be fair and wise if reasonably enforced.

Examples in German Cities

An official statement of the city of Düsseldorf, Germany, has been summarized by Frederic C. Howe.[1] It is argued that experience

[1] See his book, *European Cities at Work,* Charles Scribner's Sons, New York, 1913.

has frequently shown that a tract of land needed for some public purpose is often much more expensive at the time it is acquired than it was when the need of its ultimate acquisition first became apparent. The city should not, however, limit its acquisition of land to its own immediate needs. It is entirely proper that the city should participate in the rise in the prices of land brought about through the establishment of some municipal institution or the carrying out of some improvement that results in an increase of the value of land in its vicinity. The city should especially become the owner of land in the suburban sections and thus influence their development, the mode of building, and the creation of larger open spaces, and should promote also the opening up of land for building purposes and thus keep down the prices of land within reasonable limits.

The increase in the value of municipal lands had been, according to the experience of Düsseldorf, on an average for a long term of years, not less than four per cent annually. Even though stagnation in the rise of prices does set in at times, it is claimed that four per cent interest will be realized and that cities may even figure upon four per cent with compound interest. While an investment at four per cent doubles itself in 17 years, Düsseldorf has found that ground values treble and quadruple during the same period, and in some cases increase even more rapidly.

Düsseldorf, as a result of its policy, at the time of World War I was the owner of land equal in area to 17 per cent of the entire city in addition to its liberal park reservations and the space occupied by its streets. While some of this land had doubtless been acquired for the purpose of carrying out projected improvements, a large part of it was held as an investment and for the purpose of controlling development and discouraging speculation.

Prewar Berlin was a large investor in land, its holdings being about three times the area of the city, by far the greater portion of which was obviously outside the city limits. Strassburg was a large land owner, its holdings being said to amount to several times the area of the city, while Frankfort owned an area nearly one-half, Hamburg one-third, Cologne 18 per cent,

and Hanover 11 per cent of the areas within the limits of the respective cities.

A.-Augustin Rey has urged that, in order to secure good living conditions, cities should reserve large open spaces and keep down the price of land, and to attain this end the municipal authorities must

. . . jealously keep all the sites in their possession and never sell any of them. Those which have cost little and are not intended for laying out as parks and public gardens should be let on long leases and at low rents in order to facilitate the erection of dwellings surrounded by open spaces in which the great working class may live at moderate rents. They should seize every opportunity which arises to increase their property by purchasing, according to circumstances and at a moderate price, large areas of land. Municipal authorities should not, however, unless in very exceptional cases, themselves erect dwelling houses.[2]

Rey refers to the striking example set by the city of Ulm, where the purchase of extensive areas by the city enabled it to prevent a rise in the price of land. The dwellings have few stories and are surrounded by wide open spaces and, as a result, the healthfulness of the city is notable. Frank Koester stated that the city of Ulm actually owned 80 per cent of the land in the city and its immediate suburbs. He said that the city's real estate speculation began when the old fortifications were sold to the municipality, and the area formerly occupied by them was used in developing a comprehensive city planning and housing scheme. This resulted in a prompt advance in the land values outside the zone of the improvement, and, while the city had already been buying land, it extended its operations and secured large additional areas in order that the city itself should profit by the results of its own undertaking rather than allow the former owners to be enriched through no act of their own. It is said that in 1909 the municipality, then a city of but 56,000 population, had acquired more than 1,200 acres representing an investment of about $1,400,000, while some 400 acres had been sold for about $1,625,000, the city still having about 800 acres besides a cash profit of $225,000. Meanwhile other land in large amounts had been purchased in the old parts of the town.

[2] *Proceedings of London Town Planning Conference*, 1910, page 274.

Not only is Ulm a large land owner, but it improves its holdings by building and selling on the most liberal terms, 10 per cent cash and the balance at very low rates of interest, and with the understanding that the city may take back the property at the original purchase price in case the owner is unable to pay the interest. With this control of the nature of the development there is perhaps a better guaranty of permanence of the character of a neighborhood than is to be found in any other city.[3]

Frank B. Williams, in a report made to the Heights of Buildings Commission of New York City, gives some interesting information concerning the results of the regulations and land policies of the German cities, which were obtained by him in the course of an investigation made for the commission. In Frankfort he found that regulation did not keep land prices down. Many of the streets are claimed to be wider than necessary and the abutting property had to pay for them; the city is said to have bought land too extensively, thus lessening the supply, the city owning a third of the possible building land within its limits and a few large financial institutions and wealthy persons another third; it is also alleged that the city paid too high prices for what it bought. Owing to the high land values and the restrictions upon its use, building had practically ceased in 1910. In the central part of the town, where the restrictions were less rigid, the land was all built upon, and in the outer districts, where limitation of height and area which might be occupied were more severe, rentable space was so reduced that buildings were not profitable at rents the tenants were able to pay. To meet this situation the restrictions in the outer zone were somewhat lessened in 1910, but financial conditions were such that there was little, if any, resumption of building.

One of the objects which the German cities sought to attain by their land policies was the prevention of "wild building" or the scattered improvements which make the approaches to the average American city so ragged and irregular. German cities extend from the center outward in solid blocks, each block being almost entirely built up before building is commenced upon the next block beyond. One of the purposes of this policy was to keep down the cost of construction, repairs, cleaning, lighting, and policing. In many cities this was effectively accomplished by prohibiting the erection of any building until the street upon which it abutted had been completely paved, while no street could be paved unless the roadway and sidewalk pavement connected with a street already completely improved. It followed that no individual could erect a single building on an unimproved street unless he had first paved or paid for the pavement of the entire block, and then only if the block connected with a street already paved; that is, if he wished to build in advance of his neighboring landowners, he had to pay for the pavement in front of their property as well as for that in front of his own. The city secured his investment in the improvement to the extent that it collected and paid to him the share of the pavement chargeable to any other owner when he in turn wished to build, and would not issue a permit until such share had been paid. The result was that little, if any, individual building was possible; practically all the land was held, and all the building done, by corporations of sufficient financial resources to permit them to carry out such undertakings on a large scale. If the purpose is to reduce the amount of "building ripe" land to a minimum, such a policy will surely accomplish it.

In order to prevent speculative increases in land values, the municipal authorities of Germany did not hesitate to resort to comprehensive changes in the zoning ordinances and maps, placing areas in much more restricted districts than previously. Williams referred to such a case in Charlottenburg, where an undeveloped area was so rezoned on the grounds that high values for which it was held were purely speculative. A public official stated that the owners "must take their chances as to the ordinance they will get, and they knew it when they bought. We cannot make our rules to fit their prices; let them fit their prices to our rules."

[3] *Modern City Planning and Maintenance*, by Frank Koester, McBride, Nast & Co., 1914, pages 197–199.

It has been brought out in the discussion of the need of rezoning in Chapter 12 that many early American zoning ordinances placed excessive areas in business and multi-family districts. (See Volume I, pages 263 to 265.) Speculative land values have resulted, and many American communities are rezoning many such areas for more restrictive uses on the grounds that only if so rezoned will they be put to any efficient use. Where assessed values have risen with the speculation, they should be lowered to conform with the revised zoning.

Land Control by Taxation

The German examples discussed above depended primarily on control through regulation. Another approach is through various forms of land taxation.

Perhaps one of the simplest and most effective ways to prevent speculative increases in land values is the exaction of an unearned increment tax.[4] The right of the city to a part of the increase in the value of real estate caused by a specific improvement has already been referred to (see Chapter 23, page 175) as a justification for the adoption of the policy of excess condemnation in order to meet a part of the cost of such improvements. The unearned increment tax as imposed by the German city is, however, a revenue-producing device and may be considered as a municipal land policy. Howe says that the first instance of the imposition of such a tax occurred in 1898, when Germany acquired from China the port of Kiau Chau, and provided that the purchasers of land should pay into the city treasury a tax amounting to 33 per cent of the increased value which came to the land by virtue of the growth of the community. This was so successful that, in 1904, Frankfort adopted the policy, and it was rapidly taken up by other German cities.

In Frankfort a transfer tax of two per cent on the selling price of the property is paid whenever it changes hands, irrespective of whether it has increased in value or not. The unearned increment tax proper is imposed both upon the

increase in the value of the land which remains in the possession of the same owner, amounting to one to six per cent of the increase in value, and upon the speculative profit realized from its sale, this being much higher and ranging from two to 25 per cent, according to the amount of profit and the period within which it is realized. Within three years after this policy was adopted by Frankfort it was introduced by eleven other cities, and so rapidly did the idea spread that by 1910 it is said that 457 German cities and towns had followed Frankfort's example. Of the cities and towns of Prussia which had adopted the plan, 27 were of over 100,000 population, 72 of 20,000 to 100,000, and 64 of 5,000 to 20,000.

In most American cities nearly all the taxes are imposed upon real estate. Real property in many cities is assessed for taxation at its full market value, and as these assessments are constantly increasing with the land values the unearned increment actually is taxed, though not to the degree which prevails in Germany. In Great Britain, on the other hand, land is taxed on the basis of the returns received from it. Large tracts of unimproved land, even in London and other large cities, thus almost entirely escaped taxation during the period in which they became more and more valuable owing to the development of the property about them. The injustice of this system was so obvious that it may have been a major factor in the inclusion in Great Britain's Town and Country Planning Act of 1947 of provisions for the acquisition by the national government of all future development rights of undeveloped land and a "betterment" tax covering the unearned increment on future increased values (see Chapter 20, page 146).

Efforts to induce the provision of houses at low rents have frequently taken the form of agitation for the decrease or even the abolition of taxes on buildings, with the avowed purpose of compelling the improvement of vacant land, thereby insuring a surplus rather than a shortage of dwellings with a reduction in rentals which would naturally follow. To its advocate this single-tax theory seems the only sure remedy for many of the ills suffered by city dwell-

[4] See reference to such a tax as an aid in the prevention of blighted areas, page 37.

ers. It appears, however, to be the first step towards the complete municipalization of the land within the city, which would certainly put an effective stop to land speculation by individuals, and yet the German cities frankly maintain that such land speculation is an entirely proper as well as profitable activity for the city itself.

The advocates of this policy maintain that the halving or entire removal of the tax on buildings will stimulate better building and better architecture. If this is the case, the reason would doubtless be that the better built and more attractive dwellings and office buildings would secure tenants, rather than that the owner of the land wishes to provide for tenant or buyer the best that he possibly can. The reduction of, or even exemption from, taxation for a limited period for buildings reaching a definite standard of construction and architecture would probably accomplish this same purpose, and good building might become a habit. Awards by a competent jury of architects for the best of its type of building erected in a community within a year have in several cases done much to improve the architecture of both business and residential buildings.

Those who urge the adoption of the single-tax plan, the arguments in favor of which were so forcibly presented by the late Henry George, insist that land, being something which has not been created by personal effort or industry, is not a thing which can properly be held in private possession. They claim that the person who happens to own it should, while having the use of it, contribute some of his profit to the people whose presence on and about it has actually created its value. A fair contribution would be the increase in value which the land has acquired through no act of the owner.

There is certainly some danger that a continuation of the practice of obtaining most of the municipal operating revenues from real property taxes which fail to recognize the ability of the property to earn the tax may act as a penalty, or luxury, tax on real estate which can best be kept in residential use, on the basis of a comprehensive master plan.

Public Land Reclamation

While American cities have been hesitant to pursue a policy of acquiring upland property for private development, there are examples where water-front tidal lands have been acquired and reclaimed for such uses through the agency of a state government. An outstanding example is provided by the tidal flats along the Charles River in the Back Bay District of Boston. Although in most tide-water states the state owns the tidal flats up to the high-water line, in Massachusetts the owners of the upland water front also owned the tidal flats to the low-water mark, provided it was not more than 100 rods from the shore. The procedure followed in this case has been described by Frederic H. Fay as follows:

The extensive tidal flats which have since been developed as the Back Bay Section of Boston were separated from the main "tidal-estuary" portion of the Charles River about a century ago by the building of a tide-mill dam on what is now the line of Beacon Street. Prior to 1850, the population of the City of Boston and of the adjoining Town of Roxbury had grown to such extent that the drainage from these communities into this tidal-flat basin had created a nuisance. Shortly after 1850, the Commonwealth undertook the reclamation of these flats as a measure of sanitation. As the simplest method of procedure, the State acquired title to the area by right of eminent domain. The flats were filled and proper drainage was provided. Suitable streets and public spaces were laid out, certain portions of the lands were granted by the Commonwealth to educational institutions, and the remaining lots were sold to private parties. The reclamation of this considerable territory was of benefit not only to the inhabitants of Boston and neighboring communities in the abolition of a nuisance, but the net result financially was a substantial profit to the State. Since that time other tidal flats along different sections of the water front of Boston Harbor have been and are being similarly reclaimed by State agency.[5]

Increases in Urban Real Estate Values

It is common knowledge that increases in the value of real estate in rapidly growing cities have been enormous.

Reference is frequently made to the extraordinary increases which have taken place in such

[5] "Excess Condemnation in Massachusetts," by Frederic H. Fay, *Transactions of the American Society of Civil Engineers,* Vol. 89, 1926, page 817.

values in New York City, and yet it is admitted that if the price paid to the Indians in 1626 for the whole of Manhattan Island, which was $24.60, had been put at compound interest during the time which has elapsed since its purchase, it would by now have amounted to a sum not less than the entire assessed value of that land at the present time. Had the people not come to this island in great numbers, the land would be worth no more today than it was in 1626.

Many owners of city property do not realize as great a return upon their original investments as they would had the money been left in a savings bank. It is only through improvements placed upon the property that any return at all has been realized; that is, the land itself has simply afforded a site for a business enterprise, the success of which has given that land and other land in the vicinity an apparently greater value. It is this apparent increase in land value that the single-taxers would extinguish by taxation without penalizing the owner by imposing upon him a further tax for his enterprise in erecting useful buildings upon the land, or his public spirit in making such buildings so attractive that they add to the beauty of the city. It is urged also that, when insanitary tenements and unsightly structures are maintained upon the land, the city should have the same right to insist upon their removal without compensation that it now has to condemn and remove a building which is structurally weak and unsafe, or to take away and destroy rotten meat, spoiled fish, impure milk, or disease-infected clothing.

There are many individual cases in which apparent increases in the prices of land have brought fortunes to those who were lucky enough to acquire it at the right time. The *Single Tax Review* for November-December, 1913, gives a number of such instances, showing how slowly the land values of Manhattan Island advanced when the population was small and how they increased by leaps and bounds as the number of inhabitants began to grow rapidly. It is said that the first private sale of land recorded was in 1643, the year in which lower Broadway was laid out, when a lot on Bridge Street between Whitehall and Broad

streets was sold for a little over $9. Broadway was then the fashionable residence street, and a lot below Wall Street was sold in 1726 to a blacksmith for $250. By 1770 lots in this neighborhood had increased in value to nearly $2,000. In 1790, a lot at Broadway and Battery Place with what was then considered a fine house was worth $10,000; another, fronting on Bowling Green, the home of one of the most distinguished citizens, had the same value; another a few doors above was worth $7,000. The residence of Mayor Varick at the corner of Pine Street was worth $15,000, while a little below Wall Street stood the most palatial residence of its day, which was valued, both land and improvements, at $17,000. In 1794 the land on which the old *World* Building (Pulitzer Building) now stands was sold for $1,800; the land alone was assessed in 1913 for purposes of taxation at $1,500,000. Broadway then ended at Chambers Street, where the Lispenard farm began. Just after it was extended through this farm a small lot near the corner of Duane Street was bought for $250 and 10 years later was sold for $1,975. In 1818 this same lot was mortgaged for $7,000 and was sold on foreclosure for $8,600; it again changed hands in 1825 for $9,000; a transfer which took place in 1898 was for a consideration of $200,000, representing an increase of 2,100 per cent in 73 years.

The slow growth of land values during the century following the transfer from Dutch to English rule is explained by the small increase in population. When that change took place in 1674, there were only about 3,000 persons in the town; there was an increase of but 400 in the next three years and about 1,000 in the following 25 years, and in 1771 New York had become a city of only 21,683. From then on its growth was steady and rapid. In the last decade of the eighteenth century the population doubled, going from 30,000 to 60,000, while in the first decade of the nineteenth century it rose to 95,000. In 1845 the city had 371,223 inhabitants, which number was increased to 515,394 in 1850, a growth of nearly 40 per cent in five years. This increase in population was accompanied by an extraordinary rise in land values. In 1820 one thousand building lots between Fourth and Seventh avenues were sold for

$4,000, or at the rate of $4 a lot, while in 1852 they were sold for $780 a lot. A single lot on Fifth Avenue in this same district, having an area of 2,210 square feet, was sold in 1908 for $250,000, or $113.12 a square foot, while a corner plot at Fifth Avenue and Fifty-sixth Street, 50 by 100 feet in size, brought $725,000 or $145 a square foot. The old Fifth Avenue Hotel property fronting on Broadway and Fifth Avenue between Twenty-third and Twenty-fourth streets was sold for $7,250,000, while 60 years before it was valued at $2,000. The increases in the values of downtown property during this period were still more striking. A lot at the corner of Broadway and Dey Street, which in 1745 was sold for less than $200, brought $1,-000,000 in 1906. The land on which the old Equitable Building now stands, which is valued at about $12,000,000, was sold in 1721 for a little less than $300.

Some of the investments in land on Manhattan Island which are now seen to have been very profitable were not considered evidence of particular shrewdness by the investors' neighbors at the time. As late as 1826, when John Jacob Astor bought the Thompson farm lying on both sides of Fifth Avenue from Thirty-second to Thirty-fifth streets for $25,-000, it was thought by some to be a foolish investment, as the land was not even considered good pasture. In 1908 a single lot in this tract was sold for $400,000, and the land on which stood the old Waldorf-Astoria Hotel (later demolished to make way for the Empire State Building) had an assessed value in 1913, exclusive of the building, of $9,260,000. When Captain Randall made his will in 1801, and left a farm of 21 acres at Broadway and Astor place, the income of which was to be devoted to the support of a home for old sailors, no one imagined that the Sailors' Snug Harbor would, before the end of that century, receive an income of more than $300,000 a year from ground leases for the land comprised in that farm. The old Stewart store, now a part of the Wanamaker establishment, is on a portion of the tract, and its assessed value for land alone was $1,765,000 in 1913.

The statement in the article in the *Single Tax Review,* from which most of the preceding data

have been taken, that the land has value only because of the presence of people on it, is obviously true. The buildings which are erected on it are mere incidents, and they soon give place to others more capable of earning an income which will pay the interest on the land investment. After commenting upon the fact that few of the old buildings remain, the article closes with the following:

> But the island remains, the earth and rocks, the geologic formation, plus population; and the revenues of the great land owners remain as long as these remain. Houses, mercantile palaces, and stately office buildings come and go; but a little earth and rock and sand fronting the harbor remain as a very permanent investment, which increases constantly in value as the human tide flows in.

Land values in New York City continued to advance until the depression of the 1930's caused a general recession as a result of the countrywide drop in the market values of real estate. The assessed values are greatest on Manhattan Island, owing to its strategic location, the limited amount of land, and the shape of the island; the areas of greatest values are at the southerly end, where the financial district and the administrative center of the city are located, and in the midtown area, where the office and retail districts are centralized. In the other four boroughs the values are better distributed and will probably continue to increase, with a recession of values in some of the older districts. The trends in the assessed values of real estate in the five boroughs and the entire city during the 45 years from 1900 to 1945 are shown in Table 31, which has been compiled from the reports of the Department of Taxes.

The values given in the table include both land and buildings and the value of special franchises. Up to the year 1932 there was an increase in the total values every year, although it was slight in some years and very marked in others. At that date the total reached a peak of $19,617,000. In 1903 there was an increase of 43 per cent over the values of 1902, which was due to a consistent effort to assess all property at its full value as required by law, coupled with a desire to increase the borrowing capacity of the city in order to carry out some extensive improvements, the bonded debt of the city for enterprises which are not self-sustaining being limited to 10 per cent of the assessed value of the real estate. The total for the entire city decreased each year from 1933 through 1938 and from that date to 1945 was generally downward but irregular, with gains in some sections. The total figures for the year 1945–1946 indicated the beginning of an upward trend.

TABLE 31

TRENDS IN ASSESSED VALUES OF REAL ESTATE IN THE FIVE BOROUGHS OF THE CITY OF NEW YORK, BY FIVE-YEAR INTERVALS, 1900 TO 1945

Assessed Values in Millions of Dollars [a]

Year	Manhattan	The Bronx	Brooklyn	Queens	Richmond	Entire City
1900	2,231	138	651	104	43	3,169
1905	3,821	275	941	140	45	5,222
1910	4,744	494	1,404	335	68	7,044
1915	5,146	677	1,692	510	84	8,109
1920	5,187	753	1,938	636	112	8,626
1925	6,721	1,074	2,919	1,013	174	11,901
1930	9,593	1,998	4,272	2,040	300	18,204
1935	8,373	1,903	3,933	2,145	295	16,650
1939–1940	8,129	1,954	3,939	2,139	300	16,641
1944–1945	7,404	1,991	3,698	2,450	302	15,846

[a] Includes real estate of corporations and special franchises.
Percentage of increase during 45 years:

Manhattan	232	Queens	2,256
The Bronx	1,343	Richmond	602
Brooklyn	468	Entire city	400

The land values of New York have been discussed at some length, not because they illustrate the working of a municipal land policy, but as affording an excellent example of the results of a lack of such a policy. Many other American cities provide similar examples of rapid increases, some of them even more extraordinary during "boom" periods. In many there were recessions in values before the general recession in the depression of the 1930's.

Are the increases which have taken place unnatural and unwholesome? Are fortunes made through far-sighted investments in land in a growing city ill-gotten? Should the state or the city take for itself a considerable portion of these increased values and thus keep within reasonable limits the fortunes which may be amassed by shrewd or lucky investors and their descendants? Should the city, by judicious purchases of land in advance of development, and its improvement or resale at moderate prices and subject to restrictions which will prevent its too intensive use, effectually put a

stop to such great increases in value and the heavy tax upon business which these values involve? While the German cities evidently believe that it should, there is a feeling among many American city planners that the Germans have gone farther in this direction than is feasible for cities in the United States. Somewhere between the extremes, represented by New York on the one hand and the typical prewar German city on the other, there is doubtless a happy mean which will give sufficient opportunity for private enterprise and yet will insure to the city, or to all the people of the city, a share in the values created by their presence and their labor.

Urban Land Policy of American Institute of Planners

The writer believes that the statement of general principles relating to urban land policies adopted by the American Institute of Planners on February 17, 1946, provides a sound basis for the approach to such problems by both city planners and municipal officials. Its main features are summarized in the following paragraphs.[6]

Any sound plan for the development, rehabilitation, or redevelopment of the land resources of an urban community must be based upon "a comprehensive plan designed to promote the general welfare through improvement of facilities for living and working in the entire community or metropolitan area."

The large-scale development indicated for effective urban rebuilding requires public aid to supplement private initiative. To control and meet the costs, to assure the benefits desired, and to retain the optimum social and economic values, an unusual exercise of sovereign powers will be needed. Such powers are likely to be required to control growth in outlying areas as well as to effectuate redevelopment of built-up areas.

An urban planning program leading to the preparation, adoption, and periodic review of a

[6] For full statement see "Report of the Committee on Urban Land Policies," Journal of the American Institute of Planners, April-May-June, 1946, pages 36–43.

comprehensive master plan should be carried out by "an official planning agency in consultation with the operating official agencies and with citizen participation, and under competent professional direction." To supplement the master plan, there should be a program of land use controls which may be employed to effectuate the plan.

The most generally recognized instruments for land use control, which should be integrated in a rational urban land program, are:

a. Mapping and subdivision regulations.
b. Zoning.
c. Building, housing, sanitary codes.
d. Deed restrictions.
e. Easements or rights in land.
f. Subsidies, such as tax exemption, or direct technical and financial assistance. Subsidies present special problems and dangers and should not be employed as isolated instruments.

Other emerging types of land use controls include:

a. Improved practices in municipal assessment and tax levying on real estate, the foreclosure of tax-delinquent property, and rules for tax exemption.
b. Long-range programs for public works, through which the direction, form, and extent of land use and development may be controlled.
c. More widespread review of specific public projects in their relation to the master plan, and legislation to insure that proposed new development, rehabilitation, and redevelopment schemes conform to a comprehensive plan for the entire community, in furtherance of the general welfare.
d. Increased public ownership of land.
e. The development of practical forms of regional government and special "authorities."

Minimum standards must be determined for land use and occupancy which will produce maximum social and economic values. Further research is needed in this field, and much of it could well be undertaken by colleges and governmental agencies if given general direction and integration by the American Institute of Planners.

Land acquisition may be carried out by one or more of the following techniques: (a) purchase, (b) condemnation and excess condemnation, (c) gift, (d) exchange, (e) foreclosure, (f) reclamation, and (g) lease. Research is needed to simplify, improve, and standardize these techniques.

Some type of partnership of government and private enterprise is indicated for the actual job of urban rebuilding, and this should be so set up as to give adequate inducement to private enterprise, which may accept a lower rate of return on its capital in a modernized urban area with proper safeguards against premature depreciation.

Selected References

GEORGE, HENRY: *Significant Paragraphs from Progress and Poverty, by Henry George* (with introduction by John Dewey), Robert Schalkenbach Foundation, New York, 1931.

HOWE, FREDERIC C.: *European Cities at Work,* Charles Scribner's Sons, New York, 1913.

HOYT, HOMER: *One Hundred Years of Land Values in Chicago,* The University of Chicago Press, Chicago, 1933.

"Report of Committee on Urban Land Policies, adopted by the American Institute of Planners, February 17, 1946," *Journal of the American Institute of Planners,* Vol. XII, No. 2 (April-May-June), 1946, pages 36-43.

WILLIAMS, FRANK BACKUS: "The German Zone Building Regulations," Appendix III, *Report of the Heights of Buildings Commission to the Board of Estimate and Apportionment, City of New York,* December 23, 1913, pages 94-119.

Questions

1. What has been the main objective of those types of land policies which come within the field of city planning?
2. In what way have the land policies in German cities differed from those in United States cities?
3. How have German cities prevented scattered buildings on their edges?
4. Where did the unearned increment tax on land originate? Where has it been most extensively used?
5. What is the single-tax plan of real estate taxation? What arguments have been advanced in its favor?
6. Give an example of the public acquisition of water-front tidal lands for private development.
7. To what extent have the assessed values of real estate increased in typical American cities? What do these increases indicate in regard to municipal land policies?
8. What should be the main basis for a sound municipal land policy in any community?
9. List effective instruments for the control of land use.
10. By what different methods may land be acquired for public use?

25

THE OPPORTUNITIES AND RESPONSIBILITIES OF THE CIVIL ENGINEER

IN THE PRECEDING CHAPTERS AN ATTEMPT HAS been made to indicate what a city plan is, how it is developed, the various problems which must be studied, and the conditions which it is necessary to provide for or guard against. The unfortunate results of mistakes in the original plan have been pointed out, and the difficulty and expense of subsequent corrections have been noted. Who is primarily responsible for these mistakes? Perhaps it is unfair to call them mistakes, if the word is taken to mean blunders due to lack of ordinary foresight or to carelessness. The recent growth of cities and the changed conditions which have made possible the concentration of such numbers as are now found in our large towns could not have been foreseen by those who laid the foundations for what are now our largest cities; but many new communities have lately been established and small towns are rapidly developing into large cities.

The urban population of the United States, as shown by the Federal Census figures through 1940, continues to grow much faster than the rural population (see Chapter 2, Volume I). At the same time the central areas in the larger cities are losing population, in many cases resulting in a net loss to the entire city, while its suburbs continue to gain. The 1940 census listed 412 urban places with a population of 25,000 or more. During the decade from 1910 to 1920, 111 of these municipalities registered gains of over 50 per cent; 70 of these showed gains from 50 to 100 per cent, and 41 gains of

over 100 per cent. Hamtramck, Michigan, led with a gain of 1,266 per cent, while, of the cities which had over 100,000 population in 1920, Akron led with a gain of 201.8 per cent. During the decade ending with 1940 only 13 of these 412 communities showed gains of over 50 per cent, of which only four registered gains of over 100 per cent. Miami Beach, Florida, led with a gain of 331.4; of the cities of over 100,000 population, Miami led with a 55.6 per cent gain and San Diego followed with 37.4 per cent. Of these 412 urban places, 104 experienced population losses in the decade ending with 1940, as against 13 of the same communities which had registered losses for the decade ending with 1920.

This combination of continued urban growth and of decentralization in metropolitan areas has emphasized the need of more far-sighted planning. There will still be examples of sensational growth of cities, but the urgent need in urban planning is for better co-ordination between land use and communication facilities. Plans for the older American towns show a rather curious combination of overplanning for the intensive use of land, as particularly expressed by zoning, and underplanning for communication facilities and public open spaces. The excuse that it is impossible to foresee the future can no longer be given much consideration.

The number of cities that have given serious consideration to any kind of comprehensive planning is still discouragingly low. The survey conducted by the National Resources Committee in 1936 [1] listed only 276 municipalities with over 25,000 population in 1930 as having official planning commissions, and only 65 of these as having current annual planning appropriations greater than $500. It is significant that a number of the larger cities in the United States have recently undertaken, or are talking about, replanning. In many cases the earlier plans have either failed to realize future needs or to take account of changed and changing conditions. While some of the mistakes that have been made are chargeable to the municipal engineer, many of the earlier ones were due to the former lack of power of the municipal authorities to control the platting and development by private individuals and land companies of tracts within the city limits, or contiguous to them, which have been absorbed by its rapid growth. Through the use of planning powers now generally available, such mistakes can be avoided in the future (see Chapter 21, "Control of Land Subdivisions").

The Engineer as Pioneer and Jack-of-all-trades

The civil engineer will be the first man on the ground; he will make the first topographic surveys; his work will influence, if it will not control, the lines of transportation and the adequacy of terminal facilities; he will fix the lines and grades of the streets which are to become the traffic arteries of the town and which will make it easy or difficult for it to develop into a great city; he will decide upon the general arrangement of the streets and blocks upon which will depend the possibility of effective architectural treatment; either he will afford an opportunity to others to propose and carry out so-called city planning projects at great cost in order to correct defects in his plan or he will, by the exercise of vision and disciplined imagination, lay down the lines along which the town can develop without costly reconstruction.

[1] "Status of City and County Planning in the United States," *Circular* X, National Resources Committee, May 15, 1937.

Who is making the most substantial contribution toward the orderly development and administration of our cities? It will be admitted that the engineer is constantly assuming a position of greater importance in the physical, industrial, and commercial development of all countries, but nowhere have his services been in greater demand than in the construction and operation of cities. Where towns formerly delegated the investigation and even the execution of important improvements to committees of boards of aldermen, who might have thought it necessary to employ a party of surveyors or even one or two men who were recognized as engineers, there are now organizations of technically trained men, some of them acknowledged experts in their particular line, to whom are left both the final decision as to the plans for important projects and complete responsibility for their execution.

The variety of subjects with which the city engineer of a town of several hundred thousand population is expected to be familiar is quite bewildering. All questions relating to street and road improvement, including the various kinds of pavement and their adaptability to different conditions; the design and construction of sewers and the various methods of sewage treatment and disposal; the water supply, its development, protection, treatment where necessary, and distribution, including the construction and operation of pumping plants; the collection and disposal of wastes by the most effective and economical methods and in the least offensive manner; the lighting of streets and buildings, whether by contract with public-service corporations or by municipal plants, together with the production and distribution of electric current or other sources of power and heat, such as compressed air and steam; the construction and maintenance of local transit facilities; problems of traffic regulation and control; building regulations, including not only the code governing methods of construction, but zoning restrictions as to their use, height, and arrangement—with respect to all of these and more the municipal engineer is expected to be able to advise and frequently design and execute.

Engineers in Administration

During recent decades the engineer has found an increasing field for the use of his abilities in municipal administration or management. In selecting a business manager it is the custom to choose one who has had extensive experience with the kind of business he is expected to manage. Municipal business consists to a very large extent in the operation of engineering enterprises, the plans for which are designed and carried out by engineers. It is quite natural, therefore, that in the selection of a manager for city business a municipal engineer should be considered.

The manager form of municipal government, described in Chapter 20, "City Planning Legislation" (see page 138), has gained great headway, and new cities, towns, and villages are adopting it each year. According to the International City Managers' Association,[2] there were 726 cities and 11 counties with managers, as of March 15, 1947. Of these, 686 were in the United States, and the balance in Alaska, Puerto Rico, the Dominion of Canada, and Ireland. There were managers in 31 cities with over 100,000 population, the largest being Cincinnati, which had a population of 455,610 in 1940. In contrast with 497 managers in service December 31, 1940, there were 622 at the end of 1946; of the 506 of the latter whose education was known, 174 held engineering degrees. There were 216 city manager appointments in 1946, compared with 135 in 1945, 97 in 1944, and 98 in 1943. Of the 45 of the 1946 appointees who came from administrative positions outside the city, 14 were engineers; of those who had had no governmental experience, 19 came from engineering positions.

While this indicates an appreciation of the value of engineering training for a city manager, it is recognized that such training must be supplemented by business sense and executive capacity, and our engineering schools are only starting to realize the need to develop these qualities. At a convention of the City Managers' Association, held at Dayton in 1915,

[2] *1947 Municipal Yearbook,* International City Managers' Association, Chicago, pages 479–496.

H. M. Waite, then manager of Dayton, made some concise and forceful statements regarding the powers and duties of a city manager, among which were the following:

Men of large affairs demand broad authority. Broad lines of authority develop and attract capable executives. Broad authority carries responsibility. Responsibility attracts executives and imposes on them caution. Executives with broad authority, and using caution, accomplish results. Communities that, for any reason, cannot give broad authority to the executive, are not ready for the ideal and should accept a more modified centralized authority and not call it a city-manager form. The executive of the ideal government should have full authority in the administration of government and be held responsible for it. Lack of authority permits excuses and explanations, but clean-cut authority gets clean-cut men and clean-cut results. To get the maximum power and efficiency from the city manager he must be given the maximum authority.

Need of Broader Viewpoint

Reference has been made to surveyors who may have been employed in the establishment of a town or in the earlier period of its development, and a distinction is drawn between surveyors and engineers. While such a distinction was intentional and is warranted in the United States, it might be misunderstood in Great Britain. The head of the engineering department of the British city is frequently called the city surveyor, as the head of the engineering department of the state of New York, before the reorganization of the state departments initiated by Governor Smith, was called the state engineer and surveyor. In neither case does the title properly indicate the nature and the duties of the office. The term "surveyor" appears so often in the British Town Planning Act and in the town planning and engineering literature of that country that Thomas Adams, who served as Town Planning Expert of the Local Government and later as Town Planning Adviser to the Canadian Commission of Conservation, was requested to indicate just what the functions of this officer are. He did so in the following words:

The surveyor is the professional man who deals with all questions connected with real estate and its development for all purposes. He is also an expert in land valuation and in questions relating to the assessments of property. These men have to pass examinations which include many architectural and engineering questions, as in developing land they have to deal with sewerage, water supply and many intricate problems of land tenure. I believe that a surveyor of this kind does not exist in America, although to a certain extent the land surveyor of Canada performs part of the duties of the British surveyor. The surveyor is thus a sort of combination of a Canadian land surveyor, municipal engineer, and real estate developer. He is a very useful professional man in England and gives a status to the management and development of real estate which is badly needed over here. Such a person can bring special expert knowledge to bear on town planning. In regard to convenience, for instance, he has to deal with the problem of land values and subdivisions as they are affected by the highways, transportation, and planning of factory areas. The same points arise in connection with fixing open spaces and height and character of buildings under the heading of amenity. Finally, he is probably the most important man in connection with the ascertaining of costs and adjusting the cost of developing land to character of buildings.

The municipal engineer needs the peculiar information and experience of the British surveyor if he is successfully to cope with the problems which are now being forced upon him. It seems odd that many of the men who have been closely identified with the development of cities and with the administration of their affairs should have manifested little interest in, and should have been slow to realize their responsibility for, the general plan upon which these cities have been started and along which they will grow. They have thought much of the problems of construction and operation, but little of the appearance of the town, and their contributions to its adornment and beautification have been small.

The author has pointed out elsewhere [3] that the engineer has an esthetic responsibility and should see to it that the structures he designs are as pleasing to look at as they are efficient in serving the special purposes for which they are designed. The success of the engineer's efforts in this direction will depend to a large degree on the extent of his co-operation with those other professions or specialists that deal more directly with art. Many of the structures designed by the engineer are beneath the ground and are not seen by the public. For example,

[3] "Esthetic Responsibilities of the Engineer," by Harold M. Lewis, *Civil Engineering*, March, 1941, pages 154–156.

in the design of a sewerage system, water-distribution system, foundation for a building, power station, or other heavy structure, esthetics can have little direct relation to the project, but even in such cases the engineer may be responsible for leaving serious scars on the surface of the earth which might have been avoided if he had fully realized his esthetic duty.

For the successful esthetic development of a city or community the city planner should keep in mind the following factors. The design, both of pattern and structures, should have an apparent fitness for the type of use to be served. There should be an orderly organization of the several parts, leading to a unity of the whole. While there should be architectural harmony of units—for example, in a university campus—it should be remembered that variety is essential to prevent monotony. Use of local materials and local ideas concerning building will lead to a distinctive style or character such as is found in many European cities.

Many engineering schools have recently recognized that the young civil engineer should at least be exposed to some elementary training in architecture and city planning. Rensselaer Polytechnic Institute requires its civil engineering students, in their senior year, to take a course in architecture described as "an introduction to the principles of architecture, their historical development, and their application to the modern problems of bridge construction, housing, city planning, and industrial buildings, such as power plants and substations." The University of Wisconsin teaches city planning in the Civil Engineering Department and considers such training essential for an engineer who is to be engaged in municipal work.

As was pointed out in the introductory chapters of this book (see Volume I), the keenest interest in what we call city planning has often been shown by architects, landscape architects, artists, students of civic affairs, and social workers, while engineers have seemed to be content to carry out the physical work of city building along lines already laid down, or, when called upon to make plans for future development, to adopt the conventional features followed by their predecessors. Engineers engaged in this particular class of municipal work have so long been accustomed to leaving the determination of general plans and policies to commissioners and other public officials that they are to a large degree responsible for the generally prevailing idea that the duty of the engineer engaged in municipal work is simply to carry out the ideas and policies of others.

On the other hand, the establishment in 1923 of the City Planning Division of the American Society of Civil Engineers and its activities to date have indicated the interest of the civil engineers in that field.[4] An analysis of the professional activities of its members, as of March 1, 1937, indicated that about 54 per cent were in private practice or employment and 46 per cent in public service. Of the latter, the largest group was in municipal service, and the second largest in federal employment.[5]

Although city planning is developing as a separate branch of the technical professions and will draw more and more on those who have graduated from courses leading to degrees in that field, the engineer, as the first man on the ground, will continue to have a rare opportunity and a grave responsibility. The fundamental work of planning will continue to be his, as is recognized by the frequent use of the term "city planning engineer" in staff organizations. He should develop vision and imagination, as he will lay the foundations on which our cities are built. However important may be the function of the architect in making a city dignified and beautiful, the general city plan will have been made before he appears on the scene, and it should be such as to afford suitable sites for his great buildings without rearranging the street system. The general plan is also not the work of the landscape architect, although it should be such as to permit effective work by him in the treatment of parks and boulevards and in the selection of the areas and the streets to be so treated. The general plan is not the work of the sculptor, but it should afford suit-

able sites for the fountains, monuments, and statues which he will be called upon to design.

Too often the eyes of the municipal engineer have been so closely fixed upon the drawing board that he has seldom looked up to catch a vision of the great city that is to come—the complex organism known as the modern city with its varied activities, its difficult social problems, its ugliness or its beauty, its awkwardness or its convenience, its capacity to debase or to elevate its citizens. Every blunder that he makes will afford an opportunity for someone else to win applause for a plan to correct it through large expenditure of public funds. It often seems as if the admiration excited by what are commonly called city planning projects is in direct proportion to the amount of destruction of existing improvements and the extent of the disarrangement of the existing plan which may be involved. If you are going to dream, we are told, dream a big dream, and the people will look and admire; but these big dreams appear always to involve the spectacular making over of a big city and rarely the planning of a city not yet come into being or even of a city which is just beginning to give promise of rapid growth, although still in a formative state. Planning of this latter kind will not bring applause; genius devoted to such work will not win prompt recognition. The merits of such a constructive plan may not be appreciated during the lifetime of the man responsible for it. L'Enfant died many years before his plan for Washington was realized to be anything more than a fanciful sketch.

In Conclusion

The idea seems to be quite prevalent that city planning for any particular town is something that may be taken up whenever sufficient popular interest has been aroused and pursued with enthusiasm until, with the aid of special expert advice, a definite plan is evolved which will probably necessitate considerable rearrangement, and that the town will then have been started on the right road for its future development. It is quite probable that if, a year or so later, a new set of experts were called in and a

---

[4] Nelson P. Lewis, the author of *The Planning of the Modern City*, was the first chairman of this Division.

[5] *Handbook of the City Planning Division, 1923–1938*, American Society of Civil Engineers, September, 1938, page 43.

new diagnosis made, an entirely different remedy would be prescribed, which would in turn be discarded by a later set of experts.

A good city plan for a well-established town that wants to correct some of its old defects and properly control its future growth has rarely, if ever, been produced as a sudden inspiration, nor has it been the result of a few weeks or months of study by a man or a group of men unfamiliar with the traditions, the habits, and the peculiar needs of the people, and yet that is the usual method of procedure. Commissions have been created, experts have been retained, and acres of plans in the form of cleverly drawn pictures have been made, exhibited and admired until someone has asked how much it is all going to cost and how the funds are to be raised. It is astonishing to what an extent these simple questions tend to dampen enthusiasm. It may be that some of the projects recommended would be cheap at any price, but such an answer will not convince the taxpayer. He must be shown just how and why they will be of advantage to the city and to him as a citizen.

The creation of a proper plan will require years of patient work, and the men who do it will be forgotten before the plan is finally carried out. The task is no one-man job, and it is never actually finished. However carefully and skilfully the first plan may be made, unforeseen changes will take place, new methods of transportation will be developed, new inventions will powerfully affect the social life of the community, and the plan, where still susceptible of change, must be modified to meet these changed conditions. The city planning consultant can contribute much in directing these planning activities and will probably continue to be called on to do the entire planning job in small communities, but with the close co-operation of the local planning commission. In our larger cities the detail work of comprehensive city planning can best be done by the regularly employed technical staff of the city, but the organization created for this purpose should be carefully selected. It may be supplemented on occasion by part-time consultants. The regular staff should contain men who are familiar with the past history and traditions of the community and are in sympathy with them, but who can appreciate changing conditions and adapt the old to the new without destroying it. The work should be directed by men who do not think the exercise of imagination an engineering crime; men who are enthusiasts without being doctrinaires; men who are content to do their work well without hope of popular applause and who are willing to await the verdict on their work which will be rendered by coming generations.

The author of the original book on which these new volumes are based undertook its preparation with the chief purpose of bringing home to the municipal engineers of the United States, to whom his book was dedicated, their responsibilities and opportunities in the field of city planning. He hoped that they would thus play a major part in directing along sane and rational lines a movement to make our cities convenient and beautiful, as well as orderly and healthful. As a civil engineer who has specialized in the field of city and regional planning, the present author can testify to the increasing interest and participation of engineers in those fields, but feels that much must still be done to make urban planning a continuous and effective process in which the municipal engineer will participate with effectiveness.

Selected References

Ewing James: "The Engineer and the Town Plan" (with discussion), *Transactions of the American Society of Civil Engineers*, Vol. 91, 1927, pages 303–313.

Municipal Yearbook (*Annual*), International City Managers' Association, Chicago.

Nolen, John: "Town Planning and the Professions Involved" (with discussion), *Transactions of the American Society of Civil Engineers*, Vol. 91, 1927, pages 721–736.

"Status of City and County Planning in the United States," *Circular* X, National Resources Committee, Washington, D. C., May 15, 1937.

Questions

1. What is the most urgent need in urban planning?
2. Why, in the future, should there be far fewer mistakes in the planning of cities than there have been in the past?

3. Why has the civil engineer played a major part in the planning of cities?

4. Describe the opportunity for the municipal engineer in the city manager field.

5. What are the esthetic responsibilities of the engineer? How may esthetics contribute to better city planning?

6. What are the principal qualifications, for the practice of city planning, of men trained in the following professions: engineering, architecture, landscape architecture, sculpture, law, economics, sociology?

7. Why does successful city planning require time, patience, and co-operation?

APPENDIX A

Principal Provisions of the Scheme Advanced by the Ruislip-Northwood Urban District Council for Development of a Section of Middlesex County, England, under the British Town Planning Act of 1909

The provisions are as amended by the Local Government Board and sent by it to the District Council.

LIMITATION OF NUMBER OF BUILDINGS TO THE ACRE. In order to deal with the question of the limitation of the number of houses to the acre, the map of the area is divided into sections of about five acres. On these sections, which are known as land units, an average of four, six, eight, or twelve buildings to the acre, roads included, must not be exceeded, the number of buildings being designated for each section. These limitations of the number of buildings per acre are to be averaged over the whole land unit, but as many as 20 buildings may be built on any single acre. In the case of a dwelling house being adapted for occupation by more than two, and not more than four families, such dwelling house shall be reckoned as two buildings. If adapted for occupation by more than four families, it shall be reckoned as three buildings.

HEIGHT AND CHARACTER OF BUILDINGS. With the exception of public buildings and buildings of a warehouse class, no building shall be erected of a greater height than 60 feet (exclusive of stories in the roof, etc.) or shall be of greater height than the distance from the main front wall to the opposite boundary of the street. For the purpose of describing the character of the buildings to be erected, various special areas on the map are colored pink and yellow. No building of the warehouse class shall be erected except within a specified area, and no buildings except those erected for the purpose of, or adapted to be used as, shops or business premises shall be erected except within certain areas which include the warehouse area.

The rest of the land included in the scheme is limited to private and professional buildings. The Council may, however, on application, consent to the carrying on of handicrafts and the selling of the products thereof, but none of the products or materials used shall be exposed in the windows. Buildings to be used for agricultural or horticultural purposes may, however, be erected on any part of the area. In regard to the design of the buildings to be erected, if the Council are of opinion that the character of the buildings proposed to be erected, whether on account of the design or the undue repetition of the design, or the materials to be used would be injurious to the amenity of the neighborhood, the Council may, subject to an appeal to the Local Government Board, require reasonable alterations to be made.

Provisions are also made as to height of windows in a room, and it is also provided that no bedroom or other habitable room shall have a floor area of less than 70 square feet or contain less than 500 cubic feet. Every new dwelling house shall be provided with at least one living room with a floor space of not less than 144 square feet and containing not less than 1,132 cubic feet, and one bedroom having a floor area of not less than 132 square feet and containing not less than 1,000 cubic feet.

SPACE ABOUT BUILDINGS. Where building lines are shown upon the map, no erection other than boundary walls or fences shall be permitted nearer to the street than such building line. In streets where no building line is shown on the map no building other than boundary walls or fences shall be erected nearer to the center of the street than 30 feet, or nearer to the boundary of the street than 15 feet. This is, however, subject to modification in the case of dwelling houses erected around a quadrangle or other open space. Special provisions are also made in regard to public buildings, buildings on corner sites, shops, etc. In the case of shops, warehouses, schools, etc., such buildings shall not cover more than half of the whole area of the site. In the case of dwelling houses not more than one-fourth of the whole site shall be covered by buildings, though in exceptional cases it is provided that one-third of the site may be so covered.

OPEN SPACES. Certain open spaces indicated on the plan are set apart, some for the purpose of allotments, some for public buildings, some as public open spaces and some for private open spaces. The private open spaces shall be maintained in good order and, when required by the Council, shall be fenced by and at the expense of the owner. If such private open spaces or the fences thereof are neglected, the Council can do any works necessary and recover the cost from the owner.

STREETS. A number of new streets are shown on the map, and the widening of a number of existing streets is also shown. In respect of any of the new streets shown on the map to be made of a greater width than 40 feet, no owner shall be required to bear any greater expense in the erection of street works than that of the width of 40 feet. Any greater expense shall be borne by the Council. Various provisions are included in the scheme relative to the widening of existing streets. It is also provided that the Council may enter into agreements with owners as to the adjustment of boundaries. A clause relative to the compulsory adjustment of boundaries is also embodied in the scheme.

Anyone laying out a new street in which no buildings other than dwelling houses are proposed to be erected, may construct such street 26 feet in width if the following conditions are complied with:

a. The streets shall not be more than 900 feet in length.

b. Turning places shall be provided every 450 feet.

c. The street shall communicate at each end with a street 40 feet or more in width, and must not be in direct continuation of such a street; provided that it may communicate with any old highway of less width than 40 feet which is existing at the present time.

d. The surface of the road shall be made of the same strength and materials as are required for by-law streets.

Further relaxation of by-law requirements as to width of streets is to be given to owners who, when developing their land are prepared to set aside one-tenth of the area of such land as public or private open spaces.

These relaxations are:

a. A street not exceeding 350 feet in length may be constructed of a width of not less than 20 feet.

b. A street not exceeding 750 feet in length may be constructed of a width of not less than 24 feet.

c. A street not exceeding 1,500 feet in length may be constructed of a width of not less than 30 feet.

In all cases the provisions named above relating to turning places, communications, etc., shall apply.

Dwelling houses may be arranged around quadrangles, and in this case a street of not less than seven feet in width may be allowed, provided that it is not more than 500 feet in length and communicates with a street not less than 24 feet in width or with an existing highway. The space within the quadrangle may be laid out as gardens or as forecourts. No fence fronting on the quadrangle may be more than 3 feet 6 inches in height.

The Council may construct any of the new streets as shown on the map at any time on giving six months' notice to the owners of their intention.

The expenses of making the streets shall be deemed to be expenses of private street works, and the Council shall have power to apportion the expenses on all the lands and premises access to which is derived from such street, and which in the opinion of the Council will be benefited by such street. The Council may prescribe a period of time in which such sums shall be made payable, and in doing so shall take into consideration the time at which the construction of such street will be of benefit to the persons called upon to pay. There is a right of appeal by any person aggrieved by the decision of the Council. An important provision is that no frontager shall be called upon to pay for any street works until his land has been used for other than the purpose of agriculture, unless he has previously given his consent in writing to such charge being made upon him.

Any owner or owners of land over which a new street exceeding 40 feet in width is shown on the map to be constructed may, where such street or part thereof will, when constructed, communicate at each end with a highway reparable by the inhabitants at large, give to the Council six months' notice in writing requiring the Council to construct the said new street or the said part thereof, and the Council must with reasonable speed after the expiration of such notice construct the said street or the said part thereof. When any plan for a new street is submitted, the Council may, by notice in writing, call upon the owners of any lands, the development of which in their opinion may be affected by such street, for plans and particulars showing generally the scheme for the laying out of such estate or lands. Provision is made for the modification of the position or construction of any of the proposed new streets by an appeal to the Local Government Board. Such modifications shall not be made unless all owners affected agree.

NUISANCES. All private gardens, allotments, or private open spaces, shall be kept in such a state as not to be a nuisance or annoyance to persons using the highway or to neighbors. The Council may take steps to abate such nuisances and may recover the costs from any person served with notice. To prevent untidiness or irregularity the Council may by agreements with owners lay out, plant, and fence the forecourts abutting upon a street at the cost of the Council or the owners or of both, as may be agreed upon. No person is allowed to fix or use advertisements upon buildings, hoardings, or frame work so as to interfere with the amenity of the neighborhood.

APPENDIX B

Summary of Provisions of Alberta, Canada, Town Planning Act of 1913 [1]

A town planning scheme can be prepared for the whole area of any city and may even comprise land outside the city limits, while the minister of municipalities may approve a part of the scheme in case he does not wish to approve all. A scheme, once adopted, may be varied or revoked in case future progress renders it desirable to do so.

A town planning scheme when approved by the minister shall have effect as if it were specially enacted by law. This means that, once a scheme is approved, all future subdivisions, streets, buildings, etc., must be in accordance with the approved scheme.

The act defines who shall be the authority responsible for carrying out the town planning scheme. Such authority may be, as in the case of Edmonton, the city council itself, or it may be, as in the case of Calgary, a commission appointed by the city council, subject to the approval of the minister of municipalities. Regulations may be adopted for carrying out the objects of the scheme. No such regulations have yet been approved, and Davidson expresses the opinion that it will take the combined wisdom of the wisest of the world to make this standard set of regulations. In the meantime, the plans are prepared in accordance with the by-laws of the different cities respecting buildings, sewerage, etc.

Any money necessary can be borrowed by debentures, the same as for any other city purpose. They can be paid back either in a lump sum or by annual instalments or by means of a special local improvement tax, the same as is done in the case of pavements and sidewalks.

A special provision to cover the case of Calgary and other cities allows $20,000 to be paid for pre-liminary plans out of the current revenue without a vote of the people. If the scheme should fail of ultimate approval, there would otherwise be no money with which to pay the person or persons preparing the scheme.

Any person whose property is injuriously affected by the scheme shall be entitled to full compensation if he files his claim with reasonable promptness. If lands are increased in value by the carrying out of the scheme, the owner gets one-half of the increase and the city the other half. This is taking the unearned increment in accordance with the English theory of land taxation. One beneficial result expected from this provision is that local jealousies will be avoided, the ratepayers knowing that, although the improvement will be of local benefit, half of the benefit will be reaped by the city at large, while those who most directly profit by it are liable to a charge against their property. This half of the increased value, if not recovered by the ordinary method of taxation or by sale of the lands, may be recovered through an action at law.

The number of buildings on a given area can be limited; the space about buildings, the character and height of buildings may be prescribed; a reservation of vacant land for parks and open spaces in all new subdivisions up to five per cent of their area may be made; all without giving the land owner claim for compensation.

In cases of expropriation the city takes at the value existing before the town planning scheme came into effect. This is designed to prevent owners from holding up the city for fictitious values. On account of the publicity attached to all city enterprises, options cannot be taken as in private business; but the act provides that the city can purchase at the original value.

The minister of municipalities may force any backward city to make or execute a town planning scheme. He may also certify that the debentures by-laws of a city issuing its obligations to meet the expenses of preparing a scheme are correct, and then no court can question their legality.

[1] Based on statement submitted to the Fifth National Conference on City Planning, Chicago, May 5–7, 1913, by James W. Davidson, President, Calgary City Planning Commission.

APPENDIX C

Extract from Subdivision Platting Rules Suggested by the City Planning Division, American Society of Civil Engineers [1]

I. SUGGESTED AUTHORITY FOR RULES (STATUTE)

(For text, see source, pages 66–67.)

II. SUGGESTED ADMINISTRATION ORDINANCE

(For text, see source, pages 67–68.)

III. SUGGESTED RULES AND REGULATIONS FOR LAND SUBDIVISION TO BE ADOPTED BY THE PLANNING COMMISSION

A. *Definition.*

As used in these rules: A subdivision is the division of a lot, tract, or parcel of land into two or more lots or other divisions of land, for the purpose, whether immediate or future, of transfer of ownership or building development, including all changes in street or lot lines; provided, however, that divisions of land for agricultural purposes, in parcels of more than ten (10) acres, not involving any new street or easement of access, shall be exempted.

B. *Preliminary Plat.*

1. An application, in writing, for the tentative approval of the Preliminary Plat, together with six (6) blue prints, shall be filed with the Commission at least two (2) weeks before the meeting of the Commission, if the plat is to be acted upon at such meeting.

2. Before any subdivider or his agent contracts for the sale or offers to sell any subdivision of land or any part thereof, which is laid out wholly or partly within the unincorporated territory of _____, the subdivider or his agent shall file a preliminary plat of said subdivision with the Planning Commission of _____.
The preliminary plat shall be prepared in accordance with the regulations set forth below, and shall be submitted to the Planning Commission prior to the completion of final surveys of streets and lots and before the start of any grading or construction

[1] From "Land Subdivision," *Manual of Engineering Practice No. 16*, American Society of Civil Engineers, 1939, prepared by the Committee on Land Subdivision Manual of City Planning Division.

work upon the proposed streets and before any map of said subdivision is made in form suitable for recording. The Planning Commission shall determine whether a tentative map is in proper form and shall not receive and consider such a map as filed until it is submitted in accordance with the requirements hereof.

3. Vicinity Sketch: A vicinity sketch or key map at a scale of not more than four hundred (400) feet to the inch shall be shown on or accompany the Preliminary Plat. This map shall show all existing subdivisions, streets, and tract lines of acreage parcels together with the names of the record owners of parcels of land immediately adjoining the proposed subdivision and between it and the nearest existing thoroughfares. It shall also show how streets and alleys in the proposed subdivision may connect with existing and proposed streets and alleys in neighboring subdivisions or undeveloped property, to produce the most advantageous development of the entire neighboring area.

4. All proposed subdivisions shall conform to the City, County, or Regional Plan. Whenever a tract to be subdivided embraces any part of a thoroughfare, secondary thoroughfare, boulevard, or parkway, so designated on the City, County, or Regional Plan, such part of such proposed public way shall be platted by the subdivider in the location and of the width indicated on the City, County, or Regional Plan.

5. The street layout shall be in conformity with a plan for the most advantageous development of the entire neighboring area. All proposed streets shall be in alignment with existing planned or platted streets with which they are to connect.
a. The street layout shall include minor streets of considerable continuity approximately parallel to and on each side of each main thoroughfare, boulevard, or parkway.
b. Wherever the proposed subdivision contains or is adjacent to a railroad right of way, or super-highway, provision shall be made for a street approximately parallel to and on each side of such right of way at a distance suitable for the appropriate use of the land between such streets and the railroad. Such distance shall be determined with due consideration of the minimum distance required for approach grades to future grade separation.
c. Proposed streets shall be adjusted to the contour of the land so as to produce usable lots and streets of reasonable gradient.

d. Certain proposed streets shall be extended to the boundary line of the tract to be subdivided sufficiently to provide for normal circulation of traffic within the vicinity.

e. Wherever there exists a dedicated or platted half-street or alley adjacent to the tract to be subdivided and approved by a planning commission, the other half shall be platted.

f. Alleys will be required in all business and industrial districts. Except where justified by extreme conditions, alleys will not be approved in residential districts.

6. The horizontal scale of a Preliminary Plat shall be one hundred (100) feet or less to the inch and the vertical scale twenty (20) feet or less to the inch.

7. The Preliminary Plat shall show:

a. The proposed name of the subdivision.

b. North point, scale, and date.

c. The names and addresses of the subdivider and of the engineer or surveyor.

d. The tract designation and other description according to the real estate records of the City or County Auditor and Recorder.

e. The boundary line (accurate in scale) of the tract to be subdivided.

f. Contours with intervals of five (5) feet or less, referred to sea-level datum.

g. The names of adjacent subdivisions or the names of record owners of adjoining parcels of unsubdivided land.

h. The location, widths, and names of all existing or platted streets or other public ways within or adjacent to the tract, existing permanent buildings, railroad rights of way, and other important features, such as section lines, political subdivision or corporation lines, and school district boundaries.

i. Existing sewers, water mains, culverts, or other underground structures within the tract and immediately adjacent thereto with pipe sizes, grades, and locations indicated.

j. All parcels of land intended to be dedicated for public use or reserved in the deeds for the use of all property owners in the proposed subdivision, together with the purpose of conditions or limitations of such reservation, if any.

k. The layout, names, and widths of proposed streets, alleys, and easements.

l. The profile of each street with tentative grades.

m. The cross-section of proposed streets showing the width of roadways, location and width of sidewalks, and the location and size of utility mains.

n. A plan and profile of proposed sanitary, storm water, or combined sewers, with grades and pipe sizes indicated, and a plan of the proposed water-distribution system showing pipe sizes and the location of valves and fire hydrants.

o. The layout, numbers, and approximate dimensions of proposed lots.

8. The width of blocks shall be sufficient normally to allow two tiers of lots of appropriate depth.

9. Blocks shall not exceed 1,200 feet to 2,000 feet in length, and dead-end streets 300 feet to 600 feet.

10. A cross-walk or pedestrian way, not less than ten (10) feet in width, shall be provided near the center, and entirely across any block that is more than 600 feet to 1,000 feet long.

11. Minimum street and alley widths:

a. Main thoroughfares, secondary thoroughfares, boulevards, and parkways, as indicated by the City, County, or Regional Plan and not less than eighty (80) feet.

b. Secondary thoroughfares, sixty (60) feet.

c. Minor streets, fifty (50) feet.

d. Dead-end streets, not more than three hundred (300) feet long, forty (40) feet. All dead-end streets shall terminate in a circular right of way with a minimum diameter of seventy (70) feet, unless the Commission approves an equally safe and convenient form of paved space instead of the required turning circle.

e. Alleys, twenty (20) feet.

12. Minimum roadway widths:

a. Thoroughfares, boulevards and parkways, secondary thoroughfares, and minor streets, twenty-six (26) feet.

b. Dead-end streets not more than three hundred (300) feet long, eighteen (18) feet. All dead-end streets shall terminate in a paved turning circle with a minimum outside diameter of fifty (50) feet and a pavement at least eighteen (18) feet wide. If an equally safe and convenient form of paved space is approved by the Commission in place of a turning circle, such paved space shall extend entirely across the width of the street and shall be at least ten (10) feet wide with the flared portions rounded by minimum radii of twenty (20) feet.

c. Alleys, sixteen (16) feet.

13. Where three (3) or more lots to the acre are provided, sidewalks at least four (4) feet wide shall be provided on both sides of each street. Normally sidewalks shall be not more than six (6) inches from the property line. Cross-walks or pedestrian ways shall be not less than four (4) feet wide.

14. Grades:

a. Thoroughfares, boulevards, parkways, and secondary thoroughfares, not greater than seven (7) per cent.

b. Minor streets and alleys, not greater than ten (10) per cent.

c. Pedestrian ways or cross-walks, not greater than twenty (20) per cent, unless steps of an acceptable design are to be constructed.

15. Vertical curves: All changes in street grade shall be connected by vertical curves of a minimum length equivalent to fifteen (15) times the algebraic difference in the rate of grade for thoroughfares, boulevards, parkways, and secondary thoroughfares, and one-half of this minimum for all other minor streets.

16. Alignment and visibility: Clear visibility, measured along the center line, shall be provided for at least three hundred (300) feet on thoroughfares, boulevards, and parkways; two hundred (200) feet

on secondary thoroughfares; and at least one hundred (100) feet on minor streets.

17. Minimum radii of curvature on the center line:

a. Thoroughfares, boulevards, and parkways, three hundred (300) feet. (Note: Radii of considerably greater dimension should be used in most instances in the interest of public safety.)

b. Secondary thoroughfares, two hundred (200) feet.

c. Minor streets, one hundred (100) feet.

18. Tangents: Between reversed curves there shall always be a tangent at least one hundred (100) feet long.

19. Intersections:

a. At street and alley intersections, property line corners shall be rounded by an arc, the minimum radius of which shall be ten (10) feet and five (5) feet, respectively. In business districts a chord may be substituted for such an arc.

b. Street curb intersections shall be rounded by radii of at least twenty (20) feet.

c. The foregoing minimum radii shall be increased when the smallest angle of intersection is less than sixty (60) degrees.

20. Lots: The size, shape, and orientation of lots shall be appropriate for the location of the proposed subdivision and for the type of development contemplated, and shall conform to the following:

a. Lots for residential use shall be at least forty (40) feet wide at the building line. (In most cities a minimum lot width of fifty (50) feet is required.)

b. Every lot shall abut on a street, or on an officially approved cul-de-sac.

c. Double-frontage lots shall be avoided.

d. Reversed frontage shall be avoided in blocks exclusively residential.

e. Side lot lines shall be approximately at right angles to the street line on which the lot faces.

21. Open spaces other than streets: Due consideration should be given to the allocation of suitable areas for schools, parks, and playgrounds, to be dedicated for public use or reserved for the common use of all property owners within the proposed subdivision by covenants in the deeds. In the interest of the public welfare at least five (5) per cent of the area of every subdivision, exclusive of streets, should be set aside for recreational purposes. Where the tract contains less than forty (40) acres, such reservation for open space shall be combined, wherever possible, with similar reservations in adjoining tracts.

22. Easements at least eight (8) feet wide, four (4) feet on each side of rear or side lot lines, shall be provided for utilities where necessary.

23. The Preliminary Plat shall contain the statement that any lot transferred will have a minimum width and area substantially the same as those of the platted lots, and that only one principal building will be permitted on any such lot.

24. The proposed name of the subdivision and proposed street names shall not duplicate or too closely approximate, phonetically, the name of any other subdivision or street in _____ County.

25. Improvements: All improvements required under these rules shall be constructed in accordance with the specifications and under the supervision of the Board and to its satisfaction.

a. Roadways and sidewalks: All roadways shall be paved. Bituminous macadam is considered to be a minimum standard and will be approved. Sidewalks of concrete shall be provided where lots are less than twelve thousand (12,000) square feet in area.

b. Water lines:

1. Where a public water main is reasonably accessible, the subdivider shall connect with such water main and provide a water connection for each lot.

2. Where a public water main is not reasonably accessible, the subdivider shall place on file with the Board the prescribed form of petition for the future installation of necessary mains and connections for each lot.

c. Sewers:

1. Where a public sanitary sewer is reasonably accessible, the subdivider shall connect with such sanitary sewer and provide a connection for each lot.

2. Where a public sanitary sewer is not reasonably accessible, but where the plans for the sanitary sewer system of the district in which the subdivision is located have been prepared by the County Sanitary Engineer, the subdivider shall install sewers in conformity with such plans, although a connection with an existing main may not be immediately practicable. In such cases, and until such connection is made with the sewer system of the district, the subdivider shall provide for the disposal of sanitary sewage by a type of treatment to be approved by the Board.

3. In cases other than the foregoing, the subdivider shall place on file with the Board the prescribed form of petition for the future installation of sanitary sewers and a connection for each lot.

26. Tentative approval by the Commission is revocable and does not constitute acceptance of the plat of the proposed subdivision. It is to be considered only as approval of the design, with the understanding that the Board, the County Surveyor, the County Sanitary Engineer, and the County Health Officer will examine the grades of streets, the types of improvements, the layout of drainage and sewerage system, and the water-distribution system as proposed, and may modify any engineering or construction details submitted by the subdivider, whenever required for the protection of the public interest.

27. Tentative approval will be effective for two (2) years, unless extended by the Commission. Subdivisions, the Final Plats of which are not submitted within this time limit, must be resubmitted for tentative approval as new subdivisions.

28. Upon tentative approval of a Preliminary Plat by the Commission, one blue print of the Plat,

with the date of tentative approval stamped thereon, will be returned to the subdivider.

29. Where it can be shown that there are extraordinary hardships in the way of complete compliance with these regulations, the Commission shall have the power to vary the regulations so that substantial justice may be done and public interest secured, provided, however, that no such variation shall have the effect of reducing the traffic capacity of any thoroughfare or secondary thoroughfare below that shown on the City, County, or Regional Plan.

The foregoing regulations concerning minor and local street widths, sizes of lots, block lengths and widths, and dead-end streets may be modified by the Planning Commission in the case of a subdivision of a tract large enough to be developed as a community of not less than _____ acres in accordance with a well-studied plan, properly safeguarded by restrictions, which in the judgment of the Planning Commission adequately provides for circulation, light, and air needs and recreational requirements of the maximum anticipated population.

C. Final Plat.

30. The Final Plat shall be submitted to the Commission in the form of an original tracing on tracing cloth, together with six (6) blue-print copies. Four (4) of these will be transmitted by the Commission to the Board, which will refer one print each to the County Surveyor, County Sanitary Engineer, and the County Health Officer for their recommendations and certifications that the improvements have been completed to their satisfaction, and that the necessary petitions have been duly filed.

31. Before approving the Final Plat of all or part of a proposed subdivision, the Commission will require certification by the Board to the effect that the improvements have been completed to its satisfaction and in accordance with the approved Preliminary Plat, that the petitions for sanitary improvements have been duly filed in accordance with Sections 25 *b* 2 and 25 *c* 3 of these rules.

32. The Final Plat shall be drawn to the scale of one (1) inch equal to one hundred (100) feet or less and shall show—
a. The boundary lines with accurate distances and bearings, the exact location and width of all existing or recorded streets intersecting the boundary of the tract.
b. True bearings and distances to the nearest established street lines or official monuments, which

shall be accurately described on the plat; municipal, township, county, or section lines accurately tied to the lines of the subdivision by distances and bearings.
c. An accurate location of the subdivision in reference to the real estate records of _____ County.
d. The exact layout including:
1. Street and alley names.
2. The length of all arcs, radii, internal angles, points of curvature, length and bearing of the tangents.
3. All easements for rights of way provided for public services or utilities and any limitations of the easements.
4. All lot numbers and lines with accurate dimensions in feet and hundredths and with bearings and angles to street and alley lines.
e. The accurate location, material, and approximate size of all monuments.
f. The accurate outline of all property which is offered for dedication for public use with the purpose indicated thereon, and of all property that may be reserved by deed covenant for the common use of the property owners in the subdivision.
g. Set-back building lines.
h. Private restrictions.
1. Boundaries of each type of use restriction.
2. Other private restrictions for each definitely restricted section of the subdivision.
i. Proposed name of the subdivision.
j. Name and address of the subdivider.
k. North point, scale, and date.
l. Certification of any application filed with the Board for sewers and water extensions required under these rules, signed by the Clerk of the Board.
m. Certification by a registered professional civil engineer or surveyor to the effect that the plan represents a survey made by him and that all the monuments shown thereon actually exist, and that their location, size, and material are correctly shown.

33. The approval of the Final Plat by the Commission shall not be deemed to constitute or effect an acceptance by the public of the dedication of any street, or other proposed public way or space shown on the plat.

34. Approval of the Final Plat by the Commission shall be null and void if the plat is not recorded within ten (10) days after the date of approval, unless application for an extension of time is made in writing during said ten (10)-day period to the Commission, and granted.

APPENDIX D

New York City's Rules for Apportioning the Cost of Assessable Projects (Abstract of Resolution Adopted by the Board of Estimate, November 16, 1939)

ASSESSABLE PHYSICAL IMPROVEMENTS

Sidewalks and Curbs. 100 per cent on frontage regardless of street width.

Grading and Paving Streets. 100 per cent on local area for streets up to and including 60 feet in width. For widths over 60 feet the local area shall pay such proportion of the cost as 60 feet bears to total street width; if street width is not over 100 feet the borough shall pay any balance; if it is over 100 feet the borough shall pay only such proportion of the entire cost as 40 feet bears to the total street width, and the remainder shall be borne by the city at large.

In no case shall the local area be assessed more than the cost of paving the roadway width of a street 60 feet wide, as established by the general rules adopted by the Board; nor shall the borough's share exceed the cost of paving a strip of a width equal to the difference in roadway widths established by the Board for streets 100 feet and 60 feet in width, respectively.[1]

In general, the local area is intended to be the frontage to a depth of 100 feet.

Widening Existing Streets. Credit shall be given to the apportionment of costs made when the existing street was graded and paved.

Special Park Treatments and Other Special Work within Streets, done in connection with an assessable project, shall be paid for by the city at large.

Grading and Development of Public Parks and Public Beaches. Construction costs shall be paid for by the city at large.

Street Grade Separations. Construction costs shall be 50 per cent on the borough and 50 per cent on the city at large.

Elevated Highways. Construction costs shall be paid for by the city at large.

Boardwalks. Costs of construction shall be paid for by such local, borough, and city assessment as may be determined in each case by the Board of Estimate.

[1] These rules establishing roadway and sidewalk widths, as adopted April 8, 1926, are given in Chapter 9, Volume I.

Sewers, Other than Interceptors or Reconstruction. Sanitary sewers, 100 per cent on drainage area. Storm water sewers, combined sewers, and their appurtenances, 66⅔ per cent on drainage area and 33⅓ per cent on the city. Storm water relief sewers, equally between the drainage area, the borough, and the city.

Where sewers are reconstructed of the same capacity, the entire cost shall be borne by the city; where reconstructed of greater capacity, the city shall bear a charge equal to the original construction cost (with certain exceptions), and the remainder shall be apportioned in accordance with the rule in the preceding paragraph.

Pavement Restoration in Sewer Work. 100 per cent on the city.

Sewage Treatment and Disposal Works, Intercepting Sewers. Construction costs 100 per cent on the city.

STREET-OPENING PROCEEDINGS

Land Acquisition. For street widths up to and including 60 feet, the local area shall be assessed the full cost; for streets over 60 feet, the local area shall bear the proportion necessary to secure a street 60 feet wide; if street width is not over 100 feet the borough shall pay any balance; if it is over 100 feet the borough shall pay only that proportion necessary to secure the additional width from 60 feet up to and including 100 feet, and the remainder shall be borne by the city at large.

In general, the local area is intended to be the frontage to a depth of 100 feet.

Acquisition of Buildings, Improvements, and Damages to Buildings. Costs equally divided between the local area, the borough, and the city.

Cost of Proceedings. The city shall pay the proportionate share chargeable to any tax-exempt lands within the local area of assessment.

Acquisition of Elevated Railroads for Demolition. Apportionment of costs to be determined in each case by the Board of Estimate.

ACQUISITION OF PUBLIC PARKS, PLAYGROUNDS, AND BEACHES

Costs to be paid by such local, borough, and city assessments as the Board of Estimate may determine in each case.

ACQUISITION OF SITES FOR SEWAGE TREATMENT AND SEWAGE-DISPOSAL PLANTS

Entire cost to be borne by the city at large.

GENERAL PROVISIONS

Provision for spreading borough and city assessments over more than one year if the total amount would add two points or more to the borough or city tax rate.

Any amount of the assessment chargeable under the rules to the local area which is in excess of the amount deemed chargeable against the local area by the Board of Assessors shall be placed upon the borough.

A request for reapportionment of the cost of any improvement must be received within one year after the confirmation of the assessment in order to be considered by the Board of Estimate.

The above rules are to be observed with the reservation that in many instances conditions will no doubt arise that cannot be made the subject of fixed rules and must be dealt with according to the special features involved.

APPENDIX E

Capital Budget Provisions of the Charter of the City of New York, Effective January 1, 1938 (Chapter 9 of the Charter)

DEFINITIONS

§ 211. As used in this chapter: 1. The term "capital project" shall mean:

a. Any physical public betterment or improvement or any preliminary studies and surveys relative thereto.

b. The acquisition of property of a permanent nature.

c. The purchase of equipment for any public betterment or improvement when first erected or acquired.

It shall not include any public betterment or improvement, the acquisition of any real property, or the purchase of any equipment, any part of the total cost and expenses of which shall be paid out of the proceeds of assessments, nor the repavement of any street, avenue, highway, or public place.

2. The term "pending" shall mean authorized but not yet completed.

REPORT OF COMPTROLLER

§ 212. Not later than the fifteenth day of August in each year, the comptroller shall submit to the board of estimate, to the council, to the city planning commission, and to the director of the budget, a report which shall be published forthwith in the City Record, setting forth the amount and nature of all obligations authorized on account of each pending capital project, the liabilities incurred for each project outstanding on the first day of July and setting forth and commenting in detail upon the city's financial condition and advising as to the maximum amount and nature of debt which in his opinion the city may soundly incur for capital projects during each of the six succeeding calendar years, and containing such other information as may be required by the city planning commission or by law.

DEPARTMENTAL ESTIMATES FOR CAPITAL PROJECTS

§ 213. On such date as the mayor may direct, but not later than the fifteenth day of August, the head of each agency shall submit to the city planning commission and the director of the budget a detailed estimate of all capital projects pending or which he believes should be undertaken within the six succeed-

ing calendar years. Such estimates shall be known as departmental estimates for capital projects and shall be in such form and contain such information as may be required by the city planning commission, by the director of the budget, or by law. Such departmental estimates shall be public records and shall at all reasonable times be open to public inspection.

REPORT OF DIRECTOR OF THE BUDGET

§ 214. Not later than the first day of September, the director of the budget shall report to the mayor his recommendation as to the maximum amount and nature of debt which in his opinion the city may soundly incur for capital projects during each of the six succeeding calendar years, the probable effect of such expenditures upon the expense budgets for each of such years, and such comments and recommendations as he may deem advisable.

CERTIFICATE OF THE MAYOR

§ 215. Not later than the fifteenth day of September, the mayor shall submit to the city planning commission the report of the director of the budget, together with the mayor's certificate as to the maximum amount of debt which in his opinion the city may soundly incur for capital projects during the ensuing calendar year with his recommendations as to the capital projects to be included in the capital budget.

PROPOSED CAPITAL BUDGET; PREPARATION

§ 216. Each member of the board of estimate and such member of the council as the council shall designate shall have the right to attend in person or by a representative any and all hearings conducted by the city planning commission at which the heads of agencies or their representatives or subordinates appear to explain their departmental estimates, to ask such questions, and to require the production of such papers and records at such hearings as may seem to him appropriate and proper. The budget director shall attend in person or by a representative all such hearings and shall render to the city planning commission such assistance and advice as it may require in the preparation of the proposed capital budget. The public may be present at such hearings but shall not have the right to be heard, but the commission shall, before taking action on the proposed capital budget, hold hearings thereon at which the public may be heard. Notice of such hearings shall be published in the City Record at least five days prior thereto.

PROPOSED CAPITAL BUDGET AND PROGRAM; SUBMISSION

§ 217. Not later than the first day of November, the city planning commission shall submit to the board of estimate, to the council, to the director of the budget, and to the comptroller a proposed capital budget for all authorizations recommended to be adopted for the ensuing calendar year, the aggregate amount of which shall not exceed the amount specified in the mayor's certificate, and a capital program for the five calendar years next succeeding such ensuing calendar year, both of which shall be published forthwith in the City Record.

PROPOSED CAPITAL BUDGET AND PROGRAM; CONTENTS

§ 218. The proposed capital budget and program shall be arranged in such manner as to set forth clearly:

1. As to each pending capital project: a brief description, the original estimated cost, the date of authorization, the amount and nature of obligations authorized, the amount and maturities of such obligations issued, the amount of all liabilities outstanding, and the unencumbered balances of authorizations on the first day of July, the amount of liabilities estimated to be incurred during the balance of the calendar year, and the estimated additional appropriation required for completion.

2. As to each new capital project recommended: a brief description, the calendar year in which it is recommended to be undertaken and the total estimated cost.

3. As to each project: the estimated date of completion, the amount of liabilities estimated to be incurred in each of the six succeeding calendar years, the estimated useful existence, the amounts, the nature and terms of obligations recommended to be authorized in each of the six succeeding calendar years, and the estimated annual maintenance and service charges.

4. Any recommendation that a pending project be modified or abandoned or further authorization therefor postponed.

5. A brief description of each new project recommended in the several departmental estimates, but not recommended by the city planning commission to be undertaken within the six succeeding calendar years, with the reason why such project is not recommended.

6. Such other information as the city planning commission may deem pertinent or as may be required by law.

When a project is divisible, the information required shall be set forth for each part thereof.

RECOMMENDATIONS OF COMPTROLLER

§ 219. Not later than the fifteenth day of November, the comptroller shall submit to the board of estimate and to the council a report, which shall be published forthwith in the City Record, containing such comments and recommendations with respect to the proposed capital budget and program as he may deem advisable.

PROPOSED CAPITAL BUDGET; HEARINGS

§ 220. Between the fifteenth and the twenty-fifth days of November, both inclusive, the board of estimate shall hold public hearings on the proposed capital budget, and the officers of agencies shall have the right, and it shall be their duty when requested by the board of estimate, to appear and be heard.

CAPITAL BUDGET; ADOPTION BY BOARD OF ESTIMATE

§ 221. Between the twenty-fifth day of November and the fourth day of December, both inclusive, the board of estimate shall adopt a capital budget for the ensuing calendar year. Should the board of estimate fail within such period of time to adopt such capital budget, it shall be deemed to have been adopted in the form submitted by the city planning commission.

The capital budget shall specify the capital projects which may be undertaken during the ensuing calendar year and shall fix the maximum amount of new obligations of the city which may be authorized during such year to be incurred on account of each such project and each pending project and the nature, terms, and maximum amount of the obligations which the comptroller may be authorized to issue for the liquidation of such liabilities.

The board of estimate may include in the capital budget any capital project which was included by the city planning commission in the capital program. It may, not less than fifteen days prior to the adoption of the capital budget, request the city planning commission to furnish, with respect to a project not included in the capital program, information similar to that included in said program with its recommendations. Such information shall be submitted within ten days and shall be published forthwith in the City Record. If the city planning commission recommends such project, the board of estimate may include it in the capital budget. If the city planning commission does not recommend the project, the board of estimate may include it only by a three-fourths vote. The board of estimate shall not adopt except by a three-fourths vote any capital budget pursuant to which obligations exceeding in the aggregate the amount stated in the mayor's certificate may be issued.

CAPITAL BUDGET; ADOPTION BY COUNCIL

§ 222. Not later than the sixth day of December, the capital budget as adopted by the board of estimate shall be certified by the mayor and submitted to the council and shall be published forthwith in the City Record. Immediately upon such submission a special meeting of the council shall be called by the president of the council to consider such capital budget, which consideration shall continue from day to day, but not beyond the twenty-seventh day of December, until final action is taken thereon. Should the council take no final action on such capital budget on or before the twenty-seventh day of December, it shall be deemed to be finally adopted as submitted by the board of estimate.

The council may strike out in its entirety any authorization in the capital budget as submitted, but may not add to or increase or vary the terms or conditions of any authorization in such capital budget as submitted.

CAPITAL BUDGET; CERTIFICATION

§ 223. Not later than the twenty-ninth day of December, the capital budget as adopted by the council shall be certified by the president of the council and transmitted to the mayor.

Not later than the thirty-first day of December, the capital budget as finally adopted in such year shall be certified by the mayor, the comptroller, and the city clerk as the capital budget for the ensuing calendar year. The capital budget shall, not later than five days after such certification, be filed in the office of the comptroller and shall be published forthwith in the City Record.

RESTRICTIONS ON CAPITAL PROJECT AUTHORIZATIONS AT OTHER TIMES

§ 224. No obligations of the city shall be authorized in any calendar year for or on account of any capital project not included in the capital budget as finally adopted for such a year, or in excess of the maximum amount of obligations which may be authorized on account of such project as fixed in such captal budget; provided, however, that if the lowest responsible bid for any such project shall exceed the amount authorized therefor, the amount authorized may be increased by not more than fifteen per centum thereof by resolution of the board of estimate; and provided further, that upon receipt of a recommendation in writing from the city planning commission, approved by the affirmative vote of two-thirds of the members thereof, the board of estimate may amend the capital budget in accordance with such recommendation. Upon the adoption of any such amendment by the board of estimate adding a project to the capital budget or increasing the maximum amount of obligations which may be authorized on account of any project, it shall be certified by the mayor and submitted to the council, and if the council shall adopt the same, it shall be certified by the president of the council and transmitted to the mayor. It shall thereupon be certified by the mayor, the comptroller, and the city clerk, and the capital budget shall be and become amended accordingly. Not later than five days after such certification, such amendment shall be filed in the office of the comptroller and shall be published forthwith in the City Record.

INDEX